Principles of Plant Biotechnology

AN INTRODUCTION TO
GENETIC ENGINEERING IN PLANTS

Principles of Plant Biotechnology

AN INTRODUCTION TO
GENETIC ENGINEERING IN PLANTS

S. H. MANTELL
Department of Horticulture,
Wye College, University of London,
Wye, Ashford, Kent

J. A. MATTHEWS
Department of Clinical Chemistry,
Wolfson Research Laboratories,
Queen Elizabeth Medical Centre,
Edgbaston, Birmingham 15

R. A. McKEE
Department of Botany,
University of Leicester

BLACKWELL SCIENTIFIC PUBLICATIONS

OXFORD LONDON EDINBURGH

BOSTON PALO ALTO MELBOURNE

First published 1985
Reprinted 1987

Set by Setrite Typesetters Ltd
Hong Kong, and
printed and bound by
The Alden Press
Osney Mead, Oxford

DISTRIBUTORS

USA and Canada
    Blackwell Scientific Publications Inc
    P O Box 50009, Palo Alto
    California 94303

Australia
    Blackwell Scientific Publications
    (Australia) Pty Ltd
    107 Barry Street, Carlton
    Victoria 3053

British Library
Cataloguing in Publication Data

Mantell, S.H.
    Principles of plant biotechnology :
    introduction to genetic engineering in
    plants.
    1. Plant genetics 2. Genetic engineering
    I. Title II. Matthews, J.A.
    III. McKee, R.A.
    581.1'5   QK981.5

ISBN 0–632–01215–3 Pbk

Contents

Preface

Numerous 'new technologies' such as recombinant DNA, plant protoplast, cell and organ culture techniques, and various genetic transformation systems have been applied to plants and their component parts, generating an area of research activity known as Plant Biotechnology.

This book brings together many of the topics associated with plant biotechnology which had not previously been covered in a single volume in 1983/84 when the book was written.

The text is based on a series of thirty-three lectures on plant biotechnology given to final year biology students, in the Botany Department at the University of Leicester. The aim of this book is to provide an introduction to the subject for undergraduates and those researchers interested in the field of plant biotechnology. In so doing it assumes a limited prior knowledge of the subjects covered. As with all volumes of this size it is inevitable that certain subjects will receive less attention than others, or that they may not be covered. However, we have aimed to concentrate on those topics that we consider to be the most important and relevant to plant biotechnology as it is progressing today.

We would like to extend our sincere thanks to Professor Harry Smith, who guided and encouraged us through the initiation of the undergraduate course, and who also had the concept of this volume.

Sinclair Mantell
Jayne Matthews
Ray McKee

1 Introduction

The role of plants

Plants are the key to life on earth, principally through their unique position as primary producers in all food chains, and secondarily as the only renewable energy source available to animals.

As autotrophic organisms, plants have very simple basic nutritional requirements, these being water, carbon dioxide and various inorganic chemicals. Using sunlight as an energy source, plants make simple sugars, utilizing the complex series of reactions known as photosynthesis. These sugars may be used immediately by the plant, or stored to be converted–again using simple inorganic chemicals and water — to complex macromolecules necessary to the growth, development and survival of the plant. The trapping of light energy from the sun and the production of organic molecules through photosynthesis, provides the basis of not only all food on earth, but also all life on earth. Thus, plants provide the only renewable process capable of converting solar energy into stored chemical energy.

Plants directly supply 90% of human calorie intake, and 80% of the protein intake, the remainder being derived from animal products, although these animals have ultimately derived their nutrition from plants. The vast majority of this food (c. 90%) is produced on land. The relative amounts of protein and energy contributed by plants and animals depend largely on cultural practices, e.g. the inhabitants of Europe and North America derive more protein and calories from meat and dairy products than those of Asia.

Of the three thousand plant species which have been used as food by man, the world now depends mainly on around twenty crop species for the majority of its protein and calories, with 50% being contributed by eight species of cereals (Table 1.1). Minerals and vitamins are supplied by a further thirty species of fruit and vegetables. However, although worldwide a range of plants provide a variety of food products, local communities often rely for most of their calories on only one plant yielding the staple food. Most important of the staple foods are the cereals, particularly wheat and rice, with more than one-third of all cultivated land used to produce these two crops. Throughout North America, Europe and North Africa, in a total of forty-three countries, wheat is the dominant staple, while rice is predominant throughout Asia, being the staple food of over half the world's population.

As the global human population continues to expand, concern has been expressed in various quarters about the finite number of people world agriculture can support. Indeed, with the amount of hunger and starvation already prevalent some would argue that we have already passed the limit, while others point to the gross imbalance in the production, distribution and availability of food between developed and developing nations. Of particular relevance to this argument of just how

Table 1.1. Major food crops.

Cereals	Fruit and vegetables
wheat	banana
rice	plantain
corn	date
rye	coconut
oats	olive
barley	avocado
sorghum	mango
millet	breadfruit
	artichoke
	broccoli
Legumes	cauliflower
pea	tomato
kidney bean	pepper
soybean	okra
lentil	eggplant
chickpea	cucumber
mung bean	squash
broad bean	
peanut	
lima bean	Roots and tubers
cowpea	potato
	yam
	sweet potato
Sugar crops	cassava
sugar-beet	carrot
sugar-cane	beet

much food the earth can produce, is the comparative efficiency of food production by animals and plants. All animals either directly, or indirectly, derive their nutrition from plants. Of this intake of food energy, only a small proportion, approximately 10%, is stored and thus available to the next consumer, while the remaining 90% is used by the animal for the various metabolic processes necessary to sustain life. Thus, the transfer of protein from the primary producer (e.g. cereal) through an animal (e.g. cow) to the human consumer is inefficient, with several kilogrammes of cereal required to produce one kilogramme of beef protein. The efficiency of stored energy transfer can be improved and, for example, from feed grain to chicken may reach as high as 30%. Plants, therefore, produce more protein per unit area of cultivated land, but can an exclusively plant-based diet maintain adequate human health? The answer is yes, provided the sources of plant protein are carefully chosen to ensure a supply of essential amino acids, and also a synthetic or microbial source of vitamin B12 is included.

An estimate of how many people could be supported by world food production can be obtained from consideration of the average daily calorie requirements and the net amount of grain yield from well managed areas. Such calculations suggest that 1 hectare could support fourteen people on a strictly vegetarian diet. If half the energy in the diet is derived from animal products then only four to five people would be capable of support on 1 hectare of land. Extrapolating these figures to the estimated world range of arable land, allowing for the fact that not all available land is used to grow crops, it has been calculated that the earth can support about fifteen billion people on a strictly vegetarian diet, or five billion on a mixed diet. In 1976 the world population was over four billion with a doubling to eight billion estimated for 2001. These figures assume the application of advanced farming practices, so the need for population control in conjunction with the use of high-yielding crops and modern agricultural strategies becomes obvious.

Plant breeding and agricultural practices

The farming practices and crops cultivated today have developed over a relatively short time-span in evolutionary terms. The origins of the move from a hunter-gatherer existence, to one involving the cultivation and domestication of plants and animals, can only be speculated upon. However, during the process crop plants have changed in a number of ways, so that they now commonly bear little resemblance to their wild type ancestors. These changes have come about through selection, either conscious or not, of specific traits which are advantageous to the people growing the crops. Thus, modern wheats do not disperse their seeds, and cultivated legumes do not have pods which burst open, the process of seed dispersal is now dependent on humans. Similarly, most crop plants have lost their seed dormancy mechanisms, and varieties today are the result of generations of plants cultivated under ideal conditions, from the growers point of view, rather than in a natural environment. These practices have resulted in crop plants and man being now bound together in a mutually-dependent partnership. Furthermore, developments and improvements in agricultural tech-niques and materials (e.g. irrigation), resulted in less labour being used on the land, thus began the formation of towns and cities and the eventual birth of modern civilization.

From the beginnings of crop cultivation to the late nineteenth century all improvements in the species used were brought about by those directly involved, i.e. the farmers themselves. In the following 100 years, the laws of genetic inheritance and rules governing species variation, laid down by Mendel and Darwin, refined the breeding techniques by making them predictable and therefore quicker, more precise and more productive.

Classical genetics as applied to plant breeding cannot be divorced from other improvements in agricultural production, brought about by

Table 1.2. Increase in yield of major crops between 1930 and 1975.

Crop	Approximate average yield per acre in pounds		
	1930	1975	% Increase
Wheat	795	1714	115
Rice	2604	5056	117
Maize	1148	4827	320
Oats	1792	2693	50
Barley	1333	2464	85
Sugar-cane	35,000	84,000	141
Tobacco	776	2011	159
Soybeans	750	1590	112
Tomatoes (processing)	9632	49,500	413

improved crop husbandry and agronomic practices such as the use of fertilizers, herbicides and irrigation. However, it has been estimated that genetic improvement alone may account for 50% of the harvest increases experienced so far in the twentieth century (Table 1.2). Two outstanding examples of the success of the plant breeders techniques, and their effect on the world food supply, were the development of hybrid maize in the 1920−30s, and the 'green revolution' wheats in the 1950−60s. Improvement of wheat was achieved using controlled pollinations between superior parent strains, followed by repeated selection and crossing of desirable plants. Having obtained genotypic and phenotypic uniformity the varieties which consistently out-performed established lines were adopted. The further development of semi-dwarf varieties, exhibiting not only increased yield but also more efficient nutrient-to-seed conversion, was complemented by research which enabled the time taken to develop new varieties to be shortened, principally by selecting phenotypes at different geographical locations. This latter technique had the added bonus of producing varieties which perform well in a number of different environments. The development, by plant breeders, of successful crop varieties, has led to the large-scale implementation of these varieties by the agricultural community. In certain cases this has had the effect of standardizing that particular crop variety, with the accompanying risk of disease susceptibility on a large scale, while in other crop species the genetic base has narrowed, leading to reduced variation and difficulty in generating more new varieties. Furthermore, despite the implementation of new techniques the time taken to produce and test varieties is an important limiting consideration.

The immense complexities faced by plant biochemists and physi-ologists, in attempting to define the parameters governing such factors as photosynthetic efficiency and nutritional deficiency cannot be over-stated; indeed some models of photosynthesis indicate that the process may have an in-built inefficiency which is unavoidable. It should also be stressed that the plant breeders objectives (i.e. improving the efficiency of a crop variety) are often different from those operating in an evolutionary sense, where selection operates at the level of survival rather than efficiency. Improving efficiency is a human objective and the plant breeders' part is to trick the plant into performing in ways which do not occur in nature. The new techniques outlined below, may offer much wider scope for improving crop plants in ways that are of value to the human consumer.

New technologies

Over the past few years a number of methodologies have come to the fore which would seem to have much to offer in terms of advancing current research in the plant sciences, and exploiting the knowledge gained to develop new crops. The first of these areas is concerned with the isolation, manipulation and subsequent growth of naked plant cells (protoplasts) and cells in tissue culture. The second field, recombinant-DNA (r-DNA) technology or 'genetic engineering', has grown out of work initially carried out on micro-organisms. This technology allows for the detailed manipulation of individual genes. The importance of such developments has been highlighted recently with the investment of large sums of venture capital in small companies, whose products — or potential products — are based on the application of recombinant-DNA and tissue culture techniques.

These two areas of research have in recent years become associated with the general field of biotechnology. This is generally taken to be the use of living organisms (e.g. bacteria, yeast) or their component parts (e.g. enzymes) in the processing of materials to provide consumables or services, and it dates back a very long time including, for example, cheese, bread, wine and beer making. The central theme of biotechnology has been that the biological agent, often a micro-organism, is used in a process requiring engineering technologies, usually fermentation or controlled environment conditions, yielding a product which may require further physical processing, e.g. drying, concentration and packaging, before it reaches the market place. Plants and plant products already supply the raw materials, as well as the biological agents, involved in a number of industrial applications considered as biotechnological (Table 1.3). For example, sugar-cane provides feedstock for ethanol production in Brazil and elsewhere, and proteolytic enzymes from papaya (paw-paw), fig and pineapple are widely used in the food processing industry. The development of processes yielding various plant products such as anticancer and antileukaemic substances, alkaloids, steroids, oils and dyes from cells and organs in culture is already taking place.

However, the general term biotechnology can also be taken to

Table 1.3. Industrial sectors influenced by biotechnology.

Sector	Product/activity
Food	Dairy, fish and meat products, novel foodstuffs; starch; sugar syrups; food additives, colour, flavours, stabilizers, yeasts; vitamins; amino acids.
Agriculture	Feedstuffs; pesticides, microbial, viral; N-fixing inocculants; mycorrhizal inocculants; vegetative propagation; embryo production; vaccines.
Chemical	Organic acids; alcohols; ketones; enzymes; polymers; perfumeries; metal extraction; bioaccumulation.
Pharmaceutical	Antibiotics; diagnostics; enzyme inhibitors; vaccines; steroids.
Fermentation	Brewing, beer, wines, spirits; foods, baking, cheese, single cell proteins; chemicals, fuel alcohols; enzymes; antibiotics; drugs; vitamins; vaccines.
Energy	Biomass; ethanol; methane.
Service industries	Waste management; water purification; effluent treatment; oil recovery.

include the application of current scientific methods and techniques (the technology) to the modification and improvement of biological systems, be they plant, animal, micro-organism or cells in culture. Indeed, such applications can already be seen in the use of plant protoplast and cell culture techniques, for the mass propagation of species for which there is no other adequate way of producing large numbers of plants in a short time (e.g. oil palm and the Boston fern). Similar tissue culture techniques have also been applied to the selection and maintenance of disease-free plant stocks through the culture of meristems and, more recently, r-DNA techniques have been applied to the screening of plants for the presence of viruses.

The two areas of research associated with recombinant-DNA technology and plant cell tissue culture are potentially applicable to a wide variety of plant species, as well as offering a precision in manipulating genetic material hitherto unobtainable. Recombinant-DNA techniques in particular have already contributed much to the elucidation of basic mechanisms in plants at the molecular level. Furthermore, such techniques in the hands of plant breeders, geneticists, physiologists, biochemists, pathologists and molecular biologists, will enable the identification and eventual manipulation of single and multiple genes controlling important plant functions. In parallel, the development and construction of vectors for the transfer of genes between plants, from plants to micro-organisms, and *vice versa*, is also taking place.

All of the broad areas of application outlined above can be considered under the heading of plant biotechnology, and form the subject matter of later chapters, together with an appraisal of the complexities of the systems involved, the difficulties which may be encountered, and an indication of what may be achieved in both the short and long term.

Further reading

Apeldoorn van J.H.F. (1981) (Ed.) *Biotechnology: A Dutch Perspective*. Report by the Netherlands Study Centre of Technology Trends.

Bull A.T., Holt G. & Lilly M.D. (1982) *Biotechnology: International Trends and Perspectives*. Organization for Economic Co-operation and Development, Paris.

Chrispeels M.J. & Sadeva D. (1977) *Plants, Food and People*. W.H. Freeman & Co., San Francisco.

Office of Technology Assessment (1981) *Impacts of Applied Genetics. Micro-organisms, Plants and Animals*. Report U.S. Congress.

Science (1983) **219**, No. 4585. Biotechnology Issue.

Smith J.E. (1981) *Biotechnology*. Institute Of Biology. Studies in Biology, No. 136. Arnold, London.

2 Plant Molecular Biology

The development of a plant involves a large number of steps, each of which depends on the expression of specific genes. The structure and function of the cells is most directly determined by proteins, which are the end-product of gene expression. However, the expression of these genes can be modified by a whole range of environmental factors such as light quality and quantity, nutrient supply, pathogenic and symbiotic organisms. The situation is complicated still further by the fact that a plant cell has not one, but three interacting genomes (Fig. 2.1), making them genetically the most complex of all cells. Besides the nuclear genome, complete genetic systems are located in the plastids and the

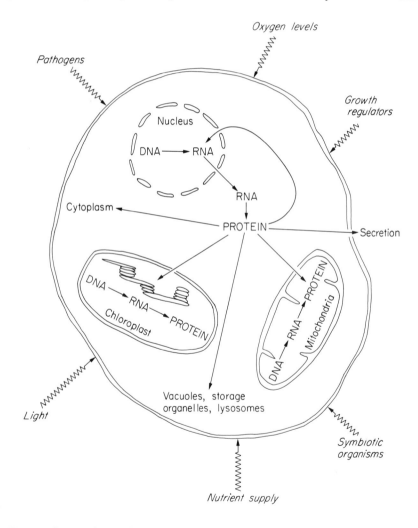

Fig. 2.1. Genome interactions. The three plant genomes interact with each other during the development of a cell as it differentiates to form part of a mature tissue. Expression of all three plant genomes is modulated by the environmental and cellular conditions prevailing.

mitochondria. However, these organelles do not synthesize all of their own proteins, the nuclear genome playing an important role in organelle biogenesis.

Our knowledge of the structure and expression of the plant genome has come largely through the use of recombinant-DNA or gene-cloning techniques. This technology allows the isolation and characterization of specific pieces of DNA, by cloning the DNA sequences into bacterial cells where they can be replicated to yield large quantities for analysis. The methods involved in recombinant-DNA technology are described in Chapter 3. In addition to supplying much basic information concerning gene structure and expression, recombinant-DNA technology provides the opportunity for specifically manipulating genetic material, and moving such material around between different organisms. To date, most gene transfers have taken place from eukaryotes to prokaryotes, and between different prokaryotes and unicellular eukaryotes such as yeast. There are only limited examples of the replacement of genes into cells of higher organisms, but attempts at such transfers are commanding considerable research effort. These types of genetic manipulation may ultimately give us the opportunity to engineer agricultural crops and industrially important plants in order to tailor them more closely to fulfil man's needs. However, before considering the feasibility of these ideas it is necessary to have a good understanding of how plant genes function and interact with environmental stimuli. A text of this length cannot hope to cover all aspects of plant molecular biology in detail, but there are many specialist books on the subject to which the reader is referred (see for example: Boulter & Parthier, 1982). In this chapter we aim to give an overview of the state of knowledge of plant molecular biology and the ways in which the subject is being investigated.

The nuclear genome

The nuclear genome is the largest in the plant cell, both in terms of picograms of DNA and in the number of genes encoded (i.e. in complexity). Nuclear DNA is packaged into chromosomes along with histones and non-histone proteins (Fig. 2.2), all of which play important roles in gene expression. These various components are held together to form chromatin by both hydrophobic and electrostatic forces. While the DNA encodes the genetic information, the proteins are involved in controlling packaging of DNA and in regulating the availability of DNA for transcription. Although the structure of eukaryotic chromatin has been fairly well characterized (Nagl, 1982) the roles of the various individual proteins in chromatin structure and gene regulation have yet to be elucidated.

One process which is basic to all development is the replication of

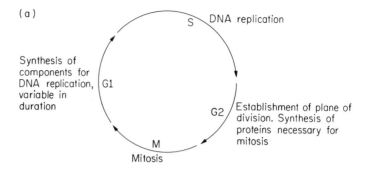

(a)

S   DNA replication

Synthesis of
components for
DNA replication, | G1
variable in
duration

G2   Establishment of plane of
division. Synthesis of
proteins necessary for
mitosis

M
Mitosis

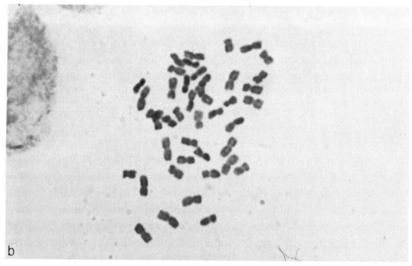

b

Fig. 2.2. Cell division: (a) diagrammatic representation of the cell cycle (see text for details); (b) mitotic chromosomes from a root tip (cell) of *Festuca rubra* (hexaploid, $2n = 42$.) The magnification is approximately $\times 1600$. (Photograph by courtesy of Mr J. Bailey, Leicester.)

the nuclear genetic material, and its equal distribution between two daughter cells during mitosis. The DNA contained in each of the daughter cells must be identical to that contained in the original cell. Without the process of mitotic division no development can occur. During the S phase of the cell cycle (Fig. 2.2) histones are synthesized and DNA is replicated. Although there are many gaps in our knowledge of the replication process, it is clear that replication is initiated at many sites along the DNA and proceeds bidirectionally (Bryant, 1982). The length of DNA synthesized from one origin of replication is termed a replicon and after synthesis the components are reassembled into chromatin as the cell enters the G2 phase of the cycle, in which preparation is made for mitosis. Following mitosis (M phase) there is a phase known as G1, during which the cell prepares for S phase by synthesizing components and enzymes necessary for replication. While the S, G2 and M phases are normally relatively constant in length for a given species, the G1 phase can vary considerably according to the cell's immediate environment. Exceptions can occur in highly differentiated tissues but, normally, once DNA replication has begun the cell is committed to completion of mitosis. In differentiated tissues the cell cycle may be arrested at different points, and changes often take place in the DNA, resulting in a loss of totipotency (see Chapter 5). It is not known whether gross changes take place or if certain genes arrive in a state where they can no longer be expressed. There is certainly no evidence for amplification of specific highly active genes in differentiated cells.

Table 2.1. Sizes of nuclear genomes for a variety of plant species.

Species	pgDNA/haploid genome
Arabidopsis (*A. thaliana*)	0·5
Mung bean (*Vigna radiata*)	0·53
Tobacco (*Nicotiana tabaccum*)	2·0
Runner bean (*Phaseolus coccineus*)	3·5
Wheat (*Triticum aestivum*)	5·1
Rye (*Secale cereale*)	8·4
Broad bean (*Vicia faba*)	26·0
Onion (*Allium cepa*)	33·5
Mistletoe (*Viscum album*)	107·0

Plant cells contain large amounts of DNA, the amount being very variable between species (Table 2.1) from the smallest (*Arabidopsis thaliana* 0·5 pg/haploid genome) to some members of the *Loranthaceae* (mistletoes) which have over 100 pg/haploid genome (Nagl *et al.*, 1983). Even the smallest plant genome is about five times larger than that found in *Drosophila melanogaster*, and contains much more DNA than is required to specify all the proteins synthesized during the course of development. What is the function of this additional DNA? Many different methods are being employed in genome analysis, ranging from examination of DNA renaturation kinetics to detailed analysis of individual sequences by the process of molecular cloning. The techniques of gene cloning are described in detail in Chapter 3.

Analysis of renaturation kinetics relies on the fact that, when double-stranded DNA is denatured into two single strands then, given a suitable temperature and ionic environment, the two strands will anneal together again. The process occurs by random collision, so the rate of reannealing depends on the initial concentrations of the different sequences present. Therefore, a sequence which is represented a large number of times in a population of sequences will reanneal more quickly than a sequence present only once. The analysis is carried out by shearing genomic DNA into small fragments (200–400 base pairs), separating the two strands and then allowing the mixture of sequences to reanneal. After various periods of time the fraction of the DNA remaining single-stranded is determined, and this fraction is plotted on a graph against the quantity C_0t, which is the time of reannealing multiplied by the initial concentration of the DNA. The time after which half of the DNA is reannealed is designated $C_0t_{1/2}$, and comparison of this value for different DNA samples allows a measure of their complexity. DNA containing sequences repeated many times will reanneal faster (i.e. have a lower $C_0t_{1/2}$) than the same amount of DNA containing unique sequences. The theory and mathematics of DNA renaturation kinetics is discussed by Britten & Davidson (1976). When this type of analysis is carried out, a large proportion of a plant genome reanneals much more rapidly than would be expected if the genome consisted entirely of single copy sequences. For pea, only about 15% of the DNA behaves as single or low copy number sequences (Murray *et al.*, 1979), while the remainder consists of sequences repeated many times. It is sometimes possible to distinguish families of moderately-repetitive and highly-repetitive sequences. Most genes occur in the non-repeated DNA, with a few notable exceptions, (ribosomal RNA genes) but not all of the non-repeated DNA is made up of structural genes. Highly repetitive DNA is often found at the centromeres in a condensed form known as heterochromatin. Many families of repetitive DNA have now been well characterized in physical terms (Flavell, 1980) but their function, along with that of excess non-repetitive DNA, is not well understood. One exception to the location of structural genes within non-repeated DNA, is the family of genes coding for cytoplasmic ribosomal RNAs: these genes are highly reiterated in plant genomes and are present in DNA located at the nucleoli. The genes coding for the 18S and 25S rRNAs are organized into a unit (Fig. 2.3) and the units are organized in tandem repeats. Transcription of a whole unit takes place into a large precursor RNA molecule, which is then processed by a number of steps to the mature sizes (Grierson, 1982). The size of the spacer regions between the coding sequences varies considerably between species, and also to a certain extent between different copies in the same species.

Plant ribosomal RNA genes and a number of other structural genes from a variety of species have now been analysed in more detail. This analysis has been made possible by the use of gene-cloning techniques (see Chapter 3), whereby quantities of a sequence can be obtained in a pure state for further study. DNA sequencing techniques have allowed fine-structure analysis of a number of plant genes. In common with many animal genes, some of the plant genes sequenced to date are found to have

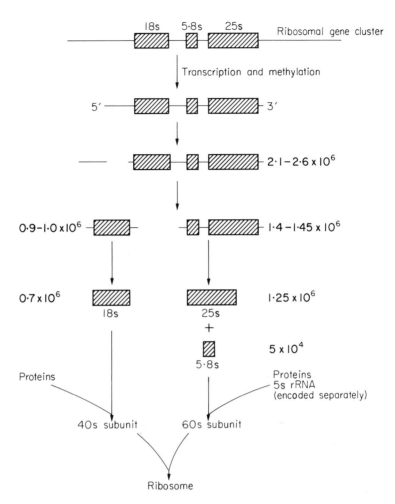

Fig. 2.3. Synthesis of rRNA and assembly of ribosomes. The ribosomal gene clusters are transcribed into precursor molecules which are processed by a number of steps to give three mature rRNAs. The first processing step (i.e. removal of 5′ region) is not well established in plants but occurs in animal cells. The numbers quoted next to the RNA molecules represent the approximate molecular weights. A further rRNA (5s) is also required for subunit assembly together with proteins which are synthesized in the cytoplasm and transported into the nucleus. Final assembly of the two subunits into a complete ribosome does not take place until initiation of protein synthesis occurs in the cytoplasm (Fig. 2.6).

their coding sequences interrupted by introns or intervening sequences. These introns are transcribed but are not represented in the mature mRNA and hence are not translated. No introns have been found in rRNA genes, but they have been demonstrated in a number of other plant structural genes; for example, in a phaseolin gene from french beans (Sun *et al.*, 1981) and in a leghemoglobin gene from soybean (Sullivan *et al.*, 1981). Sequencing of the 3′ and 5′ flanking regions in those plant genes studied has revealed potential sequences involved in the control of gene expression. Such sequences are best illustrated by examining the processes involved in the expression of a gene at the molecular level.

Expression of nuclear genes

The synthesis of a functional product within a cell, using the information contained in the coding sequence of a gene, relies on the co-ordination of a whole series of events. If the gene codes for a polypeptide (rather than a ribosomal or transfer RNA molecule) then the gene must be transcribed into messenger RNA, which is then translated to give that polypeptide. Processing of both the mRNA and polypeptide molecules may occur. There is potential for regulation of gene expression at all of these steps, and elucidation of the mechanisms and regulatory steps involved has been the subject of intensive investigation. The study of animal systems has always been at a more advanced stage than plants in this respect, but much information learned from animals can be applied to, and assist in the investigation of plant gene expression.

Transcription

A gene is transcribed into RNA by a DNA-dependent RNA polymerase, which copies a single-stranded DNA template using the four ribonucleotide triphosphates as substrates. Plant cells, in common with animal cells, contain three types of RNA polymerase which can be distinguished on the basis of physical properties, localization and function (Table 2.2). RNA polymerase II is responsible for the synthesis of mRNA precursors and is located in the nucleoplasm. RNA polymerases have been isolated and characterized from a wide range of plant

Table 2.2. Characteristics of the three types of DNA-dependent RNA polymerase found in eukaryotic nuclei.

Characteristic	Polymerase		
	I	II	III
Localization	Nucleolus	Nucleoplasm	Nucleoplasm
Sensitivity to α-Amanitin	Insensitive	Sensitive	Moderately sensitive
Mn^{2+}/Mg^{2+} activity ratio*	$1-2$	$5-10$	2
Product of transcription	Precursors of the two large rRNAs and 5·5s rRNA	Precursors of mRNA	Precursors of tRNA. 5s rRNA

* The enzyme activity is dependent on divalent metal ions and each has a characteristic ratio of activity for Mn^{2+} and Mg^{2+} ions.

species; for example, soybean (Guilfoyle & Malcolm, 1980) and wheat embryos (Jendrisak, 1980), and they carry out the first vital step in gene expression. RNA polymerase binds to a promotor region in the 5' flanking sequence of the gene, initiates a mRNA chain and then copies through the gene until it reaches a termination signal. Eukaryotic promotors are distinct from those in prokaryotes and are not recognized efficiently by prokaryote polymerases. In 1980, Benoist *et al.* put forward certain ideas as to the nature of eukaryotic promotors by comparison of the ovalbumin gene sequence with other eukaryotic genes. These workers reported a sequence homology 20–30 bases prior to the initiation point of the RNA molecule which was usually the DNA sequence TATAA followed by more A,T residues; this sequence has come to be known as a TATA or Hogness box. In addition, there is a conserved sequence CCAT which occurs 70–80 bases before the initiation point of the mRNA. Both of these sequences have been found in plant genes; for example, in the sequence of a maize zein gene (Pedersen *et al.*, 1982).

The control of transcription is a vital element in the overall control of gene expression, but is very poorly understood in plants. Studies have been carried out to look at overall levels and activities of the various types of polymerases. Guilfoyle & Malcolm (1980) found that during soybean germination the activities of polymerase I and III increased rapidly after 6 hours, whereas the increase in polymerase II was much less dramatic. An increase in polymerase activity in etiolated seedlings treated with a growth regulator, auxin, was also reported. During germination, polymerase II undergoes a change in size of its largest subunit to convert the 'A' form of the enzyme to the 'B' form. Concurrently with this change, the polymerase II activity in the seedlings increases dramatically although the amount of protein remains constant, leading to the hypothesis that the 'A' form must be converted to the active 'B' form at the start of germination for transcription to take place (Guilfoyle *et al.*, 1980).

Template availability has been studied in a few cases but it is very difficult to measure and interpret. Some increase in overall template activity can be measured after treating tissues with auxins or gibberellins, and this parameter has also been examined in wounding responses in potato tubers (Wielgat *et al.*, 1979). Template availability has been linked in some cases to the types of non-histone chromosomal proteins associated with the DNA (Kahl *et al.*, 1979).

In animal systems the control of transcription has been shown to involve changes in chromatin structure, methylation of cytosine residues of the DNA and the interaction of specific regulatory molecules with the chromatin (for a review see Lewin, 1980). Although it is thought likely that such phenomena may also be involved in plant cells, there is little direct supportive evidence as yet.

The key to this problem of the mechanism of transcriptional control will probably be found in the study of a larger number of individual genes and their expression during development in order to define consensus sequences in the 3′ and 5′ flanking sequences. Detailed studies of transcription control are discussed later, when chloroplast protein synthesis and developmental gene regulation are considered.

Processing of RNA

Almost all RNA transcripts are processed to form the mature RNA molecules which will function in the cell. Ribosomal RNA molecules are cleaved from a large primary transcript (see p. 13) and transfer RNA molecules also undergo extensive modification. Intervening sequences are removed from the tRNA precursor as well as additional sequences from the 3′ and 5′ ends. Maturation then requires the modification of several bases, and the addition of CCA at the 3′ terminus. The vast majority of tRNA studies have been carried out on yeast and animal cells (Knapp et al., 1979), but the processes appear to be similar in plants.

The processing and maturation of mRNA precursors in eukaryotic cells involves a number of steps. At an early stage a 'cap' structure is added to the 5′ end (Fig. 2.4); this consists of a 7-methyl guanosine residue attached in inverted (i.e. 5′−5′) orientation. Caps have been demonstrated in a number of plant messenger RNAs, for example, from *Avena sativa* (Haugland & Cline, 1978) and they appear to increase the efficiency of translation, although uncapped messages can also be translated.

The mRNA precursors are often modified further in the nucleus by the addition of a polyadenylic acid (poly-A) tail. This is added to the 3′ terminus by an enzyme, poly-A polymerase, which is found in animal and plant cells. Poly-A tails have been found on many plant messenger RNAs including those for hordein (Matthews & Miflin, 1980), small subunit of ribulose bisphosphate carboxylase (RUBPCase) (Highfield & Ellis, 1978) and leghaemoglobin (Verma et al., 1974). The length of the tail is variable, being up to 200 residues, and apart from a possible role in increasing the stability of mRNA, the function of the poly-A tail is not understood. It is, however, very useful to the molecular biologist in the isolation of mRNA by affinity chromatography using oligo-dT cellulose (p. 35). The signal for addition of the adenosine residues is carried in the transcript in the form of a polyadenylation site AATAAA which is usually about 20 nucleotides from the translation termination codon, and surrounded by G and C residues.

The final processing step which must be considered in mRNA maturation is the removal (or splicing out) of intervening sequences which are transcribed along with the rest of the gene. Endonucleases

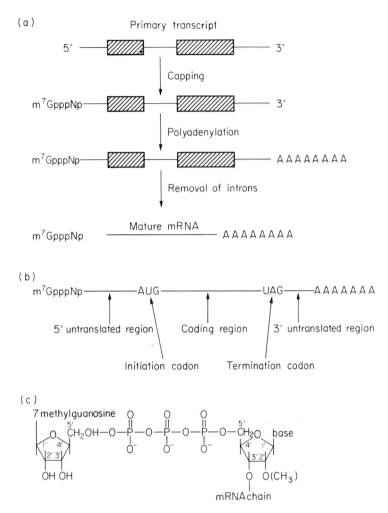

Fig. 2.4. Processing of mRNA. (a) The primary transcript is capped, polyadenylated and has introns removed to produce a mature mRNA molecule. The order in which these steps occurs is not established definitely in plants and is not necessarily exactly as indicated. (b) The coding region of a mature mRNA molecule is separated from the cap by the 5′ untranslated region (which may be very short) and from the poly-A tail by the 3′ untranslated region. (c) Structure of the cap. The cap at the 5′ end consists of a methylated guanine base joined to a ribose which is linked via the 5′ hydroxyl to the 5′ hydroxyl of the next residue. The two are linked via three phosphate groups. The penultimate residue is methylated at the 2′ hydroxyl of the ribose moiety.

specifically cleave the mRNA molecule, and the coding regions are joined to form a continuous coding sequence. The significance and mechanism of this process is not understood in plants, but junctions between introns and coding regions (exons) appear to play an important role, as there is a high degree of sequence conservation at these junctions (Fig. 2.5).

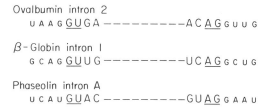

Fig. 2.5. Intron—exon junctions. The intron is represented by large capitals and the exon by small capitals. The first and last residues of the introns are commonly GU and AG respectively. There is less conservation of the exon boundary but basic amino acids are commonly found before the intron. A codon may actually be split by the intron.

After completion of these processing steps, the mature mRNA molecule is transported into the cytoplasm where it can participate in protein synthesis. Processing and transport are potential regulatory points as not all transcripts may be made available for translation. Kamaley & Goldberg (1980) suggested a major role for the post-transcriptional selection of mRNA in the control of gene expression in tobacco tissues. By hybridization techniques, they demonstrated that considerably more non-repeated DNA sequences are transcribed than eventually appear in the translated mRNA population. The amount of mRNA available for translation can also be regulated by degradation, providing yet another level of control. Studies of the control of gene expression are complicated by the problems of distinguishing between the processes of regulation of transcription, processing and degradation, and the biological activity of mRNA.

Translation

Translation is the process by which the information in the mRNA molecule is decoded into a polypeptide chain. The process is carried out by ribosomes and aminoacyl-transfer RNAs, along with a complex mixture of other factors. The mechanism of protein synthesis is essentially similar for all organisms, although there are some differences in the components and reactions between prokaryotes and eukaryotes. Three major steps can be distinguished in the synthesis of a polypeptide; these are (i) chain initiation, (ii) chain elongation and (iii) release of the completed chain from the ribosome. The details of chain initiation and of the components of the synthetic apparatus in eukaryotic cells are given in Fig. 2.6. The tRNA^{met_i} used in initiation is specific for this step and does not participate in the positioning of other methionine residues in the polypeptide chain. However, in contrast to prokaryotes, the eukaryotic initiator methionine is not formylated.

Protein synthesis proceeds from the amino- to the carboxyl-terminus of the polypeptide by step-wise addition of amino acids, brought in by

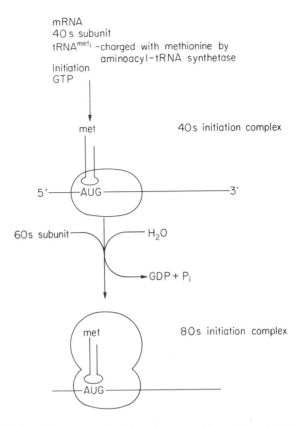

Fig. 2.6. Initiation of protein synthesis in eukaryotes. The initiator tRNA
(tRNA^{meti}) is charged with methionine, and combines with mRNA and 40s subunit of
the ribosome to form the 40s initiation complex. GTP and initiation factors (proteins)
are required. As the 60s subunit binds, GTP is hydrolysed and the 80s initiation
complex results.

tRNAs charged with the appropriate amino acid (Fig. 2.7). The specificity of protein synthesis depends on the correct charging of tRNAs
with the appropriate amino acids, by amino-acyl-tRNA synthetase
enzymes. Once the tRNA is amino-acylated its anticodon interacts with
the complementary codon on the mRNA and positions the amino acid;
this occurs independently of the nature of the amino acid carried.
Therefore, incorrect charging of tRNAs would lead to mistakes in
protein synthesis.

More than one ribosome can translate an mRNA molecule at the
same time. A polysome consists of an mRNA molecule with a number
of ribosomes at various positions along the coding sequence, all carrying
partially completed polypeptides. As each ribosome reaches the termination codons (see Appendix 1) the subunits dissociate and the newly
synthesized polypeptide is released.

The mechanism of protein synthesis is essentially the same for both

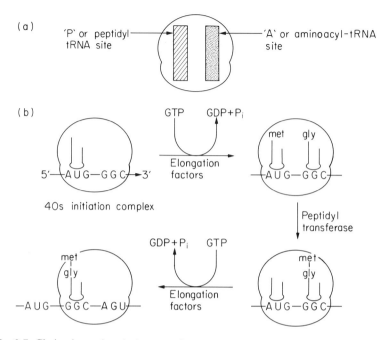

Fig. 2.7. Chain elongation during protein synthesis. (a) Two domains are recognized in the eukaryotic ribosome, although these are not defined in terms of the three-dimensional structure. The 'P' site holds the growing peptide attached to a tRNA molecule. The 'A' site accommodates the next tRNA before its amino acid is attached to the chain. The initiator tRNA binds at the 'P' site. (b) After initiation the next tRNA binds and GTP is hydrolysed. Magnesium ions are required for integrity of the ribosomes. Peptidyl transferase catalyses the transfer of the initiator methione (or the growing peptide in subsequent cycles) to the next amino acid. The hydrolysis of GTP drives the movement of the tRNA from the 'A' to the 'P' site leaving the 'A' site empty to accommodate the next amino-acyl tRNA.

plants and animals; ribosomes from one will faithfully translate mRNA from the other. This point is well illustrated by the synthesis of plant proteins in response to injection of mRNA into *Xenopus laevis* oocytes (Larkins *et al.*, 1979; Matthews *et al.*, 1981). There is little direct evidence that translational control is implicated in the regulation of plant gene expression, but this step certainly cannot be excluded as a potential control point.

Post-translational modification and compartmentation

Primary translation products undergo a whole variety of modifications, which are vital to the production of a fully functional protein. Polysomes can occur either free in the cytoplasm or bound to membranes forming rough endoplasmic reticulum. The membrane-bound polysomes are synthesizing proteins which are either secreted from the cell, form part of a membrane or are packaged into specialized organelles (e.g. seed

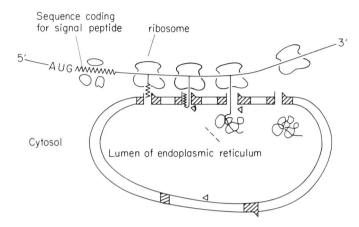

Fig. 2.8. The signal hypothesis for protein translocation. After initiation of protein synthesis, the first sequence to be produced is the signal peptide (〰). When this peptide emerges from the ribosome, it interacts, together with the ribosome, with membrane receptors (▧). The receptors assemble to form a pore through which the nascent chain passes. The signal sequence is cleaved off by a signal peptidase (◁) and degraded (----), and the remainder of the protein is translocated across the membrane as protein synthesis proceeds. After completion of synthesis and translocation, the ribosome dissociates from the mRNA. (Redrawn from Blobel, 1980.)

storage protein bodies). This latter category does not include chloroplast and mitochondrial proteins, which are considered separately later in the chapter. How is polysome attachment to membranes mediated, and how does this correlate with the transport of proteins to their final cellular locations? It has been proposed that the polypeptide itself carries a signal at or near the N-terminus which mediates the attachment to the membrane (Fig. 2.8). Translocated proteins carry a N-terminal extension of about twenty amino acids, termed a signal peptide, which binds to a receptor in the membrane as soon as it has been synthesized and has emerged from the ribosome (Blobel *et al.*, 1979). Binding initiates transport across the membrane, which occurs concurrently with translation, and is accompanied by removal of the signal peptide by a specific membrane-associated peptidase. Analysis of signal peptides from different polypeptides has shown that there is no strict sequence conservation between them. However, the central portion of each signal peptide is hydrophobic, and there often tends to be a number of methionine residues distributed along the length. Signal peptides have been found on the primary translation products of a number of plant mRNAs; for example, on zein from maize (Larkins *et al.*, 1979).

In addition to the removal of signal peptides from proteins other modifications are carried out. Glycosylation occurs during passage of proteins through a membrane, via dolicol phosphate intermediates; the protein specifies its own glycosylation sites which occur at residues

ASN-X-SER, where X is any amino acid and the glycoside unit is added to the serine residue. Many plant proteins are glycosylated in this way (Matthews *et al.*, 1981). The function of certain proteins depends on other modifications such as phosphorylation or adenylation, although these modifications are not necessarily associated with passage through membranes.

Regulation of gene expression during development

When the processes from transcription to translocation are completed, the end-products are the functional proteins which are involved in growth and development. The proteins must be produced in the correct tissue at the correct time in order that normal development can take place, so regulation of these processes is most important. The mechanisms by which a gene is expressed are now becoming well characterized, but the regulatory processes are very poorly understood. For most plant genes which have been investigated it is not yet known at which stage of the expression process regulation takes place. This question is the subject of investigation, using a number of plant developmental systems as well as responses of plants to environmental stimuli. We will consider below some of the plant systems which have been looked at in attempts to answer the question of gene regulation.

Light is vital to plants for photosynthesis, and also appears to exert many developmental effects; it is an obvious environmental factor to consider. One of the light receptors in plants, which enables the plant to respond to different light environments, is the protein phytochrome (for a review, see Smith, 1982). Phytochrome participates in many light-directed developmental responses, but it is not yet known how these effects are mediated at the level of gene expression. What is now becoming apparent is that the synthesis of phytochrome is itself regulated by light (Quail, 1984), but the mechanism of regulation is not understood. One of the major effects of light on plants appears to take place via phytochrome on the synthesis of chloroplast proteins and the biogenesis of chloroplasts. This particular development system is close to being understood at the molecular level; it will be dealt with in detail when the chloroplast genome is considered (p. 28).

The synthesis of seed storage proteins has been extensively studied in a variety of crop plants, both for their intrinsic molecular interest and for the possibility of improving the nutritional value of storage proteins by genetic manipulation techniques (Chapter 7). The synthesis of these proteins is tightly regulated, the proteins being synthesized only during one developmental phase in one tissue. In legumes they are laid down in the cotyledons, whilst the endosperm serves as the storage tissue in cereals; they are only synthesized during the phase of seed development in which the storage cells enlarge but have ceased to divide. The

overall pattern of storage protein synthesis has been extensively characterized in a number of crop species, and the effect of environmental
factors (particularly the state of nitrogen and sulphur nutrition) has been
examined. High nitrogen is correlated with increased storage protein
synthesis. This system is attractive for the study of gene regulation. How
these genes are regulated is as yet poorly understood, but now that a
number of genes have been cloned (see Table 3.2) investigation at the
molecular level can be undertaken. The mature mRNAs do not appear
to be present in tissues where the proteins are not found, indicating that
either transcriptional control or pre-translational selection is occuring.
There is some evidence that mRNA levels correlate with the rate of
accumulation of the proteins (see, e.g. Muntz et al., 1981). Certain
mRNA sequences have been described as 'superabundant' during
soybean seed development and these accumulated co-ordinately during
the early developmental stages, and then decayed before the onset of
seed maturation (Goldberg et al., 1981); they were undetectable in other
tissues. Transcriptional control is indicated in this case. Fischer &
Goldberg (1982) have analysed a number of soybean seed protein genes,
including the storage protein glycinin (see Table 7.6) and seed lectin. To
date, they have obtained no evidence for control regions in the 5'
flanking sequences of these genes specifying their co-ordinate developmental expression in the seed. These workers have also shown that a
mutant which lacks lectin has a transposable element (p. 83) in the
lectin gene which interferes with transcription (Goldberg et al., 1983).

As well as examining normal developmental processes, it is common
to use a system which can be perturbed by an external stimulus.
Examples of this type of approach would include the use of growth
regulators (auxin and gibberellins), or placing plants under stressful
conditions. When challenged with pathogens or irradiated with ultra-
violet light, plants respond by synthesizing certain proteins which are
involved in the production of protective compounds, e.g. flavonoids.
One such protein is chalcone synthase which is involved in flavonoid
biosynthesis; Hahlbrock et al. (1983) have demonstrated that in cultured
cells induction of enzymes involved in this pathway is accompanied by
the appearance of their mRNAs, suggesting control at the level of
transcription. The precise mechanism of control is unknown.

Similarly, growth regulators trigger off certain responses in plant
tissues and many studies have been carried out on this phenomenon.
Mature plant tissues have been used for some studies but most investigations have been carried out on germinating seeds, embryonic axes or
developing seedlings. For example, starch is mobilized from the
endosperm of germinating barley grains by α-amylase. Gibberellic acid
exerts an effect on α-amylase production in the aleurone cells of de-
embryonated grains. A number of hypotheses have been put forward to
explain this effect but it is still open to speculation. One suggestion is

that there is a direct effect on transcription (Ho, 1980) but others have suggested the involvement of enhanced mRNA translation. However, it is not clear whether gibberellin acts at a primary level on α-amylase synthesis, or whether increased α-amylase production is a consequence of a chain of events triggered by gibberellin. Similar studies have been carried out on isocitrate lyase in germinating castor beans but no evidence was found for translational control of the synthesis of this enzyme in response to gibberellin (Martin & Northcote, 1983). However, absolute measurements of mRNAs levels were not carried out. Many examples could be cited but there is a general lack of concensus as to the effect of growth regulators at the level of gene expression.

Germination has been studied extensively as a developmental process in its own right as well as a system perturbed by growth regulators. Mature dry seeds do not synthesize proteins nor in general do they contain polysomes, but after imbibition protein synthesis commences (within 30 min to several hours) in the embryonic axes. Ribosomes are present in the dry seed, and there is evidence that enough of all components necessary to initiate protein synthesis are present. However, very soon after the start of imbibition of isolated embryos the synthesis of components of the protein synthetic apparatus begins (Spiegel *et al.*, 1975).

One point which is far from clear is whether mRNA is conserved within the dry seed or *de novo* synthesis is necessary. The answer to this is central to examining the control of gene expression during germination, but is surrounded by some controversy (Bewley, 1982). Some mRNA is certainly conserved within the dry seed, but the population is distinctly different from that in the developing seed, suggesting that this is not simply a residue left over from seed protein synthesis. It has also been shown that newly synthesized mRNA appears on polysomes of wheat embryos at a very early stage. These types of studies depend largely on distinguishing newly synthesized mRNA from existing mRNA on the basis of polyadenylation, and it has been argued that apparently newly synthesized mRNA may in fact be newly adenylated mRNA which had been stored in the dry seed in a non-polyadenylated form (Sieliwanowicz *et al.*, 1977). This latter suggestion indicates control of processing rather than transcription but to date has only been reported by one group. The obvious question to ask is whether the population of mRNA species differs between the conserved and newly synthesized (or adenylated) mRNA. It is possible that certain proteins are encoded by conserved mRNA while transcription is necessary for the synthesis of others. This problem has been examined by translation *in vitro* of mRNA from dry seeds and imbibing seeds, and by DNA−RNA hybridization techniques. So far no significant differences between mRNA from these two sources have been demonstrated.

Although the limit of sensitivity of the techniques may not allow the detection of small, but important changes.

Developmental events in plants are increasingly being studied at the molecular level, and the information obtained may eventually allow some general conclusions to be drawn. The current state of knowledge of gene regulation is still rather sparse, both in terms of development sequences and environmental responses. This area of study is beginning to progress rapidly as more genes become available for study, but it is important to study an individual gene not only in isolation but against the background of the developmental process during which it is expressed.

Chloroplast biogenesis

The presence of a genetic system within chloroplasts was inferred from studies on non-Mendelian inheritance as long ago as 1909, but it was not until 1962 that the presence of organellar DNA and ribosomes was demonstrated (Ris & Plaut, 1962; Lyttleton, 1962). Since then it has been shown that chloroplasts and other plastids contain all the machinery necessary for gene expression. The chloroplast genetics components form a large proportion of those in the leaf, comprising up to 15% of the total DNA and up to 60% of the total ribosomes. The chloroplast genome from a variety of species has been extensively characterized, and the co-operation of the chloroplast and nuclear genomes in chloroplast biogenesis is currently under investigation.

Table 2.3. Comparison of size of some chloroplast DNAs (ctDNA) with bacterial and eukaryotic nuclear DNA.

DNA	Size in base pairs	Size of circle (μm)
Plasmid	$1-200 \times 10^3$	—
E. coli (chromosome)	3.8×10^6	—
Euglena ctDNA	1.4×10^5	40–44
Tobacco ctDNA	1.6×10^5	—
Maize ctDNA	1.36×10^5	43
Broad bean ctDNA	1.21×10^5	39
Arabidopsis total nuclear genome	2×10^8	—

Chloroplast DNA (ctDNA) consists of a circular molecule of $83-128 \times 10^6$ molecular weight ($1.21-1.93 \times 10^5$ bp, Table 2.3) which contains about 85% single-copy sequences (Bedbrook & Kolodner, 1979). The DNA is present in about 30–200 copies per chloroplast. A number of genes have been located on the circle (Fig. 2.9), and one of the principle features is the presence of two copies of the ribosomal DNA sequences.

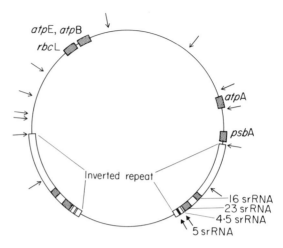

Fig. 2.9. Map of the spinach chloroplast genome. The open arrows (→) indicate restriction sites for the endonuclease Sal I. The closed arrows (→) indicate the position of genes, most of which are shown as blocked in DNA. The genes are: atpA, atpB, atpE — subunits of ATP synthetase−FI complex; psbA — thylakoid membrane protein; rbc L — large subunit of ribulose bisphosphate carboxylase. Many tRNA genes are mapped but are not indicated in order to avoid confusion.

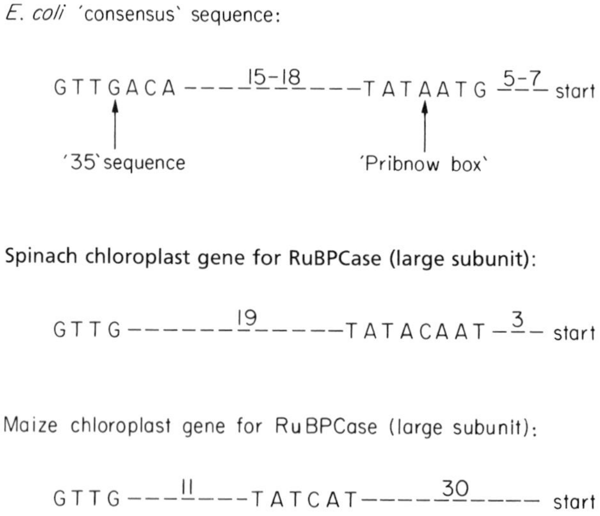

E. coli 'consensus' sequence:

$$\text{G T T G A C A} \;-\!-\!-\!-\!\underset{15\text{-}18}{\underline{}}\!-\!-\!-\!-\; \text{T A T A A T G} \;\underset{5\text{-}7}{\underline{}}\; \text{start}$$

'35' sequence   'Pribnow box'

Spinach chloroplast gene for RuBPCase (large subunit):

$$\text{G T T G} \;-\!-\!-\!-\!-\!-\underset{19}{\underline{}}\!-\!-\!-\!-\!\text{T A T A C A A T} -\underset{3}{\underline{}}-\; \text{start}$$

Maize chloroplast gene for RuBPCase (large subunit):

$$\text{G T T G} \;-\!-\!-\underset{11}{\underline{}}\!-\!-\!-\text{T A T C A T} -\!-\!-\!-\underset{30}{\underline{}}\!-\!-\!-\!-\; \text{start}$$

Fig. 2.10. Comparison of sequences preceding the initiation point of bacterial and chloroplast genes. Investigation of a number of *E. coli* genes has allowed the formulation of consensus sequences involved in the initiation of transcription. The Pribnow box and the '-35' region together form the promoter. Similar sequences have been found in a variety of chloroplast genes (Bohnert *et al.*, 1982). The genes shown here are those coding for ribulose bisphosphate carboxylase (RuBPCase), but the sequences have also been found in other chloroplast genes. The sequences are not drawn to scale.

These sequences are often — although not always — present on a large inverted repeat. Other genes mapped include those for the large subunit of RuBPCase, tRNAs, subunits of ATP synthase, and cytochrome *f*. The chloroplast genome does not have the capacity to code for all the proteins present in the chloroplast, and it is now known that there is a close co-operation between the nuclear and chloroplast genomes during chloroplast biogenesis.

The genetic system in the chloroplast is essentially prokaryotic in nature, which has given rise to much discussion as to the possible prokaryotic origin of plastids (Bogorad, 1975). Control sequences at the 5′ end of the gene which are involved in initiating transcription are very similar to the 'Pribnow' box and the '-35' region characteristic of bacterial genes (see Fig. 2.10 for explanation). In addition, chloroplast genes do not usually contain intervening sequences characteristic of many eukaryotic genes, although some introns have been found, notably in tRNA genes of tobacco and maize (Koch *et al.*, 1981; Takawa & Sugiura, 1982). The mRNA produced from chloroplast genes is not usually polyadenylated, although short sequences of up to 20 residues have been reported (Gray & Cashmore, 1976), and, of course, no transport is required as the mRNA is produced in the same compartment as the ribosome on which it will be translated. There is no evidence that chloroplast mRNA is transported out of the chloroplasts and translated on cytoplasmic ribosomes.

Chloroplast ribosomes also resemble those from prokaryotes, being 70s particles consisting of 30s and 50s subunits, and ribosomes from *E. coli* and plant chloroplasts are immunologically similar. The tRNA chloroplast population is distinctly different from that in the cytoplasm, as are the aminoacylating enzymes. The prokaryotic nature of the protein synthetic machinery is also illustrated by its sensitivity to inhibitors of prokaryotic gene expression such as chloramphenicol. This antibiotic does not inhibit eukaryotic protein synthesis. Studies with such inhibitors have been used extensively in an attempt to elucidate which chloroplast polypeptides are encoded in which plant genome. However, due to the difficulty in delivering antibiotics to their presumed site of action in sufficient concentrations, the interpretation of the results of such experiments is not easy (Galling, 1982). Molecular cloning of genes and more detailed techniques of analysis are now allowing unequivocal assignments of the genes involved in chloroplast biogenesis to a particular genome.

Ribulose bisphosphate carboxylase is the major protein component of chloroplasts and its synthesis is a good example of co-operation between the genomes (Fig. 2.11). The enzyme consists of eight identical, large, catalytic subunits encoded by the chloroplast genome and eight identical, small, regulatory subunits encoded in the nucleus. After synthesis, the large subunit (which has limited solubility) is

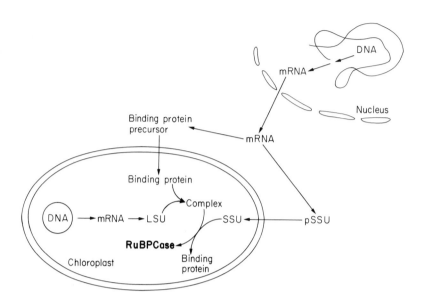

Fig. 2.11. Synthesis of RuBPCase. The small subunit is synthesized as a precursor (pSSU) on cytoplasmic ribosomes and transported into the chloroplast. The binding protein probably behaves similarly but the precursor is less well characterized. The large subunit (LSU) is synthesized on chloroplast ribosomes.

probably bound by a stabilizing protein to maintain solubility prior to assembly into active enzyme. The small subunit is synthesized in the cytoplasm, on free ribosomes, with an N-terminal leader peptide of about 20 amino acids. The complete peptide is then taken up into the chloroplast in an ATP-dependent manner, accompanied by removal of the leader peptide by a stromal peptidase (Smith & Ellis, 1979). This mechanism is not analgous to that involving signal peptide cleavage described by Blobel (1980). The synthesis of this important enzyme clearly depends on the co-ordinate expression of genes in different genomes.

The development of photosynthetically-competent chloroplasts depends on light, and many workers have examined the effect of light on chloroplast protein synthesis. Many polypeptides can be synthesized in the dark, but light has a stimulatory effect on the synthesis of certain proteins. The synthesis of the nuclear-encoded small subunit of RuBPCase in pea and *Lemna* is stimulated by light via a phytochrome-mediated response (Tobin, 1981) which apparently acts at a transcriptional level (Gallagher & Ellis, 1982). A wider range of proteins was studied by Thompson *et al*. (1983), who reported the involvement of phytochrome at the transcriptional level for the control of both chloroplast and nuclear genes. General conclusions are very difficult to draw, however, because different species react very differently to light. For example, mung beans contain high levels of small subunit mRNA in dark-grown seedlings, and cereal plants contain very high levels of the protein in the dark, whereas dark-grown pea seedlings contain negligible amounts of both the mRNA and polypeptide. In pea seedlings, the synthesis of the light harvesting chlorophyll *a/b* binding proteins is controlled by light in an apparently different manner from the small subunit of RuBPCase. No polypeptides are detectable in dark-grown peas but, in light conditions which allow the synthesis of both chlorophylls *a* and *b*, the polypeptides will accumulate. In intermittent light, when there is little or no chlorophyll *b* synthesis, the mRNA but not the polypeptides accumulate (Tobin, 1981). This has led Bennett (1981) to conclude that turnover of the polypeptide is also involved in the control of gene expression.

The many studies on chloroplast protein synthesis have led Ellis (1983) to formulate certain principles to describe the interactions involved.

1 'The majority of chloroplast polypeptides are encoded in nuclear genes and are synthesized by cytoplasmic ribosomes.'

2 'Those chloroplast polypeptides synthesized by cytoplasmic ribosomes are transported into the chloroplast by a post-translational mechanism based on the chloroplast envelope.'

3 'The chloroplast genetic system is essential for chloroplast development and contributes of the order of 100 polypeptides.'

4 'Chloroplast-encoded polypeptide and RNA molecules function entirely within the organelle.'

5 'Synthesis, transport and assembly of the majority of chloroplast polypeptides can occur in both the dark and the light, but illumination has a stimulatory effect at several different levels on the accumulation of these polypeptides.'

These principles make useful working hypotheses to summarize the current state of knowledge of the interactions of the chloroplast and nuclear genome. Some are well substantiated but others may have to be expanded or modified in the light of new discoveries.

The mitochondrial genome

In contrast to the DNA of chloroplasts which is relatively conserved, the DNA of mitochondria exhibits a wide variation in size and form. Animal mitochondrial DNA (mtDNA) is circular and approximately 15–20 kbp in size. Higher plant mtDNA, on the other hand, can be circular or linear and varies from 200 kbp (in brassicas) up to greater than 2500 kbp (in muskmelon). The genome of plant mitochondria is, therefore, very large and may also be divided between one or more DNA molecules (Leaver & Gray, 1982). The situation is further complicated by small, plasmid-like molecules which are present in the mitochondria of some species (see also Chapter 4). Plant mtDNA is more commonly found in a linear arrangement, but in many species it has proved difficult to make a positive identification of the morphology. Some bizarre arrangements have been demonstrated; for example, Palmer & Shields (1984) reported in mtDNA of *Brassica campestris* a circular master copy of 218 kbp which carries a 2 kbp sequence repeated 83 kbp further round the circle. Two smaller circular molecules (135 kbp and 83 kbp) are also present, apparently formed by reciprocal recombination at the repeated sequence.

The amount of mtDNA in plants is less than 1% of the total cellular DNA; however, it plays a vital role in the development and reproduction of the plant. The genetic system within the mitochondria of all organisms is unusual in that it is neither wholly prokaryotic nor eukaryotic in nature. Some similarities to bacterial protein synthesis have been observed, such as sensitivity to antibiotics, sequence homology of rRNAs and the use of N-formyl-methionine to initiate the polypeptide chain. However, the diversity of mitochondrial tRNAs and their structure differs from those found in prokaryotes, the eukaryotic cytoplasm or chloroplasts. Mitochondrial ribosomes range from 55S (in animals) up to 77–78S in plants, in contrast to 70S chloroplast ribosomes and 80S cytoplasmic ribosomes. The major difference between the mitochondrial genetic system and all other systems is that mitochondria use a slightly altered genetic code. Prior to this discovery, it was thought that the genetic code was universal. For example, in the 'normal' code the triplet UGA specifies chain termination, whereas it codes for tryptophan in mammalian and fungal mitochondria. Similarly, in the maize cytochrome *c* oxidase (subunit II) gene, CGG codes for tryptophon, whereas it normally specifies ariginine. The altered genetic code makes many *in vitro* experiments difficult as *in vitro* protein synthesizing systems from both pro- and eukaryotes are based on the use of the 'normal' genetic code. Successful translation of yeast mtRNA has been achieved *in vitro* but only by the inclusion of bacterial suppressor tRNAs.

What function does this genome carry out in the cell? Like the chloroplast, the mitochondrial genome codes for a small, but important, number of mitochondrial polypeptides. There is no evidence that it codes for extra-mitochondrial components (Fig. 2.12). The mtDNA appears to have a similar function in cells of all species, and so some extrapolation can be made from work on yeast. Major products which have been identified include three subunits of cytochrome *c* oxidase, two subunits of the oligomycin-sensitive ATPase complex, a subunit of the cytochrome *bc* complex, and some mitochondrial ribosome components.

The contribution of mitochondrial gene expression to plant development is only poorly understood, but several groups are now investigating this topic. Protein synthesis using intact, isolated mitochondria

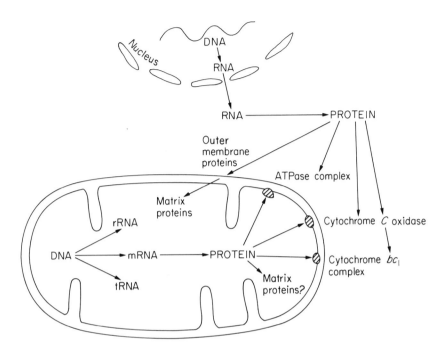

Fig. 2.12. Function of the mitochondrial genome. The mitochondrial genome codes for subunits of three inner membrane complexes, and some matrix proteins (including some of the ribosomal proteins).

has been studied in early seedling development in *Vicia faba* (Leaver & Gray, 1982), although few conclusions could be drawn. The most extensively studied phenomenon involving the mitochondrial genome is cytoplasmic male sterility (CMS). CMS has been exploited by breeders in the production of hybrid lines of crop plants, particularly maize, and there is now a large body of evidence implicating the mitochondrial genome in this phenomenon. The evidence comes firstly from restriction endonuclease analysis which shows differences between the mtDNA from normal and CMS cytoplasms (Spruill *et al.*, 1981). Secondly, changes have been demonstrated in the products of protein synthesis in isolated mitochondria, and these have been correlated with the cytoplasm type, and with the presence or absence of nuclear genes which restore fertility ('restorer' genes). For example, in Texas-type maize (CMS-T) the mitochondria synthesize an extra 13000 MW polypeptide but a 21000 MW polypeptide characteristic of normal cytoplasm is missing. When T-type cytoplasm is restored by its nuclear restorer gene, the 13000 MW polypeptide is no longer synthesized, but the 21000 MW polypeptide does not reappear. A third line of evidence comes from ultra-structural studies of developing anthers; in maize S-type cytoplasm, the first sign of abnormality is mitochondrial degeneration in the tapetal cells. Cytoplasmic male sterility is also correlated with the plasmid-like DNA molecules found in the mitochondria, S-type maize cytoplasm carries two linear molecules of 6·2 kbp (S_1) and 5·2 kbp (S_2). They have inverted terminal repeats of 200 bp, show some sequence homology and can be integrated into the mitochondrial genome. Other maize CMS cytoplasms have different combinations of plasmid-like elements. In *brassica* species, the presence of an 11·3 kbp plasmid is strongly correlated with CMS (Palmer *et al.*, 1983), but this plasmid is not homologous to any found in maize. Thus, there is a general consensus of opinion that cytoplasmic male sterility resides in the mitochondrial genome. One group (Jigeng & Yi-nong, 1982) have reported changes in chloroplast DNA in sterile lines of maize, wheat and rape, but they have not ruled out the additional involvement of mtDNA.

The genetic basis of CMS is of great interest, as the use of these lines can lead to a high degree of cytoplasmic uniformity in a crop. Such uniformity is undesirable as it can render a crop vulnerable to damage by pathogens or extreme environmental conditions. This problem is well illustrated by the massive losses suffered to the American maize crop in 1970, due to a race of southern corn leaf blight which preferentially infected plants with CMS-T-type cytoplasm. Over 85% of hybrid maize carried this cytoplasm.

The identification of 'promiscuous' DNA has come out of the study of plant mtDNA in conjunction with the study of other genomes. Ellis (1982a) used this term to describe DNA sequences which are found in more than one genome of the plant. Maize mtDNA carries a 12 kbp sequence which is homologous to the part of the inverted repeat of the chloroplast genome which encodes the 16S rRNA and two tRNAs (Stern & Lonsdale, 1982). This sequence is not transcribed in mitochondria but appears to be important as it is altered in certain male-sterile lines. Homology between sequences on the nuclear genome and some plasmid-like elements of the mitochondrial genome has also been detected in maize (Kemble *et al.*, 1983). The suggestion was put forward that these plasmid-like elements may provide a mechanism for the transfer of genetic information between genomes.

The mitochondrial genome is perhaps the least well understood in the plant in terms of function, structure and the relationship to development of the plant. Recently, however, there has been an increase in interest as the importance of the genome to normal development was realized and techniques for its analysis became available. The phenomenon of cytoplasmic male sterility provides a good example of abnormal plant development brought about by a cytoplasmic genetic lesion.

Conclusions

It is fairly clear from this survey that, although mechanisms of gene expression in plants are becoming well characterized, we are a long way from understanding how genes are regulated. The interactions between the three genomes and the environment in the development of a healthy plant are still to a large extent shrouded in mystery. If the biotechnologist is to utilize the modern DNA manipulation methods available as a tool for the improvement of crop plants, then understanding these interactions is vital. Specific manipulations of plant genes must result in healthy viable plants for such techniques to be of any practical value, and success in these types of manipulations will almost certainly depend on our obtaining a much greater understanding of the regulation of gene expression.

Further reading

Boulter D. & Parthier B. (1982) (Eds) *Nucleic Acids and Proteins in Plants*. Encyclopaedia of Plant Physiology, Vols 14A & 14B. Springer-Verlag, Berlin.
Grierson D. & Covey S. (1985) *Plant Molecular Biology*. Blackie/Chapman & Hall.
Hall T.C. & Davies J.W. (1979) (Eds) *Nucleic Acids in Plants*. CRC Press, Boca Raton, Florida.
Lewin B. (1980) *Gene Expression 2*. 2nd edn. Wiley Interscience, London.
Szekely M. (1980) *From DNA to Protein*. Macmillan, London.

3 Cloning Plant Genes

Introduction

The development of sophisticated DNA handling techniques dating from the 1970s has made possible the isolation or 'cloning' of genes. Gene cloning can be defined as the isolation and amplification of an individual gene sequence, by insertion of that sequence into a bacterium where it can be replicated. There are many methods involved in cloning but the common principle is to isolate the gene sequence from the many millions present in the organism, and to amplify it for study by replication in a bacterial host, usually on a bacterial plasmid. It is of course essential that the sequence be replicated accurately.

But why do we wish to clone plant genes? Firstly, molecular cloning of genes allows the investigation of gene structure and the sequences which control gene expression. Much of the information presented in Chapter 2 has been obtained using these techniques. Cloning provides the basic information which forms the starting point for many more sophisticated studies. Further, gene-cloning technology may find a place in the manipulation of plants for exploitation by man. This technology could provide an additional tool for the plant breeder, who is trying to improve crop yield, nutritional quality and many other characters by traditional methods. In addition, plants can be viewed as a genetic resource, genes being cloned into, and expressed in, bacteria. These bacteria may then be used to produce desirable plant products on an industrial scale using fermenters.

In order to understand these potential applications, it is necessary to look at the techniques of gene cloning, and also in later chapters at the methods for replacing genes in the plant. This chapter will discuss the underlying principles of gene-cloning techniques, and in particular the problems encountered with applying these techniques to plants. It will not attempt to provide detailed methods; this type of information can be found in specialist monographs such as Old & Primrose (1981) or laboratory manuals such as Maniatis et al. (1982). Although problems can arise when working with plants, much progress has been made, and cloning techniques have been successfully applied to many plant genes.

Principles of complementary DNA cloning

The strategy of complementary DNA (cDNA) cloning involves the copying of mRNA transcripts into DNA; these DNA copies are inserted into bacterial plasmids and then placed into bacteria by transformation. The colony of bacterial cells (clone) carrying the copy of interest is then selected from the many thousands of transformed bacteria. The method was developed following the discovery of the enzyme, reverse transcriptase, which synthesizes DNA from an RNA template. The principle steps involved are summarized in Fig. 3.1 and will now be described in more detail.

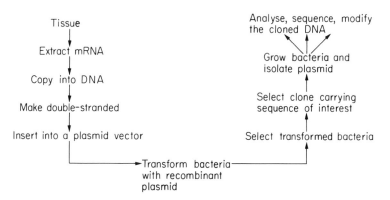

Fig. 3.1. Overall scheme for cDNA cloning (see text for details).

Isolation and characterization of mRNA

The initial isolation of a mRNA preparation can often be a difficult and time-consuming step. Although there are many individual methods available there are two main approaches to the problem. One approach is to prepare polysomes from the tissue, this only being of use if the mRNA is being actively translated. It is possible to separate free cyto-plasmic polysomes from membrane-bound polysomes (Larkins *et al.*, 1976) both of which can then be disrupted, and mRNA extracted from them. Alternatively, total RNA can be prepared prior to mRNA puri-fication. A crude extract of the tissue is prepared and then freed of protein, polysaccharides and other contaminants (see for example, Noyes *et al.*, 1979; Chirgwin *et al.*, 1979; Hall *et al.*, 1978).

Many eukaryotic mRNAs can be further purified from the total or polysomal RNA fraction using the technique of oligo-dT cellulose chromatography (Aviv & Leder, 1972; Bantle *et al.*, 1976). This technique exploits the string of adenosine residues (or poly-A tail) present at the 3′ end of many eukaryotic mRNAs. Under appropriate conditions this tail will bind to a string of thymidine residues immo-bilized on cellulose; the polyadenylated (or poly A+) fraction can then be eluted. Two or three passages of the poly A+ fraction through such a column produces a fraction highly enriched for mRNA. Figure 3.2 summarizes the extraction of mRNA.

The major problem encountered in RNA isolation is that of degradation. RNA is not particularly stable and it is readily attacked by the ubiquitous enzyme ribonuclease. At all stages great precautions must be taken to exclude ribonuclease by sterilization of solutions and equipment. Endogenous ribonuclease action in the tissue must also be avoided by harvesting tissue freshly or storing it at −80°C prior to use, and by the inclusion of potent ribonuclease inhibitors.

An mRNA fraction prepared in any of these ways will contain many different mRNA sequences, but certain techniques can be employed to

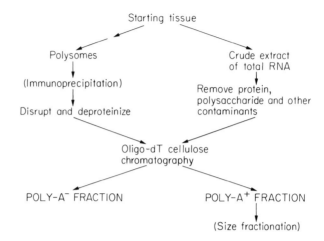

Fig. 3.2. Preparation of eukaryotic mRNA using oligo-dT cellulose chromatography to separate polyadenylated RNA from non-polyadenylated. The steps in brackets indicate optional steps used to enrich mRNA for a particular sequence.

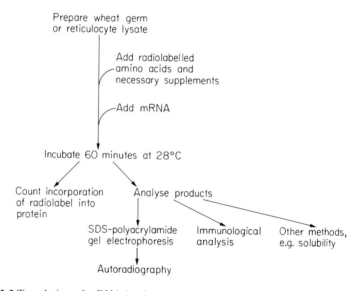

Fig. 3.3 Translation of mRNA *in vitro*.

enrich for a particular mRNA species. At the beginning, careful selection of a tissue in which the mRNA is abundant can be a great help. The use of bean cotyledons harvested during their phase of maximum storage protein synthesis, combined with size fractionation of the mRNA, produces a highly purified storage protein mRNA preparation from french bean (Hall *et al.*, 1978). Size fractionation can be conveniently carried out by sucrose density gradient centrifugation. Considerable purification can be achieved when mRNA is prepared via polysomes if a specific antibody is available to the protein of interest. Immunoprecipation of polysomes has been successfully applied to the purification of lectin mRNA and kunitz trypsin inhibitor mRNA from soybeans (Vodkin, 1981). This powerful technique may well become more widely used in the future.

Having prepared an mRNA fraction, enriched or otherwise, it is necessary to check that the sequence of interest is present. This is done by translation of the mRNA *in vitro* and identification of the appropriate polypeptide in the products obtained (Fig. 3.3). It was found that lysates prepared from wheat germ (Roberts & Paterson, 1973), or from rabbit reticulocytes (Pelham & Jackson, 1976), would faithfully translate eukaryotic mRNAs. These lysates contain most of the components required for protein synthesis but are supplemented with a radiolabelled amino acid and an optimum concentration of magnesium ions. In addition, the wheat germ lysate requires ATP, creatine phosphate, GTP and spermidine. Table 3.1 gives a comparison of the two types of lysate; but the choice of which to use remains very much a matter of individual preference.

Table 3.1. Comparison of rabbit reticulocyte and wheat germ cell-free lysates for *in vitro* protein synthesis.

	Rabbit reticulocyte	Wheat germ
Preparation of lysate	Complicated. Can be purchased but expensive.	Straightforward. Low cost.
Ease of use	Reaction mixtures are quick and easy to set up.	Many components have to be added (e.g. ATP, GTP, creatine phosphate).
Fidelity of translation	Good. Excellent for high molecular weight proteins.	Good but premature termination can occur in some preparations.
Endogenous mRNA	High. Lysate must be treated with micrococcal nuclease.	Low. No nuclease treatment is necessary.
Translational activity	High.	Intermediate.
Analysis of products	Analysis can be complicated by the large amounts of globin.	Usually straightforward.

Once the *in vitro* polypeptide products are synthesized, a suitable method of analysis must be chosen. The first step is generally to analyse the ·products by SDS-polyacrylamide gel electrophoresis (Fig. 3.4) which separates the polypeptides on the basis of molecular weight (Laemmeli, 1970). The gel is then exposed to an X-ray film (autoradiographed) in order to visualize the radiolabelled products. If the protein is labelled with a tritiated amino acid then the gel must first be treated

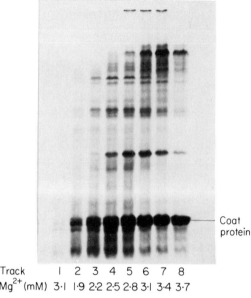

Track   1 2 3 4 5 6 7 8
Mg^{2+}(mM) 3·1 1·9 2·2 2·5 2·8 3·1 3·4 3·7

Fig. 3.4. Analysis of translation products by SDS-polyacrylamide gel electrophoresis and fluorography. The figure shows the fluorograph. Brome mosaic virus (BMV) RNA was translated in a wheat germ lysate. Track 1 shows the background incorporation in the absence of exogenous RNA, in the presence of 3·1 mM magnesium ions. The remaining tracks are BMV products synthesized in the presence of increasing magnesium concentration. The optimum incorporation occurred at 3·1 mM magnesium ions. The top major bond is a polypeptide of 110,000 m.w. and the position of the viral coat protein is indicated.

with a fluor (Laskey & Mills, 1975). However, [^{35}S]-methionine is the most commonly used label and does not require fluorography.

This method is definitely not satisfactory for an absolute identification of products. Co-electrophoresis of an *in vitro* synthesized product with the reference protein does not prove its identity, merely that the two polypeptides are of similar molecular weight. In addition, many *in vitro* synthesized products will not co-migrate with the corresponding authentic protein because wheat germ and reticulocyte lysates do not carry out secondary modifications such as glycosylation or cleavage of signal sequences. Lack of these modifications affects the electrophoretic mobility of the polypeptides, hence further analysis is required. The most specific method available is to immunoprecipitate the products with antibodies. The technique is widely used but can run into difficulty as the antibody may not recognize the primary translation product. It is sometimes necessary to raise antibodies to SDS-denatured antigens which appears to open up more antigenic sites on the protein. Alternative techniques are also available, usually exploiting unusual characteristics of the protein. For example, barley storage proteins have been identified in *in vitro* translation products on the basis of their solubility in 55% iso-propanol (Matthews & Miflin, 1980). Whatever characteristic is chosen, some other means of identification must be used in addition to electrophoretic mobility.

Construction of cDNA clones

The conventional method of cDNA cloning (Higuchi *et al.*, 1976) is illustrated in Fig. 3.5, and has been widely used. Many sophisticated variations are now being developed but this conventional method serves well to illustrate the principles. Certain tools are required in addition to

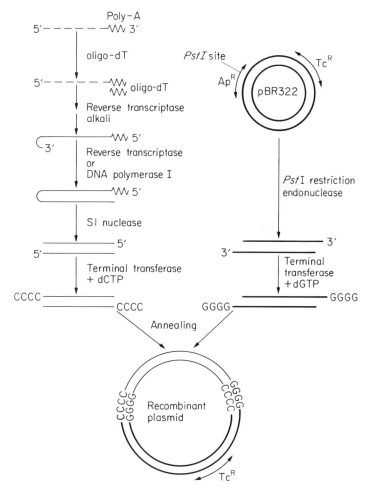

Fig. 3.5. Synthesis of cDNA and insertion into a plasmid: (---) mRNA, (—) cDNA and (━) the plasmid. The plasmid, pBR322 carries ampicillin resistance (Ap^R) and tetracycline resistance (Tc^R). After insertion of foreign DNA the ampicillin resistance gene is destroyed and bacterial clones carrying recombinant plasmids can be selected on the basis of drug resistance.

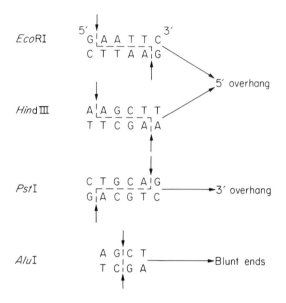

Fig. 3.6. Cleavage sites of some commonly used restriction endonucleoses. The diagram shows the position of cleavage and the type of ends left after the cleavage. Tables of restriction sites can be found in Appendix 2 of Old & Primose (1981).

reverse transcriptase and are worth mentioning before the steps are described in detail. Almost all current DNA handling techniques rely on a group of bacterial enzymes termed restriction endonucleases which cut DNA at specific sites. These sites are usually tetra-, penta-, or hexanu-cleotides (Fig. 3.6), and the cut often leaves overhanging ends which can anneal to each other again or to another piece of DNA with the same complementary single-stranded ends. The other vital tools are plasmid cloning vectors, which will carry the cDNA in the bacterium. A plasmid is an extrachromosomal, circular DNA molecule which may be capable of autonomous replication, and can be introduced into the bacterium by the process of transformation. Maps of some commonly used plasmids are given in Appendix 2.

The mRNA fraction is copied into single-stranded DNA using reverse transcriptase. This enzyme can only add residues to a 3'-OH group of an existing primer, which is base-paired with the template. Oligo-dT is hybridized to the poly-A tail in order to supply this primer. The RNA strand of the resulting RNA−DNA hybrid is destroyed by alkaline hydrolysis prior to second-strand synthesis. The second-strand synthesis reaction is carried out using either DNA polymerase I or reverse transcriptase, and is self-priming. The single-stranded cDNA has a transitory hairpin structure at the 3'-end which is stabilized by second-strand synthesis. The hairpin loop and any single-stranded overhang at the other end are then digested away with the single-strand specific S1 nuclease. The final product is a population of double-stranded, blunt-ended DNA molecules complementary to the original mRNA fraction.

The double-stranded DNA is now ready for insertion into the plasmid. Homopolymer tailing is probably the most commonly used, but not the only, method of inserting cDNA into a plasmid. A string of cytosine residues is added to the cDNA using the enzyme terminal transferase, to form oligo-dC tails on the 3'-ends. Similarly, a plasmid is cut open at a unique restriction endonuclease site and tailed with oligo-dG. The homopolymer tails of the cDNA and plasmid then pair to form a circular recombinant plasmid carrying a cDNA insert (Fig. 3.5).

The recombinant plasmids are used to transform bacteria, usually the *E. coli* K12 strains. *E. coli* cells treated with calcium chloride will take up plasmid molecules from the surrounding medium (Cohen *et al.*, 1972), and the host cell will repair any gaps in the recombinant plasmid. If the plasmid has been chosen carefully, it is possible to select transformed from non-transformed bacteria on the basis of antibiotic resistance. Many cloning plasmids contain two antibiotic resistance genes, one of which is destroyed during cloning. In the case of pBR322, cloning into the unique PstI site destroys ampicillin resistance but leaves tetracycline resistance intact (Fig. 3.5). Bacteria transformed with a recombinant plasmid will be sensitive to ampicillin but resistant to tetracycline. This simple selection tells the investigator which colonies carry a cDNA copy of some sort.

Clone selection strategies

The antibiotic resistance selection carried out already has identified which clones carry a recombinant plasmid, but there will be many thousands of different inserts. The cloning procedure usually begins with a whole population of mRNA sequences. In addition, some plasmids may have undergone recircularization or generated deletions which failed to reconstruct the ampicillin resistance gene. The most difficult part of cDNA is selecting which of these clones carries the sequence of interest. If the gene is expressed (p. 54) then the simplest selection is to screen for the presence of the protein, either by the bacterial phenotype it produces or by protein detection methods usually based on immunological or other (for example, enzymological) techniques. More often than not the protein is not expressed and other methods have to be used, many of which are based on nucleic acid hybridization. One of the most important techniques was developed by Grünstein & Hogness (1975), which involved the detection of DNA sequences in transformed colonies by hybridization *in situ* with a radioactive probe (Fig. 3.7). Depending on the specificity of the probe (see below), this can lead to the rapid identification of one colony among many thousands. A nitrocellulose filter disc is placed on the

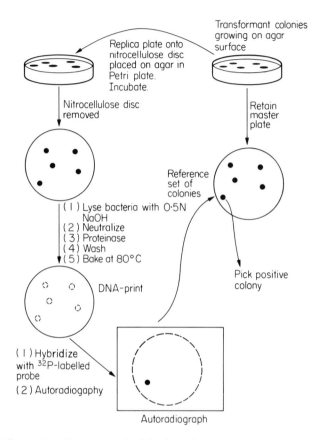

Fig. 3.7. Grunstein–Hogness method for detection of recombinant clones by colony hybridization. (From Old & Primrose, 1981).

surface of an appropriate agar plate and the colonies are transferred to this disc. A replicate agar plate is retained as a reference set. The colonies are grown up and the nitrocellulose disc carrying the colonies removed. The bacteria are lysed and the DNA is denatured by treating the disc with alkali. The DNA will adhere to the nitrocellulose while protein is removed and debris washed away. DNA is firmly fixed in position by baking at 80°C.

A radiolabelled probe is hybridized to the DNA on the filter. The DNA probe can be labelled by 'nick'-translation, a process in which nicks are introduced into a DNA sequence and then the enzyme, DNA polymerase 1, digests away from the nick while replacing the strand as it proceeds. A labelled nucleotide is incorporated into the replacement strand (Rigby *et al.*, 1977). Any colony carrying a sequence complementary to the probe will, during hybridization, become radiolabelled and can be identified by autoradiography. Any clone showing a positive result can be picked from the master plate and grown up to provide DNA for further analysis.

What is the nature of the probe used in the procedure outlined above? On some occasions a specific probe will be available in the form of a closely related DNA sequence; an example of this would be the use of globin gene sequences from one species as a probe for those from another species. Alternatively, a specific probe can be constructed if the protein sequence of the gene product is known. The gene sequence for about fifteen nucleotides can be deduced from the known amino acid sequence and the oligonucleotide synthesized chemically. More often a specific probe is not available, nor can one be constructed. In this case very specific clone identification may not be possible but it should be possible to use the following technique to narrow down the numbers of potential positive clones. A highly enriched mRNA fraction can be copied into $[^{32}P]$-cDNA (single stranded) and hybridized to the filter. This probe will pick out clones which carry an insert to any of the messages in the enriched fraction. After this positive selection, a negative selection can be carried out by using mRNA from the same organism, but from a tissue which does not express the gene of interest. Any positively selected colonies which now hybridize to the negative probe can be discarded (see for example, Forde *et al.*, 1981). A manageable number of colonies should now remain.

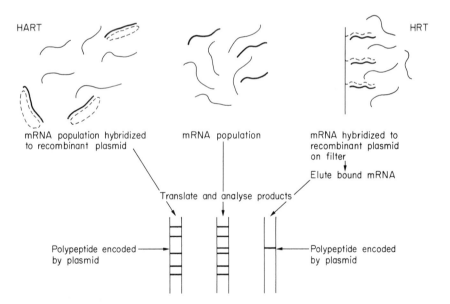

Fig. 3.8. Hybrid-arrested (HART) and hybrid-released (HRT) translation. For HART, the plasmid under test is hybridized to the mRNA and the whole mixture translated *in vitro*. The plasmid is identified by the polypeptide missing from the translation products. For HRT, the plasmid is immobilized on a filter and hybridized to the mRNA. The filter is washed, and then the bound mRNA eluted and translated. The plasmid is identified by the polypeptide product. These two techniques provide useful, complementary tests of plasmid identity.

Two methods based on *in vitro* protein synthesis provide additional tools in clone identification. Hybrid-arrested translation (HART; Paterson *et al.*, 1977) relies on the fact that, if mRNA is hybridized to its complementary DNA, then it is not available for translation (Fig. 3.8). The recombinant plasmid under test is denatured and hybridized to an mRNA preparation under conditions that favour the formation of RNA−DNA hybrids. The hybridized mixture is then translated *in vitro* but mRNA complementary to the recombinant plasmid will not be translated. The absence of the protein of interest confirms the identity of the clone. Heating of hybridized mRNA prior to translation should restore translational activity. Hybrid-released translation (HRT; Alwine *et al.*, 1980) is a more direct method. In this case, cloned DNA is immobilized on a nitrocellulose filter and hybridized to RNA. The mRNA complementary to the cloned DNA will stick to the filter and, after washing, can be eluted and placed in an *in vitro* translation system. The identity of the *in vitro*-synthesized product confirms the identity of the cloned DNA. These two methods are very valuable in the identification of clones from a population of different mRNA species.

The methods described so far have covered the construction and selection of cDNA clones. Much can be learned by analysis of these clones but before turning to this subject, it is appropriate to look at the cloning of genomic sequences.

Principles of genomic cloning

Why are genomic clones necessary in addition to cDNA clones? Although useful, cDNA clones themselves can only yield information about sequences which reach the mature mRNA molecule. Information about the structure of the gene in the chromosone and about sequences surrounding it can only be obtained from genomic clones. The structure of sequences flanking genes has been analysed in a variety of genomic clones (e.g. β-globin genes; Jeffreys & Flavell, 1977). Comparison of the two types of clones (i.e. cDNA and genomic) reveals the presence or absence of introns or intervening sequences which interupt the gene sequence, but which are not present in the mRNA (e.g. Breathnach *et al.*, 1977). The first published report of the phenomenon in plants was for the french bean seed storage protein, phaseolin (Sun *et al.*, 1981). From a biotechnological point of view, if genes are to be modified and returned to plants, it is likely that genomic sequences will be more useful.

Isolation of nuclear DNA

For genomic cloning, nuclear DNA must be isolated from the tissue in a high molecular weight form, largely free of organelle DNA and RNA.

Although at a later stage the DNA will be restricted to more manage-able lengths, preparation of high molecular weight DNA is desirable to ensure that minimum shearing and non-specific damage has occurred. DNA must be free of contaminants which will interfere with subsequent manipulation, particularly with restriction enzymes (see for example, Murray & Thompson, 1980). To facilitate the separation of nuclear DNA from organellar DNA, preparation often proceeds via isolated nuclei (Bedbrook *et al.*, 1980a). Nuclei remain whole under conditions which will lyse mitochondria and chloroplasts, and can then be collected in a reasonably pure form. A more detailed discussion of the separation of nuclear and organellar DNA can be found on p. 49. The DNA preparation can be rendered RNA-free by digestion with ribonuclease, which has been freed of deoxyribonuclease by heat treatment. The size of nuclear DNA is monitored by agarose gel electrophoresis (Fig. 3.9).

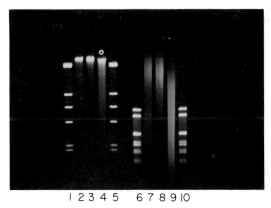

1 2 3 4 5   6 7 8 9 10

Fig. 3.9. Agarose gel electrophoresis of DNA, in 0·4% agarose stained with the intercalating dye ethidium bromide. Tracks 1−5 show double-stranded DNA (0·25 μg) and Tracks 6−10 show single-stranded DNA (1 μg), denatured with 0·15M NaOH. The marker tracks (1,5,6,10) are bacteriophage digested with *Hind* III. Tracks 2 and 7 show owl monkey DNA; 3 and 8 show paw-paw (*Carica papaya*) DNA, and 4 and 9 show dwarf lemur DNA. The dwarf lemur DNA is of poor quality as shown by the low molecular weight smear in the single-stranded track. The owl monkey and paw-paw DNA are of good quality. (By courtesy of Dr S. Adams.)

Cloning genomic sequences

Plasmids are usually used for cDNA cloning, but they will only accom-modate a relatively small piece of DNA due to problems with transfor-mation using very large plasmids. It is generally desirable to clone larger pieces of genomic DNA as a large clone is more likely to contain an intact copy of a gene plus some of the flanking sequences. Cloning large pieces also brings the number of different clones needed to cover the entire genome down to a manageable number.

Genomic cloning is often carried out by using bacteriophage lambda

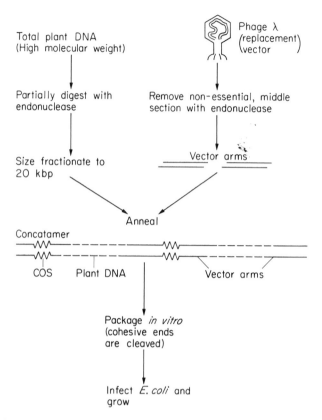

Fig. 3.10. Genomic cloning into bacteriophage λ.

(λ) as a vector (Fig. 3.10). The phage genome is double-stranded and approximately 50 kbp in length. It is amenable to genetic manipulation and the structure of the genome is well understood. Since its first use as a cloning vector in 1974 (Murray & Murray, 1974) many different vectors have been constructed which enable replacement of part of the λ genome with foreign DNA (Brammar, 1982). Part of the central portion is non-essential, so can be replaced without detriment to phage reproduction; this type of construct is termed a replacement vector.

High molecular weight genomic DNA is partially digested with a restriction enzyme and then size fractionated to about 20 kbp. The non-essential region of the phage genome is removed with the same enzyme and the vector arms purified (Fig. 3.10). These vector arms and the genomic fragments are annealed together. The genome has cohesive ends so as well as annealing to the foreign DNA, the genomes will anneal to form a concatamer. During *in vitro* packaging endonucleolytic cleavage occurs at the cohesive ends (the 'cos' site) to reduce the DNA to unit lengths. The phage particles are then used to infect *E. coli* for amplification of the DNA, and clone selection can subsequently be carried out.

If the cohesive ends are separated by the correct length of DNA (of whatever origin), the DNA will be cleaved and packaged *in vitro* into particles. Plasmids have been constructed which contain these cohesive ends (Collins & Hohn, 1979) and when foreign DNA of approximately 28−42 kbp is inserted into this vector, the cohesive ends are the correct distance apart. The DNA is packaged into phage particles, and infection of *E. coli* takes place in the normal way (Fig.

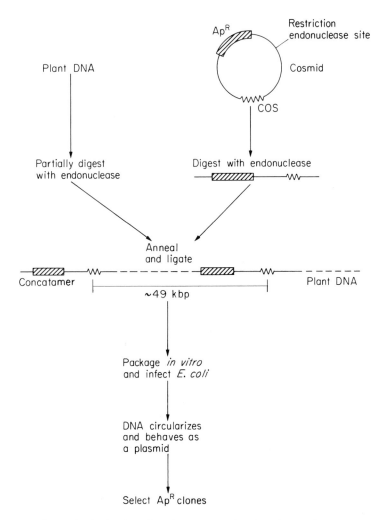

Fig. 3.11. Genomic cloning into Cosmid vectors. The plasmid contains the 'COS' site of bacteriophage and ampicillin resistance. The 'COS' site allows packaging into particles but once the DNA is in the bacterium it behaves as a plasmid. Ampicillin resistance colonies have been transformed with a cosmid.

3.11). Once inside the host, the DNA replicates as a plasmid because the phage genes required for replication are not present. These vectors are called Cosmids, and recombinants can be selected on the basis of drug resistance in a similar manner to ordinary plasmids (p. 41).

Once cloned DNA has been produced, hybridization techniques similar to those used for cDNA clones can be applied to identify individual clones. However, as cDNA cloning of a gene is frequently carried out first, a specific probe is often available. These probes can greatly simplify selection of genomic clones from the very large number produced.

Problems specific to plant material

The techniques described so far are of general applicability to DNA or poly-adenylated RNA from any source, but it is worth considering at this point a few problems which are specific to plant material. The study of the molecular biology of plants has not progressed as rapidly as similar studies in animal systems. When starting experiments now, we know less about the system to begin with than do many animal re-searchers. Therefore, a lot of groundwork often has to be covered before gene cloning can begin at all. Plant tissue can present a number of practical problems for the isolation of nucleic acids. Tough cell walls can make effective homogenization of the tissue difficult, and this fact coupled with the large amount of nucleases (particularly ribonuclease) present in many plant tissues, makes for very low yields of nucleic acid per gram of tissue. This is especially true if mRNA must be extracted from a difficult tissue such as mature leaves or certain seeds. RNA extraction is much easier if young seedlings can be used. Purity of RNA preparations can also be a problem. Plant cells contain large quantities of polysaccharide which, being a negatively charged polymer, can some-times co-purify with RNA. Persistent polysaccharide contamination is a difficult problem to solve.

Isolation of DNA from the nucleus requires the removal of both chloroplast and mitochondrial DNA, although chloroplast DNA is quantitatively the larger problem. This problem, coupled with that of low yield can be circumvented to an extent by careful choice of tissue. Nuclear DNA is often isolated from embryonic axes which have a high proportion of nuclear to organelle DNA; collecting the embryonic axes can, however, be a tedious process. None of these problems are insoluble but it is important that they are considered when planning plant molecular biology projects.

Cloning plastid and mitochondrial genes

Cloning organellar genes presents rather a different prospect to nuclear genes. Most mRNA molecules transcribed from organellar genes are non-polyadenylated so conventional oligo-dT primed cDNA synthesis is not possible. However, the genomes are small — approximately 150 kpb for chloroplasts — therefore cloning of the genes directly from purified organellar DNA is relatively straightforward compared with nuclear DNA.

The first problem is to prepare, from the organelles, DNA which is free of contaminants. Chloroplast DNA, free from nuclear contamination, has been prepared reliably from intact, purified chloroplasts, which are treated with DNase prior to DNA isolation (Herrmann et al., 1975). Many modifications of the basic procedure have been published (Bohnert & Crouse, 1981). Other methods have also been used for chloroplast DNA; if it differs in bouyant density from nuclear DNA sufficiently, chloroplast DNA can be isolated by CsCl density gradient centrifugation. However, this method is more applicable to algae, these differences in bouyant density often being too small in higher plants.

A number of chloroplast genes have now been cloned and it is apparent that some homology exists between species. A method often used now is to take cloned sequences from one species and use these to probe for genes from different species (Bohnert et al., 1982). This homology greatly facilitates organellar gene cloning and analysis of the structure of the genome.

For a number of reasons, mitochondrial DNA has been studied less extensively compared with that from the chloroplast but interest in it is increasing. Quantitatively it is the smallest genetic component of a plant cell, often contributing less than 1% of the total cellular DNA (Palmer & Thompson, 1980). In spite of the small amount present, mitochondrial DNA has been successfully prepared from purified, DNase-treated, mitochondria (Kolodner & Tewari, 1972). As with chloroplasts, DNase treatment is necessary to remove nuclear contamination.

Analysis of cloned genes

Once cloned, the DNA must be analysed if it is to yield information regarding gene structure and function, and if biotechnological applications are to be considered. A detailed account of the techniques of nucleic acid analysis would be inappropriate in a book of this type. Omission of techniques, such as the electron microscopy of nucleic acids, does not indicate a lack of importance of information derived from them. To keep this chapter to manageable proportions, three analytical techniques will be covered. These are restriction enzyme analysis, DNA sequencing and the technique referred to as 'Southern blotting'.

Restriction enzyme analysis

As a restriction enzyme cuts DNA at a specific tetra-, penta-, or hexanucleotide sequence, it is possible to map the position of these particular sequences along the length of a DNA molecule. Digestion with one or more restriction enzymes generates a series of fragments, the size of which can be determined by agarose gel electrophoresis. The electrophoretic mobility of the fragments can be compared with that of known size markers. From these types of data, a map of restriction sites can be constructed, and some information can be obtained from a restriction map alone. For example, intervening sequences in a gene will mean that two restriction sites in the coding region will be further apart in a genomic clone than in a cDNA clone (Fig. 3.12). The mRNA precursor to the cDNA clone does not carry the intervening sequences, so the cDNA clone also will not carry this intron. Although restriction maps provide some information *per se*, it is the useful reference points they provide which makes them most valuable. Once the position of these sites is known, the restriction enzymes can be used to cut the DNA specifically for manipulative and analytical procedures. An obvious example of this has already been mentioned: the map of a plasmid allows the selection of a suitable site for insertion of foreign DNA. Restriction site information is vital for many other analytical techniques.

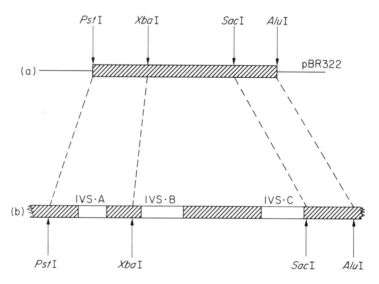

Fig. 3.12. When a genomic clone (b) contains intervening sequences the restriction sites are further apart than in the corresponding cDNA clone (a). These clones are of the plant gene phaseolin which contains, in the section, three intervening sequences (IVS A,B and C), but this is not the whole gene. (Redrawn from Sun *et al.*, 1981)

Southern blotting

There is often a need to determine which particular fragment of DNA is complementary to another fragment. Restriction fragments of cloned or total genomic DNA can be mapped by hybridization to a probe. The technique known as 'Southern blotting' (Southern, 1975) allows this to be done. It is sensitive enough to map restriction sites around single-copy genes in total genomic DNA, if a suitable probe is available (Jeffreys, 1979).

The method is summarized in Fig. 3.13. Restriction fragments of the DNA to be tested are prepared and separated by agarose gel electrophoresis (for a review see Southern, 1979). These fragments are transferred, or blotted, to a nitrocellulose filter and are fixed firmly in place

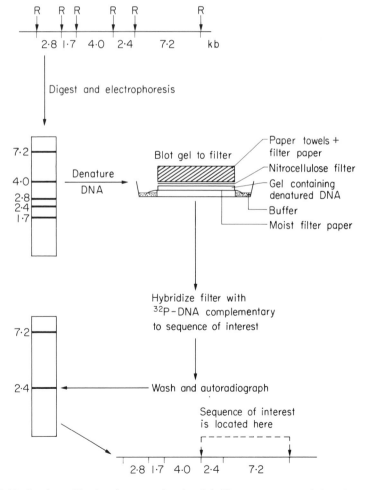

Fig. 3.13. Southern blotting (see text for details). R represents restriction sites.

by baking at 80°C. The filter is then incubated with the radiolabelled RNA or DNA to be used as the probe, and hybridization occurs between complementary sequences. After washing, hybridization sequences are detected by autoradiography. The development of this powerful technique made this type of analysis much easier, and obviated the need for lengthy procedures involving eluting nucleic acids from gel slices. Southern blotting is simpler to carry out and gives much higher resolution. In plant molecular biology it has been used extensively to map chloroplast genomes using probes from a different species (see for example, Van Ee *et al.*, 1982).

DNA sequencing

At one time, sequencing nucleic acids was extremely difficult; even if enough could be obtained in a pure state, the actual sequencing process was prohibitive. Some molecules, such as tRNAs, were sequenced but the technique was not widely used. Protein sequencing was time-consuming but could be achieved if the protein was of sufficient purity. Protein purification is still a problem, whereas now pure DNA sequences can be obtained in large quantities by molecular cloning. DNA sequencing was revolutionized by Maxam & Gilbert (1977, 1980) and their method relies on our ability to manipulate DNA with a variety of enzymes (Fig. 3.14).

A restriction fragment of DNA is labelled at either its 5' or 3' with [^{32}P] using either polynucleotide kinase or terminal transferase. From a restriction map, an enzyme is chosen which will remove a small piece from one end of the molecule leaving just one end labelled. In five different reactions the DNA is then chemically cleaved at specific residues, but the reactions are only partially completed. The partial digestion products are separated on a polyacrylamide gel and auto-radiographed. Only fragments containing the labelled terminus will be visualized; the sequence can then be deduced from the order of the fragments from the different digestions. The interpretations of sequence data is explained more fully in Fig. 3.14.

A different method was described by Sanger *et al.* (1977), known as the 'dideoxy' or chain terminator method. Again, a series of radio-labelled fragments of increasing size are generated, but this time by copying single-stranded DNA in the presence of a labelled nucleotide, with DNA polymerase. The polymerase will also incorporate dideoxy-nucleotides into the strand, but once incorporated there is no free hydroxyl to accept the next residue and the chain is therefore ter-minated. By using a carefully selected ratio of a dideoxy nucleotide to its deoxynucleotide, the terminator is put in randomly, terminating different chains at many different points. The fragments are analysed in essentially the same way as those from Maxam and Gilbert sequencing.

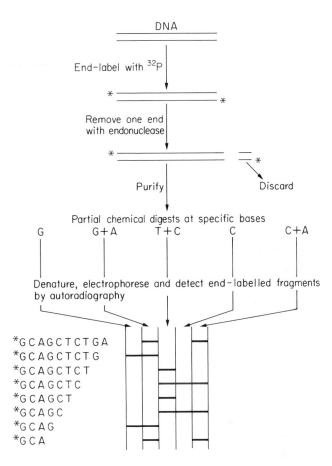

Fig. 3.14. DNA sequencing by the Maxam–Gilbert method (see text for details). The DNA can be labelled at either the 5' ends (using polynucleotide kinase) or 3' ends (by terminal transferase). This allows the sequencing of both strands as a check. The details of the chemical digestions can be found in Maxam & Gilbert (1980).

This method requires a primer to be used in order to initiate DNA synthesis. Generally the DNA to be sequenced is cloned into a phage known as M13 which has been carefully manipulated to allow a 'universal primer' to initiate sequencing (Messing *et al.*, 1981). This subject is reviewed by Old & Primrose (1981).

Sequence analysis of cloned DNA has yielded a large amount of information, particularly about sequences at the beginning and end of genes involved in the possible control of the expression of the gene. Sequencing is a powerful tool and provides by far the most detailed analysis of a particular piece of DNA. The technology does however rely on information obtained by using other techniques — restriction maps, for example — and cannot stand alone. The information obtained must also be coupled with other investigations before interpretation of the function of any specific sequences can be made.

Expression of cloned genes

In addition to purely physical analysis, investigations into the expression of cloned genes in host cells have been carried out. Many processes are involved in the expression of a gene and, although some early experiments with hosts such as yeast and fungi were successful, (e.g. Struhl *et al.*, 1976) transferred eukaryotic genes are often not expressed in their new host. Expression of cloned genes could be expected to yield valuable information into the processes involved and, from a biotechnological view point, expression of plant genes in bacteria may be of commercial significance. A few problems will be discussed briefly here, to set in context the later discussion of the uses of cloned plant genes.

For a cloned gene to be expressed in a bacterial cell, it has been found that it is necessary to place it under the control of an *E. coli* promotor. Many different plasmids have been constructed which allow insertion of a gene near to a promotor (see for example, Backmann *et al.*, 1976; Mercerau-Puijalon *et al.*, 1978). A detailed discussion of the construction of these plasmids would be inappropriate here, but a number of different strategies have been used. Some genes are inserted such that the protein produced is actually fused to part of a bacterial protein, often β-galactosidase (e.g. β-endorphin; Shine *et al.*, 1980), whilst others are inserted such that the promotor is correctly placed for protein synthesis from the correct N terminus. An example of this latter type would be the maize gene coding for the large subunit of ribulose bisphosphate carboxylase (RuBPCase, Gatenby *et al.*, 1981).

Bacterial genes do not contain intervening sequences nor the machinery for removing them from the primary transcript. Any eukaryotic genes containing introns will not give a functional mRNA molecule in bacteria even if transcribed efficiently. It is necessary, therefore, to use cDNA clones of this type of gene for expression studies (e.g. sweet protein, thaumatin; Edens *et al.*, 1982). A functional mRNA also depends on the coding sequence being in the correct reading frame if it has been fused to a bacterial coding sequence. Three vectors were constructed by Charnay *et al.*, 1978) which allow cloning into the *lac Z* gene of *E. coli* in all three possible reading frames relative to the initiation codon, and similar vectors have been constructed by a number of other workers. If placed in the correct reading frame relative to the initiation codon and with a ribosome binding site present the mRNA should be translated into a primary translation product.

The problems do not end there, however; many proteins are modified in some way either by the removal of the polypeptide or by addition of various groups. Signal sequences, which allow passage through membranes, need to be cleaved (Blobel, 1980) and other modifications include glycosylation, adenylation and phosphorylation. While bacteria may be able to cleave signal sequences in some cases, glycosylation certainly does not occur. In the case of the sweet protein, thaumatin (Edens *et al.*, 1982), neither the N nor C terminal extensions of the primary translation product were removed in *E. coli*. Likewise, the glutamine synthetase gene from *Anabena* functions in *E. coli* but no adenylation of the enzyme occurs (Fisher *et al.*, 1981).

Lack of these modifications may have certain consequences. If a functional protein is sought, for some commercial application, lack of these modifications could be a serious problem. From an investigative point of view, the primary products may be very unstable; if rapid degradation occurs, detection of the products would be difficult. The expression of a cloned gene requires the correct functioning of a complex series of events, and perhaps we should not be surprised that many problems are associated with the expression of foreign genes in bacteria. Application of knowledge obtained will doubtless assist in future expression studies, and the range of hosts extended to include other organisms. A eukaryotic host, such as yeast, may have considerable advantages for some application as modification of primary translation products is known to occur in these organisms.

Applications of molecular cloning to plant genes

The techniques of gene cloning and analysis are tools of the molecular biologist, but how have these tools been applied to plants? Until 1980 very few plant genes had been cloned but since 1980 the number has increased dramatically. Table 3.2 contains a selection of the major plant genes which have been cloned. It is not possible to discuss every one of these genes in detail, but some of the information obtained from cloning has already been presented in Chapter 2. In this section we will consider what type of genes have been studied and why they were chosen.

One of the biggest groups to be investigated is the seed storage proteins of a number of major crop plants. These storage proteins are synthesized rapidly over a short period during seed development, their expression is both tissue- and time-specific. The rapid synthesis correlates with high levels of mRNA, up to 50% of the mRNA in the cells, so cDNA cloning of these genes is an attractive proposition. Clones have been prepared from maize, barley, soybean, french bean and pea, all of which are important sources of human or animal nutrition. Potential biotechnological applications of cloned seed protein genes are considered in Chapter 7; however, some basic information regarding gene structure and function has come from storage protein studies. The gene for phaseolin, from french beans was the first plant gene to have the presence of intervening sequences demonstrated (Sun *et al.*, 1981). Some unusual structures have been revealed in certain storage protein genes. The protein sequence of the maize storage protein, zein (derived from the gene sequence) has a repeating unit (Pedersen *et al.*, 1982), and similar results have been obtained for hordein from barley.

Table 3.2. Cloned plant genes.

Gene or type of DNA	Source	Genome	Reference
Alcohol dehydrogenase	Maize	Nuclear	Gerlach et al., 1982
α-Amylase	Barley	Nuclear	Muthukrishnan et al., 1981
Auxin-regulated mRNA	Soybean		Walker & Key, 1982
Bowman−Birk Protease inhibitor	Soybean	Nuclear	Spencer et al., 1982
Catalase	Maize	Nuclear	Sorensen, 1981
Chalcone synthase[*]	Parsley, Antirrhinum	Nuclear	Wienand et al., 1982
Chloroplast components:			
ATP synthase (and subunits)	Wheat, spinach	Chloroplast	Howe et al., 1982a; Zurawski et al., 1982
ATP synthase (proton translocating)	Wheat	Chloroplast	Howe et al., 1982b
Chlorophyll a/b binding protein	Pea	Nuclear	Broglie et al., 1981
Cytochrome f	Pea	Chloroplast	Willey et al., 1983
Elongation factor TU	Euglena	Chloroplast	Passavant et al., 1983
RuBPCase LSU[†]	Tobacco, wheat	Chloroplast	Shinozaki & Sugiura, 1982; Gatenby et al., 1981
RuBPCase SSU[‡]	Pea	Nuclear	Broglie et al., 1981 Bedbrook et al., 1980b
rRNA[§]	Pea, broad bean	Chloroplast	Chu et al., 1981; Sun et al., 1982
tRNA[§]	Maize	Chloroplast	Schwarz et al., 1981
Cytochrome c oxidase (subunit 1)	Maize	Mitochondrial	Fox & Leaver, 1981
Glutamine synthetase	Anabena		Fisher et al., 1981
Heatshock proteins	Soybean		Schoffl & Key, 1982
Highly repetitive DNA	Wheat	Nuclear	Hutchinson & Lonsdale, 1982
Highly repetitive DNA	Secale	Nuclear	Jones & Flavell, 1982
Highly repetitive DNA	Pea	Nuclear	Cuellar & Thompson, 1981
Insertion element CIN-1	Maize	Nuclear	Shepherd et al., 1982
Leghaemoglobin	Soybean	Nuclear	Brisson & Verma, 1982
Meiotic-specific poly-A[†] RNA	Lilium		Appels et al., 1982
Nitrogenase	Anabena		Rice et al., 1982
Phytochrome	Oat	Nuclear	Quail, 1984
rRNA[§]	Wheat, barley	Nuclear	Gerlach & Bedbrook, 1979
Satellite DNA	Cucurbitaceae	Nuclear	Hemleben, 1981
Seed lectin	Soybean	Nuclear	Goldberg et al., 1983
Seed storage proteins			
β-conglycinin (7s)	Soybean	Nuclear	Beachy et al., 1981
glycinin (11s)	Soybean	Nuclear	Fischer & Goldberg, 1982

Table 3.2. Cloned plant genes (continued).

Gene or type of DNA	Source	Genome	Reference
hordein	Barley	Nuclear	Forde *et al.*, 1981
legumin	Pea	Nuclear	Croy *et al.*, 1982
phaseolin	French bean	Nuclear	Sun *et al.*, 1981
vicillin	Pea	Nuclear	Croy *et al.*, 1982
zein	Maize	Nuclear	Burr *et al.*, 1982; Wienand *et al.*, 1981; Viotti *et al.*, 1982
Sucrose synthetase	Maize	Nuclear	McCormick *et al.*, 1982
Superabundant embryo mRNAs	Soybean		Goldberg *et al.*, 1981
Thaumatin	*Thaumatococcus*	Nuclear	Edens *et al.*, 1982
Tubulin	*Chlamydomonas*	Nuclear	Minami *et al.*, 1981

* Key enzyme in anthocyanin biosynthesis.
† Large subunit.
‡ Small subunit.
§ These genes have been cloned from a number of species; a few examples are given.

Chloroplast biogenesis provides a useful system for the study of gene expression. The synthesis of chloroplast proteins involves the co-operation of two genomes, and some steps are regulated by light. Molecular cloning has assisted in the assignment of genes to either nuclear or chloroplast genomes, and the availability of cloned genes as probes is proving valuable in the study of the control of gene expression. Recently, genes coding for the small subunit of RuBPCase and the light-harvesting chlorophyll *a/b* binding protein of *Lemna gibba* have been used to study the effect of light quality on gene expression (Stiekema *et al.*, 1983). This study indicated the involvement of phytochrome in the regulation of either transcription rates of mRNA degradation for these particular genes.

The synthesis of many plant proteins is regulated by external stimuli. The molecular biology of a number of these systems is being studied, particularly in relation to the application of a number of hormones, e.g. auxins. Stress situations produce gene expression changes; for example, certain pathogens invoke an increase in anthocyanin synthesis. Studies have been carried out into the synthesis of certain key enzymes involved (Chalcone synthase: Wienand *et al.*, 1982) in an attempt to unravel the molecular biology of the response. These types of genes are useful in the study of gene expression as the investigator can manipulate the plant's conditions in order to perturb mRNA and protein levels, which can then be quantified.

A well studied case of a plant organ responding to its immediate environment is that of the symbiotic association between nitrogen-fixing bacteria, *Rhizobium* and the roots of legumes. The association of these two organisms results in the formation of symbiotic nitrogen-fixing nodules, and the process involves dramatic changes in gene expression in both. The plant responds by producing large quantities of leghaemoglobin which seems to protect the bacterial nitrogenase enzyme from oxygen. Leghaemoglobin genes from soybean have been cloned and extensively analysed. Further applications of this system are considered in detail in Chapter 7.

Many other plant proteins are being studied for their own sake and some of these may turn out to have biotechnological applications. One example is the work of Edens *et al.* (1982) on the sweet-tasting plant protein, thaumatin. This protein is considerably sweeter than sucrose on a weight-for-weight basis and is of interest to the food processing industry. A thaumatin gene has been cloned and expressed in *E. coli*, demonstrating the presence of an amino acid extension at both the N and C termini. These extensions are not processed by *E. coli* but manipulation of the gene or use of a different host could lead to the formation of a mature protein. Production of thaumatin in fermenters on a large scale is certainly a potential direct application of molecular cloning technology.

From this brief survey and the list of cloned genes in Table 3.2 it is clear that information concerning plant genes is accumulating rapidly. This information must be examined in a broad context and interpreted with care. It is vital to try and draw out the underlying principles of gene structure and expression, rather than simply accumulate sequence data. There is, as suggested by Ellis (1983), a great danger of biological 'stamp collecting'. From a biotechnological viewpoint it must be stated that, although ideas abound, no cloned plant genes have yet found any direct applications in the improvement of crops or commercial production of plant products.

Future steps

Where does the application of cloning technology go from here? Although information is accumulating rapidly these is still a great need to consolidate the position in order to understand the working of the plant genomes. Manipulation of a plant genome to advantage can never be successful without a deep basic knowledge. In addition to the basic information obtained from cloning there may also be more direct uses for cloned genes. There are three basic approaches: (i) the removal of genes from the plant and their return to the same or a different species after modification; (ii) the use of plant genes in a unicellular organism to produce desirable plant products, using fermenter technology and

(iii) the introduction into plants of desirable genes from other organisms such as bacteria (e.g. those encoding salinity tolerance). Fig. 3.15 demonstrates some possible strategies.

At present there are many difficulties to be overcome before genes can be returned to plants. One difficulty, and by no means the least, is that of deciding which genes you wish to move around. Certain possible genes have been cloned, and these could include cereal and legume seed storage proteins. Modification of the amino acid composition of these proteins could lead to nutritionally superior seeds (see Chapter 7). Unfortunately, many traits which could be usefully transferred between species are not fully understood in molecular terms. Resistance to disease or tolerance of extreme environmental conditions would fall under this heading. The ability to associate with nitrogen-fixing *Rhizobia* in a symbiotic relationship is confined to legumes but might be of great advantage to cereal crops, allowing a reduction in nitrogen fertilizer use, but again, the genes involved are only partially characterized.

Having selected candidate genes, the problems are not over. At present there is no reliable way available to place genes into plant cells, particularly in monocotyledonous plants. Lack of well developed vector systems and the lack of success in regenerating crop plants from single

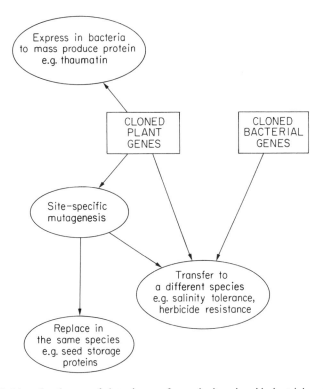

Fig. 3.15. Ideas for the use of cloned genes for agricultural and industrial applications. The examples given are discussed in later chapters.

cells are among the stumbling blocks. These topics need considerable investigation and the state of knowledge on them is covered in Chapters 4 and 5. The one stage of the process which is possible is the alteration of genes by site-specific mutagenesis, for which sophisticated techniques are available (e.g. Gillam *et al.*, 1980).

When all of these processes are possible and plant genes can be moved around between species or returned to a species in a modified form, it may appear that the aim of using the new technologies to improve crop plants has been achieved. However, it is most important not to lose sight of the overall goal, i.e. to use these technologies to produce superior, agronomically-viable cultivars of crop species. It is absolutely pointless to produce a cultivar of, for example, tomatoes which is resistant to the *Solanum* pathogen *Phytophthora* if it produces no fruit. Any new genetic combinations must be employed in an extensive breeding programme in order to be of use. The consequence to the plant of genetic manipulation must always be considered. Cloning technology will never replace the breeder but probably can provide an additional, powerful tool.

The concept of expressing plant genes in a unicellular host is rather different. In this case selection of possibly useful genes is particularly difficult. Many desirable plant products are produced by a whole series of enzyme reactions, e.g. alkaloids. It would be extremely difficult to isolate and transfer all genes necessary for the pathway to the host and then obtain correct expression. For the time being at least, the choice of genes for expression in bacteria or yeast must be limited to single proteins or very simple pathways. One example of such a gene has already been mentioned, i.e. the sweet-tasting protein thaumatin. Another candidate would be amylase enzymes from plants which are used in industry.

As with transferring genes between plant species, the choice of gene is not the end of the problem. Correct expression of the gene in the host involves many processes, particularly post-translational modification of the polypeptides. For successful biotechnological application, the host must be capable of cleaving signal sequences, glycosylating and modifying as necessary. Yeast cells may prove to be a more viable proposition than bacteria as a host for expression of transferred plant genes. This sort of technology has been successfully applied to certain animal proteins (e.g. insulin, Goeddel *et al.*, 1979) and should certainly, in the long term, be applicable to plants for the bulk production of proteins in fermentors.

There are many steps required before plant gene cloning can produce any benefits to agriculture or industry, but the abundant ideas are now beginning to be backed up by the necessary research and development. This exciting area will surely provide some applications and agricultural improvements in the future.

Conclusions

The current state of cloning plant genes can be summed up in the following points.

1   There are powerful techniques available for molecular cloning of genes from all three plant genomes.

2   Complementary DNA clones are prepared from mRNA and do not contain intervening sequences or promotors. These clones are useful for expression in bacteria under the control of a suitable prokaryotic promotor.

3   Plant genes can be cloned directly from plant DNA for structural analysis. Genomic clones will find more applications in the transfer of genes between plant species or for returning genes to the same species in modified form.

4   The cloning of plant genes is providing much information about gene structure and function.

5   As yet, gene cloning has not lead to any direct commercial applications.

6   Putting genes into plants requires much additional work into potential vectors and tissue culture systems.

7   When all the techniques are finally assembled, the new technologies will have to interact with breeding programmes to be used to their full advantage.

Further reading

Old R.W. & Primrose S.B. (1981) *Principles of Gene Manipulation*. Blackwell Scientific Publications, Oxford.

Wu R. (1979) (Ed.) *Recombinant DNA*. Meth. in Enzymol., 68, Academic Press, New York.

Maniatis T., Fritsch E.F. & Sambrook J. (1982) *Molecular Cloning*. Cold Spring Harbor Lab., Cold Spring Harbor.

Williamson R. (1981−83) (Ed.) *Genetic Engineering*, Vols 1−4. Academic Press, New York.

4 Vectors for Gene Cloning in Plants

Over the past few years much has been written on the need for an efficient and reliable plant gene vector. A vector may be defined as an agent which will facilitate one or more steps in the overall process of placing foreign genetic material, from whatever source, into plants or their constituent parts. Such steps would include uptake, incorporation (possibly including stable covalent integration), transcription, translation, maintenance and passage through mitosis and meiosis of the exogenous material. The term 'plant gene vector' applies to potential vectors both for the transfer of genetic information between plants, and also the transfer of genetic information from other organisms (bacteria, fungi and animals) to plants. A vector then is a go-between, transferring genetic information from one organism, the donor, to another, the recipient, and in the case of plants we are looking for the equivalent of bacterial vectors such as bacteriophage λ, cosmids and plasmids (Old & Primrose (1981) and Chapter 3). Several plant DNA viruses have been proposed as candidates for such a role, but do we need such complicated and, with regard to host range, possibly limited systems? What is wrong with naked plant genes? The plant cell wall, long regarded as a barrier to plant DNA uptake experiments is not found to be so, and the use of protoplasts provides an even more ammenable system. However, the fate of the genetic material once inside the cell is usually that of rapid degradation.

The use of natural vectors such as viruses, Agrobacterium Ti plasmids and transposable elements is being explored because it is envisaged that their normal host plant association will be advantageous in introducing new genetic material. The list of cloned plant genes is lengthening rapidly, and the situation may soon arise where one would wish to study the uptake, integration and expression of a gene, or a modified form of it, in a different host plant. The availability of a suitable vector system would be crucial to such studies.

In this chapter we will discuss the three major groups of gene vectors for plants; these are the Ti plasmids of *Agrobacterium tumefaciens*, the Caulimoviruses and the Gemini viruses. We will also consider systems which may, in the future, become potential vector candidates, as well as the delivery systems which may prove useful, or necessary, for their transfer to the host organism. As we shall see, the first group has already successfully fulfilled all that is required of a fully operational vector system. The others are not as yet at the same stage of sophistication.

Agrobacterium tumefaciens plasmids

The development of Agrobacterium plasmids as vector systems for plants is a natural progression of studies on this organism: firstly, on the plant disease associated with it, and secondly in respect of the similarity of the disease symptoms to certain cancers. When details of the true relationship between the bacterium and the host plant were elucidated its potential as a vector was realized. We now know that Agrobacterium and its Ti plasmids have evolved solely for the benefit of the bacterium. The infected plant produces a localized proliferation of undifferentiated cells which, under the direction of integrated bacterial genetic information (DNA), produce metabolites which are utilized by free-living *Agrobacterium tumefaciens* bacteria as their sole nitrogen and carbon source (Fig. 4.1). The potential of the Agrobacterium Ti plasmid as a vector arises from the ability of the bacterium to somehow transfer, and stably integrate, a piece of the plasmid DNA into the plant nuclear genome, a natural vector system.

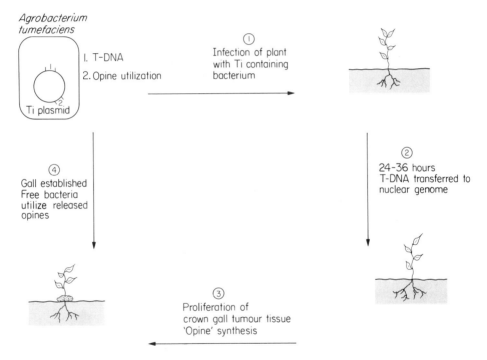

Fig. 4.1. *Agrobacterium tumefaciens*: relationship between the bacterium and host plant.

Features of the crown gall infection

Crown gall disease is the infection inflicted mainly on young fruit trees by *Agrobacterium tumefaciens*. In the UK outbreaks are few and symptoms are mild but elsewhere, particularly the USA, losses are more severe. Infection occurs at wound sites on the plant, although wounding may not be an absolute requirement for infection; rather, access to a constituent of the primary cell wall may trigger establishment of the disease. The bacterium is needed for infection to occur, but its continued presence is not required for the subsequent maintenance of the gall. Material from an established gall may be removed and kept in sterile culture, free of the bacteria, for considerable periods of time up to several years. Furthermore, unlike normal plant cells, these tumorous cells can grow on a chemically defined medium lacking added auxins and cytokinins (plant growth substances), and the genes responsible for this phenomena also reside in the transferred bacterial DNA. The disease has been known and studied for a long time, but a proper understanding of the bacterial interaction came about through (i) an intense study of the bacterium itself, and (ii) the development of extremely sensitive techniques for the detection of specific pieces of DNA.

Petit *et al.* (1970) observed that there were two families of bacteria, and the crown galls they established differed in that they produced two different amino acid derivatives subsequently called octopine, [N-α-(D-1-carboxyethyl)-L-arginine] and nopaline [N-α-(1,3-dicarboxypropyl)-L-arginine]. The ability to produce these 'opines' was specified by the transferred bacterial DNA and not by the host plant genome; indeed the plant cannot metabolize these products. The ability to produce tumours on plants, and the specificity of the opine produced was found to be associated with the possession by the bacterium of a large Ti (*T*umour *i*nducing) plasmid (Tables 4.1, 4.2.). Avirulent bacteria (unable to elicit

Table 4.1. Ti plasmid encoded functions.

Crown gall tumour induction
Specificity of opine synthesis in the transformed plant cell
Catabolism of specific opines
Agrocin sensitivity
Conjugative transfer of Ti plasmid
Catabolism of arginine and ornithine

Table 4.2. Ti plasmid groups.

Group		Opine
Octopine	also	octopinic acid
		lysopine
		histopine
		agropine
Nopaline	also	ornaline
		agrocinopine
Agropine		

crown galls on susceptible plants) do not carry a Ti plasmid. Transfer of the plasmid from a virulent to an avirulent strain results in that strain becoming virulent; moreover, it can now utilize the specific opine produced in the crown gall tissue which it initiates. The ability of virulent strains to transfer the Ti plasmid is found to be dependent on the presence of the particular opine encoded by that plasmid. A search for the presence of Ti plasmid in the genome of infected tumour cells failed, initially because the techniques were not sensitive enough, and as was later revealed, only a small part of the Ti plasmid, the T or *Transferred DNA*, is transferred to and integrated into the host plant nuclear genome (Chilton *et al.*, 1977; Thomashow *et al.*, 1980; Lemmers *et al.*, 1980).

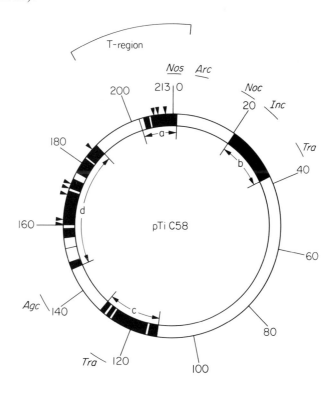

■■■■■ Regions of homology with octopine plasmid

▼   Insertions affecting tumour formation

Fig. 4.2. The nopaline Ti plasmid. Regions a, b, c, d represent areas of homology between the nopaline and octopine Ti plasmids. Other mutations shown are nopaline synthase (*Nos*), arginine catabolism (*Arc*), nopaline catabolism (*Noc*), incompatability (*Inc*), transfer functions (*Tra*), and agrocinopine catabolism (*Agc*). (Adapted from Schell, 1982.)

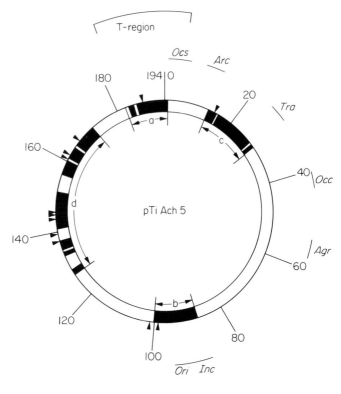

Fig. 4.3. The octopine Ti plasmid. The regions of homology with the nopaline Ti plasmid are shown, a, b, c, and d. Other mutations shown are octopine synthase (*Ocs*), arginine catabolism (*Arc*), transfer functions (*Tra*), octopine catabolism (*Occ*), agropine catabolism (*Agr*), incompatability (*Inc*), and origin of replication (*Ori*).

Organization of the Ti plasmid

The Ti plasmids of Agrobacterium are large, up to 200 kbp in length (Figs 4.2, 4.3). They have been studied in detail using molecular techniques such as restriction mapping and insertional mutagenesis. The two families of Ti plasmids differ in their properties. The octopine group are closely related and show extensive homology to one another, while the nopaline family are less closely related. Comparison of the octopine and nopaline groups show that overall they exhibit about 30% homology, this homology residing in specific regions of the Ti plasmid. Restriction endonuclease digestion, and *in vitro* DNA/DNA hybridization studies established the size and location of the T-DNA on the Ti plasmids. Insertional transposon mutagenesis localized the regions on the Ti plasmid concerned with the major functions specified by the plasmids, for example virulence, origin of replication, oncogenicity and catabolism of opines. These functions, with the exception of some of those controlling tumourigenicity, do not reside within the T-DNA (Figs 4.2, 4.3).

Incorporation, localization, organization and expression of the T-DNA in plants

The T-DNA is transferred to, and stably incorporated into the nuclear genome of the infected plant cells; there is no incorporation into plastid or mitochondrial DNA. How this is accomplished by the bacterium is not known; it is the least well understood process in the crown gall story. The site of integration of the T-DNA on the plant chromosomes appears to be random, but presumably there would be a selective advantage to the bacterium in having the DNA integrated in a region of the plant chromosome which is constantly actively expressed.

In the tumour there are recognizable left- and right-hand borders to the T-DNAs. In T-DNA from nopaline Ti plasmids these borders consist of 14 bp direct repeats, overlapped by 25 bp imperfect repeats.

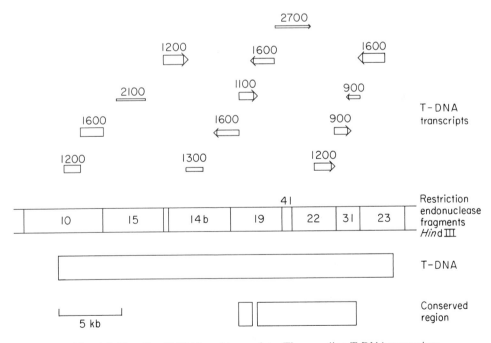

Fig. 4.4. Nopaline T-DNA and transcripts. The nopaline T-DNA transcripts positions are indicated by separate boxes, the length of each box indicates the relative abundance of the transcript in tumour tissue. The sizes of each transcript (uncorrected for length of Poly-A tail) are given in bases, and the 5′−3′ polarity where known is indicated. (Adapted from Willmitzer *et al.*, 1983.)

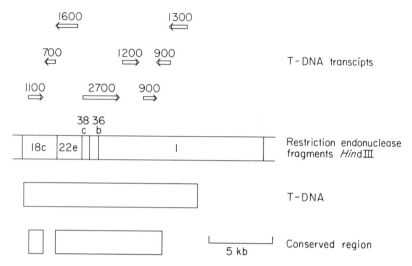

Fig. 4.5. Octopine T-DNA and transcripts. The positions, sizes (in bases), and polarity (5′−3′), of octopine T-DNA transcripts are shown. (Adapted from De Greve *et al.*, 1982a.)

The left border of octopine T-DNA is fairly constant whereas the right border is more variable, and there may in fact be duplications of all or part of the T-DNA. T-DNA of nopaline tumours has a more simple arrangement with fixed borders and colinearity with T-DNA of the Ti plasmid. The organization of, and functions associated with, the integrated T-DNA of octopine and nopaline Ti plasmids are shown in Figs 4.4 and 4.5, along with recent transcription data. The observation that genes on the T-DNA are linked to typical eukaryotic control sequences was unexpected. T-DNA is transcribed in the plant cell by host DNA polymerase II, the polyadenylated transcript being translated on plant ribosomes. All of the above information was gathered by different groups of investigators over a number of years, and such knowledge is vital for the design and construction of Ti vector plasmids carrying foreign genetic information.

Use of Ti as a vector

There are several problems associated with the use of Ti plasmids as vectors. Firstly, the plasmids are large and this does not allow for easy manipulation of their DNA; also, they have a large number of restriction sites which are not usefully distributed. Secondly, the plasmids transfer functions on the T-DNA which specify production of substances which effectively convert the infected cells into tumour cells, and these cannot readily be regenerated into whole plants. A further consideration should be that Agrobacterium only infects dicotyledonous plants, whereas many of the major food crops tend to be monocotyledonous. The development and use of plant protoplast systems may go some way towards circumventing this problem; however, successful regeneration of protoplasts derived from cereals has not yet been reported. Several groups worldwide have contributed greatly to the development of the Ti plasmid as a generalized vector for gene transfer, and also to our basic knowledge of the Agrobacterium–plant interaction. These include those led by Mary-Del Chilton in the USA; Marc Van Montagu and Jozef Schell in Belgium and Germany; and R. Schilperoort in the Netherlands.

Initially, foreign DNA in the form of a bacterial transposon Tn7, was inserted at random sites on the Ti plasmid. The insertions may occur in functional genes thereby inactivating them, and this allows a functional map to be constructed of genes on the Ti plasmid, and also of course within the T-region itself. By this means it has been found that none of the genes of the T-region are essential for the transfer and integration of the T-DNA. Also Tn7 integrated into the T-region is transferred to, and integrated into, the plant nuclear genome. This result indicates that the size of the T-DNA may be increased, without affecting its transfer and integration into the plant nuclear genome. Furthermore, expression of the transposon-encoded functions in the infected plant can be studied, and indeed transcription and possibly translation of the methotrexate-resistant dihydrofolate reductase gene of Tn7 has been reported. However, such early experiments lacked precise knowledge of the control signals associated with the genes carried on the T-DNA, and whether or not bacterial DNA integrated into the T-region could be transcribed in plant cells. When this was forthcoming the way was clear for construction of sophisticated vectors to test the ability of the Ti plasmid to transfer, integrate, stably maintain, express and transmit to progeny, exogenous genetic material integrated into the T-region. Numerous foreign genes have been inserted into the T-region of the Agrobacterium Ti plasmid from animal, bacterial and unrelated plant sources, and although they are subsequently transferred to the plant nuclear genome and are present in the integrated T-DNA, until recently none was shown to be expressed (transcribed and translated).

To gain an understanding of the mechanism by which natural T-DNA encoded genes are expressed in transformed plants, several groups have studied the precise organization of the octopine and nopaline synthase genes, *ocs* and *nos* respectively (De Greve *et al.,* 1982a; Depicker *et al.,* 1982; Bevan *et al.,* 1983).

Although these genes are coded on bacterial plasmids they have more in common with eukaryotic genes, having in the 5′ region, upstream of transcription start, sequences resembling the TATA or Hogness box, and near the 3′ end a sequence 'AATAAA' resembling the eukaryotic polyadenylation signal. The failure of previous attempts to obtain expression of foreign genes integrated in the T-DNA may have been due to the failure of the host plant enzymes to recognize the control signals of these genes. To circumvent this problem Herrera-Estrella *et al.* (1983) constructed a number of chimaeric genes, consisting of the coding sequences of the foreign gene and the promotor region of the nopaline synthase gene. These constructs can then be introduced via Ti plasmid vectors into tobacco plants and the resulting transformed cells tested for the ability of the chimaeric gene to produce a functional protein. The promotor region of the nopaline synthase gene (*nos*) was linked to the coding sequence for the octopine synthase (*ocs*) gene. This strategy was followed for a number of reasons: (i) *nos*, and separately *ocs*, are expressed constitutively in callus cells and also in the tissue of plants regenerated from T-DNA transformed cells; (ii) there exist rapid and sensitive assays for the detection of octopine and nopaline, and neither has been found in untransformed plant cells; (iii) a great deal is now known about the structure and organization of the *nos* and *ocs* genes.

Construction of the expression vector, using the *nos* promotor, the *ocs* cassette fragment (consisting of the *ocs* coding sequences with the promoter region deleted), and the *nos−ocs* chimaeric gene is outlined below and in Figs 4.6 and 4.7, a more detailed account is found in Herrera-Estrella *et al.*, 1983. A restriction endonuclease fragment *Hind* III-23 from Ti plasmid pTi C58 (Fig. 4.4) carries the complete coding and control sequences needed for expression of nopaline synthase in plant cells. From a pBR322 derivative carrying this *Hind* III-23 fragment a smaller *Sau* 3A fragment carrying the 5′ transcription signals and the coding region for the first fifteen amino acids of the *nos* gene is isolated to a second plasmid vector pLGV13. As eukaryotic ribosomes preferentially use the AUG most proximal to the 5′ end of the mRNA to initiate translation, this second plasmid vector underwent a number of treatments designed to remove the *nos*-coding sequences. A number of such pNOS△ (△ = deletion) plasmids were isolated and, following nucleotide sequencing, shown to have 3′ ends in different positions of the 5′ untranslated region of the *nos* gene. One such deletion, which removed the *nos*-coding region and two nucleotides of the 5′ un-translated region, was selected for further use.

A fragment of this pNOS plasmid (*Sac*II to *Bam*H1) is cloned back to the pBR322 derivative, pGV0601 which carries the complete *nos* coding and control regions. The large *Sac*II−*Bam*H1 fragment on pGV0601 is replaced by the smaller fragment from pNOS, generating the plasmid pLGV2381 which has the following features. Three-quarters of the *nos* coding region has been deleted but the 5′ and 3′ control sequences remain intact, with a *Hind*III restriction site conveniently placed behind the promoter. To determine whether this expression vector would promote the expression of other foreign genes, it was first

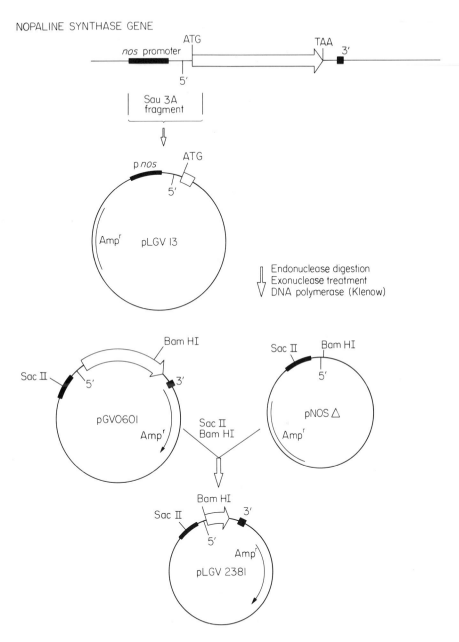

Fig. 4.6. Construction of *nos* promoter expression plasmid. See text for details.

combined with the coding region of the octopine synthase gene isolated as described below (Fig. 4.7).

A pBR322 derivative carrying the complete coding sequence, and part of the promotor, of the *ocs* gene, from Ti plasmid pTi B6S3, was treated in order to remove the 5′ upstream promotor sequences. A set

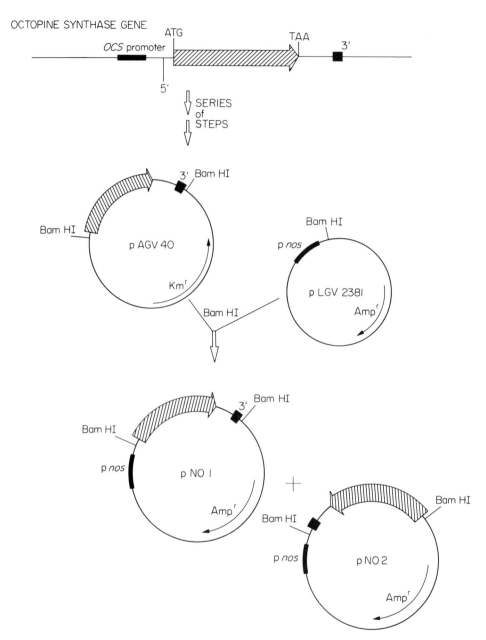

Fig. 4.7. Construction of plasmid expressing octopine synthase (*ocs*) from the nopaline synthase (*nos*) promoter. See text for details.

of plasmids carrying the complete coding sequence for the *ocs* gene and with different deletion end-points in the non-translated 5′ leader sequence were isolated: one plasmid (pAGV 40) containing only seven nucleotides of the 5′ region, the complete coding region and the 3′

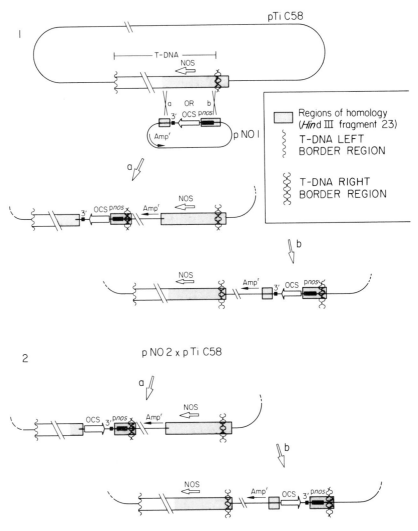

Fig. 4.8. Possible structure of co-integrates between plasmids. Plasmids pNO1 and pNO2 can integrate via homologous recombination with plasmid pTiC58. The four possible structures resulting are shown. (Adapted from Herrera-Estrella *et al.*, 1983.)

untranslated sequence, including the AATAAA polyadenylation signal from the *ocs* gene, was used in further studies.

Chimaeric genes linking the *nos* promoter to the *ocs* coding sequences were constructed, with the *ocs* coding sequences in each of two orientations shown in Fig. 4.7. These plasmids are then transferred by conjugation to Agrobacterium and recombined by homologous recombination with an acceptor pTi C58 plasmid (Fig. 4.8). The four possible results of such a co-integration are shown, and the resultant plasmids have two right-hand border fragments.

Plants were infected with the pTi C58 hybrid plasmid constructed from the *ocs* coding regions in all orientations shown in Fig. 4.8, types 1 and 2. Subsequent analysis of tumour extracts show that only type 1 produce octopine, whereas both type 1 and 2 produce nopaline, irrespective of whether they are type a or b. This suggests that both genes are transferred, despite their partition, on either side of an internal right-hand border of the T-DNA. The results may also reflect several independent integration events.

From these results it is clear that the isolated *nos* promotor is capable of promoting the transcription of the octopine synthase coding sequence. What of other coding sequences placed downstream from the *nos* promoter region?

The chimaeric nos−cat *gene*

The same authors then chose to test the *nos* promoter in combination with the coding region of the bacterial chloramphenicol acetyl trans-ferase (CAT) gene. A simple and sensitive assay exists for the CAT gene product, but the gene already shown to be capable of expression in yeast and mammalian cells, is not known to be present in plants.

Using similar constructions to those outlined above the *cat* gene coding sequence was 'hooked up' to the *nos* promotor, again in both orientations, and then transferred to plasmid pTi C58. Tumours were induced on tobacco seedlings and extracts, from axenic culture, tested for CAT activity. The extract from tumour tissue infected with plasmid having the *cat* coding sequences in the correct orientation with respect to the *nos* promoter was positive for CAT activity, whereas the other orientation was negative. Again the tumours contained nopaline, further suggesting that the external right-hand T-DNA border is involved in integration of the T-region. Suitable controls ensured that the CAT activity found was not due to contaminating Agrobacterium strains.

The above experiments clearly demonstrate that foreign genes can be transferred to, integrated into the nuclear genome of, and expressed in plants using the approach of constructing chimaeric genes, consisting of the coding region of the gene under study and the promoter region of the nopaline synthase *nos* gene. Other studies indicate that where plants are regenerated from such transformed tissue the genes will be inherited in a simple dominant Mendelian fashion.

These experiments also raise several other interesting points. The *nos* promoter may be a particularly useful one, since it is found to be functional in callus derived from all dicotyledonous plants so far tested, as well as being expressed in most tissues of regenerated *nos*-containing plants. Yet another application with wider implications is the con-struction of selectable marker genes for plants. Using the above *nos* promoter system Herrera-Estrella *et al.* have constructed chimaeric

genes containing the coding sequences of the neomycin phospho-
transferase gene from transposon Tn5 and the dihydrofolate reductase
gene of plasmid R67. Transformed tobacco cells were shown to express
resistance to the antibiotic G.418 and the drug methotrexate respectively, substances normally very toxic to plant cells. The potential
usefulness of these integrated chimaeric genes as selectable markers is
under study. Following on these results it is to be expected that the
recombinant DNA techniques so far elegantly applied to bacterial and
mammalian systems will find applicability in the plant field.

Design of Ti plasmid vectors

The large size of the Ti plasmids, and the lack of suitable restriction
endonuclease target sites in the T-region, for the cloning of foreign
DNA, has been the impetus for the development of smaller Ti cloning
vectors. Allied to this is the requirement for other functions on the Ti
plasmid which are essential for the transfer and integration of T-DNA
into the plant genome. These virulence genes must therefore be present
on any vector plasmid, or their functions available in *trans*. Also, there
is the situation that plant tissue, transformed with T-DNA with or
without inserted sequences, will give rise to tumorous plant cells with
grossly altered growth and differentiation characteristics. Ideally, one
requires transformed cells to be capable of normal growth and development. Each of these problems has been overcome to a greater or lesser
extent. Perhaps the easiest problem to overcome is that of tumorous
growth of the plant cells. This was achieved by deleting from the T-
region of the bacterial Ti plasmids all the genes concerned with
tumorous growth, while conserving those concerned with opine
synthesis (Leemans *et al.*, 1982; Matze & Chilton, 1981; Klee *et al.*,
1982). Normal plants develop from infection with Agrobacterium strains
containing such a deletion plasmid, and the presence of a functional
octopine synthase gene has been demonstrated in their tissues. Moreover, they have been shown to be fertile and to sexually transmit the
introduced gene as a single dominant Mendelian locus (De Greve *et al.*,
1982b).

In an attempt to reduce the overall size of the Ti plasmid and yet
retain an infective agent capable of gene transfer to plant cells, Chilton
and her collaborators have set about placing the minimum number of
essential functions onto smaller plasmids — the Mini Ti strategy. As we
have seen, the Ti plasmid is large and contains numerous functions not
essential for transfer and integration of the T-region. Any mini plasmid
must contain the T-region, and by a series of *in vivo* manipulations
Framond *et al.* (1983) have placed the T-region on a plasmid which is
capable of replication both in *E. coli* and *A. tumefaciens*. This mini Ti
by itself is avirulent, i.e. it will not induce the formation of tumours or

production of opines in infected plant cells. However, in the presence of a second plasmid which carries the *vir* genes (responsible for transfer of the T-region from bacteria to plant) the mini Ti is virulent.

As the above workers point out even this mini Ti is too large to allow easy manipulation. Their aim is to delete all the T-region functions with the exception of the border regions, and to replace them with foreign genes or genetic markers.

This approach is very similar to that of Zambryski *et al.* (1983) who propose a modified Ti plasmid with the following T-region characteristics: only the border recognition sequences; no *onc* gene functions; a marker gene, preferably dominant and selectable, and a sequence derived from a widely used cloning vector, such as pBR 322. It is envisaged that a single *in vivo* cross-over event between an intermediate vector, a pBR 322 plasmid carrying the gene of interest, and the acceptor Ti plasmid, described above will generate a Ti plasmid with the inserted gene within the T-region. The plasmid may then be transferred to the plant via normal Agrobacterium infection.

Caulimoviruses

Among the plant viruses the type virus of the caulimovirus group, cauliflower mosaic virus (CaMV), is often cited as the most likely potential vector for introducing foreign genes into plants. This is mainly because caulimoviruses are unique among plant viruses in having a genome composed of double-stranded DNA, which of course lends itself more readily to the manipulations involved in recombinant DNA technology. We will first of all consider the salient features of the CaMV particle and life cycle, and then look at its potential as a plant gene cloning vector.

Again, the impetus for development of CaMV as a vector stems from study of the virus itself, as a consequence of its pathogenic activities on susceptible plants. An immediately apparent drawback of this potential vector is the limited host range of CaMV, the virus mainly affecting the Cruciferae. Symptoms of infection vary, depending on the virus isolate, time of inoculation and condition of the plant, from mild vein clearing to more severe leaf stunting. The virus is transmitted by aphids and this ability may be controlled by the virus itself. However, one of the main attractions is that both the virus and the isolated DNA are infectious, easily transmitted by abrasion of the leaves. The infection becomes systemic yielding very high replication of the virus — 10^5 virions/cell. Virus accumulates in the cytoplasm in inclusion bodies which consist of a protein matrix with embedded virus particles. It is rare to see free virus in the cytoplasm, and the inclusion body may be the site of virion assembly. The virus particle is spherical, isometric, about 50 nm in diameter, and may be isolated from the inclusion body using urea and non-ionic detergents. Extraction of DNA from the virus particle is particularly difficult involving the use of ionic detergents and proteolytic enzymes. The DNA molecule is about 8 kbp long and several varieties (totalling 50,000 bases) have been sequenced. The DNA exists in linear, open circular and twisted or knotted forms; however, none of the circular forms is covalently closed due to the presence of site-specific single-strand breaks (Fig. 4.9). These S1 nuclease-sensitive single-strand breaks are not true gaps but short oligonucleotide overlapping regions, having sequence complementarity, and thus forming short triple-stranded structures with a fixed 5' end. There are three such sites, one (1) in the minus (coding or transcribed) strand yielding the large α fragment and overlapping by eight residues. The other two (2 and 3) are in the plus (non-coding or non-transcribed) strand yielding the β and γ fragments having eighteen and fifteen residue overlaps respectively. One of the plus strand discontinuities is dispensable (Gardner *et al.*, 1980), and none are required for infection, as virus DNA previously cloned in bacteria and lacking the 'gaps' is as infectious as native DNA (Fig. 4.10; Howell *et al.*, 1980).

The sequence data obtained from CaMV have revealed, by analysis of open reading frames and stop codons, six major and two minor, tightly packed, potential coding regions distributed between the three reading frames (Fig. 4.11). On either side of coding region VI there are

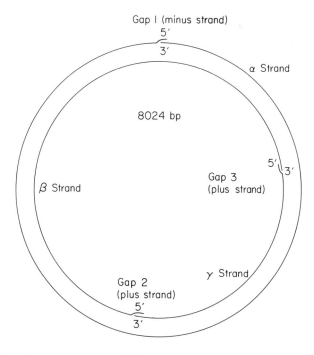

Fig. 4.9. Cauliflower mosaic virus DNA.

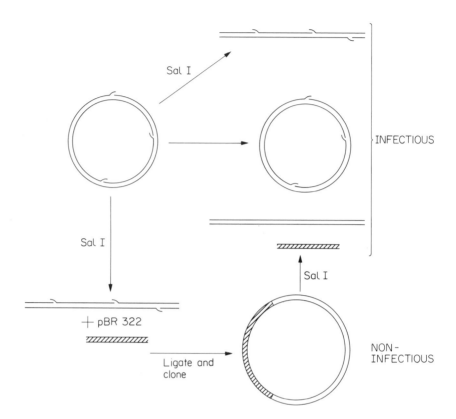

Fig. 4.10. Infectious and non-infectious forms of CaMV DNA.

two 'intergenic regions' (IR) one large of approximately 1000 bp, and one small of roughly 100 bp. The large IR flanks the α-strand break. From the projected amino acid composition of the protein derived from the DNA sequence, coding region IV has the capacity to code for a protein of 57,000 MW which correllates closely with the viral coat protein. Region VI codes for a non-viral protein of 61,000–66,000 MW (P66) thought to be involved in the viral inclusion body found in the cytoplasm. The proposed protein from region II is implicated in aphid transmissibility, as mutations in this region can abolish this capacity. The putitive 18,000 MW product may be a 'transmissibility' protein.

Viral-specific RNA isolated from infected tissue is analysed using Northern Blots. Transcription of CaMV is found to be asymmetric, with only the α-strand producing stable transcripts. The map location of only two major transcripts is known (Fig. 4.11). The smaller of these is a 1·9 kb (19S) RNA derived from coding region VI, proposed to code for the 62,000 MW inclusion body protein, the 5′ end of which originates in the small IR between coding region V and VI. The other transcript is an 8 kb (35S) RNA of the whole α-strand, transcribed in a clockwise

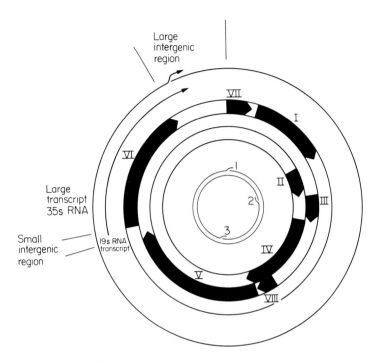

Fig. 4.11. Major CaMV RNA transcripts and potential coding regions.

direction with the 5′ end in the large IR near the end of coding region VI. Upstream of the 5′ end of both transcripts are found typical eukaryotic promotor signals, 'TATA' and 'CAT' boxes, and at the 3′ end a polyadenylated signal is present; the two transcripts have a common 3′ end. The large 35S RNA transcript also has terminal repeats of 180 b. The accumulation of start and stop signals before the first open reading frame makes the transcript an unsuitable messenger and, unlike the 19S RNA, it is not translated *in vitro*.

The various features of CaMv have led two groups of investigators, Hull & Covey (1983) and Pfeiffer & Hohn (1983) to propose a mechanism for replication based on that found in retroviruses. Briefly, the proposed mechanism is as follows. The infecting CaMV DNA enters the plant nucleus, where the single-stranded overlaps are digested and the gaps ligated to give a supercoiled minichromosome. The function of this minichromosome is to act as a template for plant nuclear RNA polymerase II. The transcript thus formed is transported to the cytoplasm where it is either translated, or replicated by reverse transcription. A site 600 b downstream of the promotor of the large transcript binds the proposed primer of reverse transcription, methionine tRNA. The RNA transcript is then copied into minus strand DNA. Synthesis of the plus strand DNA starts at two primer binding sites near 'gaps' 2 and 3. From gap 2 synthesis proceeds to the 5' end of the minus strand DNA, whereas synthesis from gap 3 continues to gap 2. Template switching and displacement of 5' termini are proposed to account for the terminal repeats/overlaps at the three strand irregularities. This DNA molecule may then be packed into virus particles, or re-enter the nucleus and undergo another round of transcription and/or translation/replication (Pfeiffer & Hohn, 1983).

If this model turns out to be the case it has certain implications for the use of CaMV as a possible gene vector. Transcription takes place in the nucleus, but unlike retrovirus, where integration is a prerequisite for transcription, there is no evidence that CaMV DNA integrates into the plant genome, indeed the symptoms of infection are not transmitted through seed.

Use as a vector

There are several problems associated with the use of CaMV as a gene cloning vector for plants. Firstly, the genome is so tightly packed with coding regions that there is little room to insert foreign DNA. The question then arises as to whether any of the genome is dispensable for viral functions? Most deletions of any significant size destroy virus infectivity, except for small modifications in coding region II. Random insertion of 8 bp restriction site linkers also destroys infectivity, again except in coding region II and the large intergenic region. Coding region II is highly polymorphic and has natural deletions and insertions; however, inserts up to 0·4 kbp long are tolerated, but those over 1·3 kbp destroy infectivity of the DNA.

Attempts have been made to side-step this size limitation problem by using a helper virus system, where a substantial proportion of the viral genome is deleted and replaced with foreign DNA. The loss of function could be complemented by co-infection with a normal viral DNA, or viral DNA deleted for a different function. However, the rescue of viral functions in all cases occurred by recombination between the inactive viral genomes, and only normal infectious virus was recovered. For this system to be of any use the recombinational rescue of altered genomes must be suppressed, although the 'retroviral like' mode of replication produces a high recombination frequency and alteration of this would affect viral replication.

The second potential problem with CaMV is that infection, once established, becomes systemic, spreading throughout the whole plant. This lack of inheritance through the germ line, may be advantagous in that the CaMV DNA, and any inserted gene sequence, would be highly amplified in the host plant cells, potentially permitting the expression of large quantities of the foreign gene product. However, it appears that to propagate CaMV and to allow its movement throughout the vasculature of the plant, the DNA must be encapsidated and this would impose serious constraints on the size of foreign DNA which can be inserted into the viral genome.

The problems outlined above have come to light through a detailed study of CaMV and its mode of replication and transcription, and there may be as yet unrecognized properties of the virus which will be exploited in its future development as a cloning vector. Also, one can envisage the possibility of introducing into the CaMV DNA short regions of host plant DNA, or the border regions from the T-region of the Agrobacterium Ti plasmid, to aid integration of CaMV DNA into the plant nuclear genome through these regions of homology. Subsequent infection using CaMV, containing integrated DNA, would allow integration via the homologous CaMV DNA already in the plant nuclear genome. Such inserts, stably maintained, may also be inherited through the seed.

To date the infectivity of the virus particle, and its naked DNA, are the most useful assets as regards the use of CaMV and its development as a gene cloning vector for plants.

Gemini viruses

As with the Ti plasmid of Agrobacterium, and cauliflower mosaic virus, the potential of gemini viruses as gene cloning vectors for plants, stems from work on several plant diseases now recognized as being caused by these agents. Both curly top virus (CTV), which causes major disease in several crops in the western US and the Mediterranean, and maize streak disease (MSV) — one of the most important diseases of maize in Africa — have been major economic factors in the development of agriculture in the areas where they occur. The gemini viruses recognized by the International Commission on the Taxonomy of Viruses in 1978, are characterized on the basis of their unique virion morphology and possession of single-stranded (ss) DNA.

Structural features of gemini viruses

The most suprising features of this virus group are the small capsid size, $18-20$ nm $\times$ 30 nm, their geminate (paired particles) morphology, which sets them apart from all other classes of viruses, and the unexpected covalently closed circular (ccc) topography of the ssDNA which is in the molecular weight range $7 \times 10^5 - 9 \times 10^5$. All gemini viruses recognized so far have a single major coat protein subunit in the range $2 \cdot 7 - 3 \cdot 4 \times 10^4$ daltons.

These features raised questions about the genome size of gemini viruses, and the biological or genetic significance of the geminate structure. Bean golden mosaic virus (BGMV) DNA was found to be

2510 nucleotides long, and if this was the complete genome it would be less than half the length of any other known autonomously replicating plant virus. By comparing the ssDNA of the virus particle with the viral dsDNA found in infected plants, it was found that the nucleotide sequence had a complexity twice that expected on the physical size of the viral DNA (Haber *et al.*, 1981). This indicates the BGMV DNA is heterogenous, the virus having a divided genome consisting of two DNA molecules of approximately the same size, but different genetic content. It would appear that gemini viruses consist of two populations of paired particles, differing only in the nucleotide sequence of the DNA molecules they contain.

Little is know about the replication of gemini viruses except that it occurs in the nuclei of infected plant cells — both DNA synthesis and viral assembly take place here — and may be associated with the fibrillar rings seen in the nucleolus. A dsDNA intermediate has been found in infected plant cells and DNA synthesis may occur on a circular template using, at least in part, host enzymes. No DNA/RNA hybrid molecules have been observed. Transmission of the virus in nature occurs by leaf hoppers (*Circulifer tenellus*, *Cicadulina mbila*), or the tropical white-fly (*Bemisia tabaci*).

Use as a cloning vector

The potential of gemini viruses as vectors for the transfer of genes to plants is only beginning to be considered. As is usual with potential vectors, particularly viruses, the first step is to determine which genes carried by the virus are essential, their location and promotor sequences. Such details have yet to be determined for these viruses.

One advantage this group of viruses does have is that they contain DNA which, although single-stranded, appears to replicate via a double-stranded intermediate, which would make *in vivo* manipulation in bacterial plasmids more convenient. The dsDNA is known to be present and possibly replicated in the nucleus, as well as being infectious to plant protoplasts (Goodman, 1981a). The virus group are known to infect a wide range of crop plants including monocots, dicots and legumes (Goodman, 1981b).

A potential disadvantage may relate to the observation that in infected plants BGMV particles are limited to phloem-associated elements. With BGMV this may not be such a problem as the DNA can infect mesophyll protoplasts *in vitro*, and these could be used to regenerate whole plants. However, the transformation of protoplasts with BGMV DNA is a very inefficient process requiring 10^6 DNA molecules per cell to achieve 1% infection.

Gemini viruses are not readily transferred by mechanical means from plant to plant, being transmitted in nature by insects in a persistent fashion. The small particle size may present packaging problems for modified DNA molecules, and any useful genetic modifications will have to solve the problem of a vector which in its natural state causes significant, sometimes severly debilitating, diseases in susceptible plants.

Other possible vector systems

There are several other potential vectors for gene transfer to plants, which although they are not at the same stage of development as the Ti plasmids, are none the less worth bearing in mind. One class, the transposable or controlling elements such as those found in maize, may indeed eclipse the Ti plasmid vectors, if their proposed application to cereal crops becomes a reality.

Transposable elements

These are segments of DNA which are not autonomous, and spend most of their time integrated into the genome. They have been described as introgenic parasites, and they have the ability to integrate at different sites within the genome and to move around the genome, i.e. transpose. Transposable elements are found in a wide range of species — bacteria, yeast, insects, plants, animals — and they may be ubiquitous in nature. They are a diverse class of elements with some properties in common, detected usually by classical genetics, and more recently by hybridization probes. These elements are the source of 'genetic noise' in many organisms, i.e. they can cause spontaneous mutations such as deletions, reversions and transpositions (Bukhari *et al.*, 1977).

It is satisfying to note that in the discovery of controlling elements, plant science was ahead of both animal and bacterial research. The elegant work of Barbara McClintock in the 1940s and 50s with maize was the first description of the action of these elements (McClintock, 1951, 1956, 1965). The effects of nuclear controlling elements are seen as unusual variegation patterns on maize kernels, and several types of elements have been recognized. The initial discovery was largely ignored and only recently has it come to the fore, through the recognition of similar phenomena in other species, and a description of the molecular basis of the proposed mechanism (Fincham & Sastry, 1974; Starlinger, 1980; Federoff 1982). The pioneering work of Barbara Mclintock was rewarded in October of 1983 with the award of a Nobel prize in medicine.

In general, what happens is that a controlling element inserts into a particular locus and thus disrupts gene expression, giving rise to a mutant recessive phenotype. This insertion may be very unstable and revert to wild type at high frequency, other insertions are inherently stable, cause stable mutations, and become unstable in the presence of another type of controlling element (Federoff, 1982). Several maize controlling elements of the DS (dissociation) type (causing stable mutations) have now been cloned and analysed (Marx, 1983). They vary enormously in size (402 bp, 2500 bp and 20,000 bp), although they may all have in common the presence of inverted terminal repeats of approximately 11 bp. In at least one case these are bounded by 8 bp direct repeats of the host DNA at the insertion site of the gene into which they integrate (Marx, 1983). However, Döring (1984) has reported that the structure of the integrated DS element may be much more complex than at first thought, with one element possibly integrating into the middle of another.

How would these transposable elements be used to transfer genes to plants? A precedent already exists in that similar smaller elements found in *Drosophila*, the P elements, which also have inverted terminal repeats and behave like the DS elements of maize, have been used by Rubin & Spradling (1982) in the USA to transfer foreign genes into the fruit fly. The work of W.J. Peacock (see Marx, 1983) in Canberra, Australia would seem to offer the best approach to this research in plants. What they have done is to clone the gene coding for the enzyme alcohol dehydrogenase (ADH) from maize. Cells deficient in this enzyme cannot grow in the absence of oxygen. If the ADH gene coding for this enzyme is transferred to the mutant plant cells they should grow anaerobically. This is proposed as a selectable marker system, in that this gene (ADH) could be transferred together with another desired gene to the ADH-deficient plant and transfer detected by the ability to grow in media lacking oxygen. These workers also had a mutant *adh* locus with an inserted transposable DS element. This gene was 402 bp longer than the wild type, and the wild type revertants lacked this insert. The idea is then, to insert the cloned ADH locus into a DS element, and to determine whether this hybrid can confer ADH enzyme activity on maize cells lacking the enzyme. If this turns out to be the case then other genes would be inserted into DS and this linked to an ADH gene, thus giving a selectable marker linked to sequences capable of insertion into the nuclear DNA. The main advantage of this system is its applicability to monocotyledonous plants, whereas Ti only infects dicots. However, problems remain: for example, whole maize plants have not been grown from protoplasts, although progress towards this end is being made (Green, 1978). Other plants can be regenerated from protoplasts, however, and one interesting study would be to compare the Ti and DS element vector systems in the same plant.

Maize mitochondrial elements

Studies of cytoplasmic male sterility have revealed several of these extrachromosomal DNA elements. Unlike nuclear elements these appear to replicate autonomously in the mitochondria and may integrate into the mitochondrial genome. The cytoplasm of plants exhibiting cytoplasmic male sterility (CMS) are classified into three types, T, C and S-CMS, (p. 31) based on their response to nuclear restorer genes (Duvik, 1965), and this division correllates well with features of the mitochondrial DNA, and the presence of DNA elements. Wild type mitochondrial CMS cytoplasms contain a 1·95 kbp circular element, a small cryptic self-replicating plasmid; all except T-CMS contain in addition a 2·4 kbp linear element. As well as these, C-CMS cytoplasm has two small circular elements of 1·55 and 1·42 kbp, and S-CMS cytoplasm contains two linear molecules of 6·2 kbp and 5.2 kbp called S_1 and S_2 respectively. These two elements have an inverted terminal repeat of 200 bp, sharing a region of homology of 1·3 kbp near to one end and, although they are linear and non-integrated, they appear to be capable of transposition within the mitochondrial genome. Indeed they may have been derived from this genome as regions of homology exist between S_1 and S_2 and normal mitochondrial DNA. The use of these elements as cloning vectors is speculative, considering they do not carry any known markers, and their exact relationship to cytoplasmic male sterility is not yet clear.

Nuclear genomic components

The potential for development and use of plant nuclear genomic components stems from similar successful applications in yeast. From yeast chromosomal DNA, vectors have been constructed which allow integration into the host genome without (Hinnen *et al.*, 1978), or with (Scherer & Davis, 1979) replacement of the homologous host loci. As yet in plants a homologous transformation system does not exist; however, in mammalian cells integration of DNA does not occur by homologous recombination, the inserted DNA integrating at random (Pellicer *et al.*, 1980). If the case in plants turns out to be similar there may be no need for specialized vectors derived from nuclear components. One other important feature of transformation in animal (mammalian) cells is the phenomenon of competence, i.e. not all cells are able to take up DNA. However, competent cells integrate a selectable marker gene into their genome and appear also to incorporate any non-selectable DNA which is present. These two DNAs are linked in the recipient host cell (Perucho *et al.*, 1980; Wigler *et al.*, 1979). Nevertheless, the availability of selectable marker systems for plant cells may pre-empt such studies.

Another type of successful yeast vector has been constructed using autonomously replicating DNA sequences (ARS), which may represent origins of DNA replication. Yeast vectors of this type give higher transformation frequencies with (Struhl *et al.*, 1979), or without (Clarke

& Carbon, 1980) selection pressure being applied to maintain the vector, which is retained in an autonomously replicating form. These latter types of vector (Clarke & Carbon, 1980; Hsiao & Carbon, 1981) turn out to be portions of the centromeric fragments of the chromosome, and it may be that they behave as such, allowing normal segregation at cell division. Recently progress has been reported in the construction of artificial chromosomes in yeast (Murray & Szostak, 1983).

RNA viruses

These viruses are not high on the list of potential vectors for plant gene transfer. They do have a few properties, however, which may be exploited at some future date. There are two basic types of single-stranded RNA virus. The 'monopartite' viruses have undivided genomes containing all the genetic information present in these viruses, and are usually fairly large, for example tobacco mosaic virus is of the order of 2×10^6 MW. Their large size is a major disadvantage rendering *in vitro* manipulation difficult. The 'multipartite' viruses as the name suggests, have their genome divided among small RNAs, either in the same particle, or separate particles. For example, brome mosaic virus (BMV) contains four RNAs divided between three separate particles. The RNA components of 'multipartite' genomes are small and appear to be able to self-replicate in plants. With some members of the group the genes encoding the coat protein may be dispensable, in that loss does not affect viral DNA multiplication. From the vector construction point of view this would enable the RNA to move systemically through the plant in an unencapsidated form. Compare this with the situation in CaMV. The second group, subgenomic RNAs (for example, RNA IV of BMV) are unlikely to find application as cloning vectors as they are unable to self-replicate in infected plants. The third group, satellite RNAs have perhaps the greatest potential being totally dispensable to the virus. They vary in size from 270 bases (tobacco ringspot virus satellite) to 1·5 kb (tomato black ring virus satellite). These satellites appear to share little homology with the viral genomic RNAs, the templates for their own replication, and utilize the machinery for replication set up by the virus. They are not required for virus replication, but are capable of altering the pathogenicity of the viral infection, usually moderating the symptoms but sometimes making them worse. These satellite RNAs have a number of other unusual properties, including the ability to code for proteins and stability in the plant in the absence of other viral components (Howell, 1982). However, their use as cloning vectors will have to be evaluated when cDNA copies or RNA derived therefrom have been assessed for infectivity, and the fate of such constructions can be determined in the whole plant.

Viroids

The smallest and indeed simplest pathogenic agents known have also been proposed as plant gene vectors. They are small, 300–400 bases long, circular, single-stranded although they undergo extensive base pairing, and consist of naked RNA (Sänger *et al.*, 1976). These non-protein coding viroids replicate in the host using host enzymes, probably host RNA polymerase II (Rackwitz *et al.*, 1981). They may cause quite severe symptoms in infected plants such as coconut Cadang-Cadang disease, and their mechanism of action, although not certain, may involve interference with RNA processing in the affected plant.

Despite the obvious limitations they have several features attractive to vector development. They are mechanically transmissible, able to move through the sap and infect other parts of the plant, and some may also be transmitted through the seed (vertical inheritance). They infect a wide variety of plants — mainly tropical — and may replicate in, and are certainly associated with, the nucleus.

Delivery systems

The development of gene cloning vectors for plants aims at introducing foreign DNA into that plant using some 'natural' system, viral or bacterial. However, where this is not possible or desirable, other methods of introduction must be sought. The introduction of biologically active nucleic acid into plant protoplasts has been investigated (Fernandez *et al.*, 1978), and in these systems various agents have been used to protect that nucleic acid from nuclease digestion, or physical disruption (Takebe, 1975). These have included polycations such as poly (L-ornithine), poly (L-lysine), protamine sulphate, various metal cations, Zn^{2+}, Ca^{2+}, and polyethylene glycol. In animal cells larger pieces of DNA and whole chromosomes have been transferred (Willecke, 1978). Plant chromosomes have also been isolated from protoplasts (Malmberg & Greisbach, 1980), and their uptake in this system studied (Szabados *et al.*, 1981).

Another possible delivery system might involve the direct micro-injection (Steinbiss & Stabel, 1983) of nucleic acid into plant cells using techniques described for cultured mammalian cells (Gordon *et al.*, 1980; Capecchi, 1980). The system currently receiving most attention, and considered to hold the most promise involves the use of liposomes (Fraley *et al.*, 1982; Ohgawara *et al.*, 1983). These are small artificial lipid vesicles prepared (Uchimiya & Harada, 1981) from phosphatidyl choline and stearylamine by a process known as reverse-phase evaporation. Nucleic acid entrapped in such liposomes renders it highly tolerant to attack by nucleases. More recently, techniques for fusing these liposomes to plant cell protoplasts have been described (Uchimiya

& Harada, 1981; Ohgawara *et al.*, 1983; Matthews & Cress, 1981).

A further technique which would be useful when transferring DNA present in bacteria to higher plant cells involves the direct fusion of bacterial and plant cells. Such techniques have been described in mammals for the transfer to SV40 DNA cloned in bacteria to cells in culture (Schaffner, 1980), as well as transfer of the Ti plasmid from *Agrobacterium tumefaciens* to tobacco cells in tissue culture (Marton *et al.*, 1979). Recently, *E. coli* cells and sphaeroplasts have been introduced into protoplasts of *Vinca rosea* using polyvinylalcohol to mediate fusion (Matsui *et al.*, 1983).

Techniques for the successful delivery of nucleic acids to plant cells and protoplasts will be developed and extended to complement the use of intact vectors.

Further reading

Kahl G. & Schell J.S. (1982) (Eds) *Molecular Biology of Plant Tumours.* Academic Press, New York.

Kosuge T., Meredith C. & Hollaender A. (1983) (Eds) *Genetic Engineering of Plants. An Agricultural Perspective.* Plenum Press, New York.

Wettstein von. D. (1983) Genetic engineering in the adaptation of plants to evolving human needs. *Experientia* **39**, 687–713.

5 Cultural Tools and Technique

Undoubtedly one of the significant contributions to the manipulative powers of modern biologists has been the development of tissue culture technique. Tissue culture is the process whereby small pieces of living tissue (explants) are isolated from an organism and grown aseptically for indefinite periods on a semi-defined or defined nutrient medium. This original definition now has to be extended in the case of plants to include a range of 'explants' as large as seedlings and organs (as in ovule and embryo cultures) and as small as single cells and protoplasts (as in cell and protoplast cultures, respectively). Such developments have broadened the scope of operations possible for use in the diverse plant-based biotechnological fields dealt within the proceeding chapters of this book.

Scope and perspective

Successful attempts were made to culture animal tissues aseptically in the early part of this century (Paul, 1975). Plant-based tissue culture methodology lagged somewhat behind and developed in conjunction with related advances in the plant sciences. With the discovery of auxin and cytokinin and their effects on cell growth and division, along with the advantageous inclusion in media of natural substances such as coconut milk (which *in vivo* support growth and development of embryos in certain plants), it was shown that plant tissue explants could proliferate by repeated cell divisions. When appropriate cultural conditions were provided, cell masses could then proceed along various developmental pathways to regenerate shoot and root organs and eventually whole plants. Much has been written on the subject of plant tissue and cell culture from the point of view of its elegance as a research tool and its potential application in many biological fields. It is intended that this chapter introduce the topic to those unfamiliar with the essentials of the methods and technique. Greater detail is supplied in the texts listed at the end of this chapter and elsewhere in the literature.

Differentiation, totipotency and meristems in plants

Development of single cells into complex multicellular organs and tissues is a natural progression common to all higher forms of life. It constitutes that spectrum of development known as differentiation and is a series of highly co-ordinated and genetically determined processes through which single or fused gametes (spores and zygotes, respectively, in plants) and somatic initials derived ultimately from a single cell primordium develop into whole plants. As described in Chapter 2, the paths of differentiation along which plant maturation proceeds are ultimately determined by the constitutive nature of inherited genes, the expression of which is modulated by cellular and environmental inter-actions. Patterns of plant development are reasonably consistent within definable ranges of genotype, i.e. taxonomic groups, so much so that the genetic constituents of the original germ cell in theory contain all the critical determinates of patterns of differentiation. It is upon this basis that the concept of totipotency has arisen. Since somatic tissues of a plant are ultimately the products of mitotic divisions, each cell within that organism should be capable of regenerating further replicas of the same organism provided appropriate conditions for this are supplied. By definition, totipotency is the capacity of a single cell to regenerate the phenotype of the complete and differentiated organism from which it is derived. In plants, most co-ordinated cell division takes place in con-centrated areas known as meristems and these are distributed at various sites within the organism as it develops. The activity of meristems can be activated or suppressed according to patterns of differentiation dictated by genetic and/or environmental control mechanisms (Wareing, 1982).

The totipotency concept, however, requires that somatic cells derived from these meristems retain functional and conserved DNA during differentiation processes, and that differential gene expression mechanisms do not result in permanent modifications to the genomes during differentiation. It is clear that such modifications in gene expression and DNA content do occur (see Chapter 2) such that totipotency theory, although satisfactory in principle, should be qualified to distinguish certain states of differentiation or determination. Cells at a relatively early stage of development — such as quiescent (non-dividing) types of parenchyma and the cells in meristems, vascular cambial tissues and embryonic tissues — are in a condition referred to as 'undetermined'. Undetermined cells are by definition capable of switching to different pathways of development depending on the environments imposed on them. Undetermined cells can also rapidly proliferate (dedifferentiate) to produce cell masses known as calluses. This type of tissue is often naturally produced in plants as a response to wounding and its development normally persists for only a short time before cells become rapidly infiltrated with polyphenolic substances, sealing off the wound from the environment (Yeoman & Forche, 1980). By contrast, cells that have developed to a point beyond which they are destined to produce specialized cell types, e.g. lignified vascular elements of the xylem phloem and suberised cork cells, have reached a more 'determined' state.

Consequently, undetermined plant cells can exhibit totipotency in addition to a high degree of plasticity in their response to physiological and environmental stimuli. This feature of vascular plants is possibly attributable to their adaptation to the sedentary habit which necessitates various degrees of evasiveness in order to respond to injury caused by herbivores, pests and pathogens and to the requirement in perennials for survival by means of prodigious vegetative propagation mechanisms whenever unfavourable environmental conditions prevail.

Development of plant tissue culture technique

Historical events

It was in 1878 that the German botanist Vochting, after attempting to investigate factors which play a role in the control of organ formation and differentiation in plants, stated that in every plant fragment, be it ever so small, rest the elements from which, by isolating the fragments under proper external conditions, the whole body can be built up. Such foresight was followed in 1902 by Haberlandt who predicted that one day 'one could successfully cultivate artificial embryos from vegetative cells' (from Krikorian, 1982). The work of Haberlandt on single cells derived from palisade tissue of leaves, pith tissue of stems and the glandular and stamen hairs of *Tradescantia*, demonstrated that it was possible to support cells in a viable state for up to 20–27 days in a Knop's mineral solution containing sucrose, asparagine, and peptone. However, these cells although showing up to eleven-fold increase in original volume did not divide. Concurrently, major advances were being made in animal tissue culture in which frog neuroblasts were grown in clotted lymph. Also, other excised animal tissues were cultured in nutrient media containing blood plasma and embryo sac fluid. In 1922, Kotte (a student of Haberlandt's) succeeded in culturing excised root tips of pea and maize for limited periods using an animal-based culture medium (Liebig's meat extract). Shortly afterwards, it was demonstrated that the sustained growth of excised maize roots could be achieved for up to 20 weeks in media containing yeast extract. The milestone for satisfying the major criteria of plant tissue culture, i.e. potentially unlimited growth and undifferentiated growth, came when White (1934) achieved indefinite culture of tomato roots on a defined nutrient medium (for White's Medium, see Appendix 3) and Gautheret (1934) concurrently developed unorganized ('dedifferentiated') callus cultures from the cambial (meristem) regions of three tree species. Thereafter, the course of history reveals some dramatic advances in tissue culture technique. Some of the major ones are listed in Table 5.1.

Culture media

With the identity of mineral nutrients and growth regulators required to sustain cell division and proliferation of tobacco and carrot explants, the same technique was applied with limited degrees of success to numerous other species including many crop plants. It was recognized early on that

Table 5.1. Major landmarks in the development of plant tissue culture technique (pre-1960).

Period	Achievements	References[*]
1920–1934	Limited culture of excised pea and maize roots	Kotte (1922)
	Limited culture of excised maize roots	Robbins & Maneval (1923)
	Discovery that auxin IAA promotes cell growth	Went (1927)
	Indefinite culture of tomato roots	White (1934)
	Indefinite callus cultures of tree species	Gautheret (1934)
1935–1940	Use of IAA in media (carrot cultures)	Nobecourt (1937)
		Gautheret (1937)
	Use of tumour hybrid *Nicotiana glauca* × *N. langsdorffii* to produce callus cultures	White (1937)
	Recognition of role of vitamin B1	Gautheret (1939)
1941–1950	Use of coconut milk to support embryoids of *Datura* hybrids	Van Overbeek *et al.* (1942)
	Discovery that adenine derived from nucleic acids enhances cell proliferation and bud formation in callus cultures	Skoog (1948)
	Endosperm cultures established	La Rue (1949)
	Cultures of monocotyledons established using coconut milk additive to media	Morel (1950)
1951–1960	Discovery that the cytokinin, kinetin, promotes cell division	Miller *et al.* (1955)
	Effects of graft transmissible growth regulatory substances on differentiation	Wetmore & Sorokin (1955)
	Roles of auxin and cytokinin on shoot and root induction in tobacco callus cultures established	Skoog & Miller (1957)
	Discovery of somatic embryogenesis in carrot callus cultures	Reinert (1958)

[*] Cited in Gautheret (1982) and Krikorian (1982).

different tissue explants taken from different parts of a plant within and between genotypes have varying growth regulator requirements for callus growth. Also, due to the natural variation in endogenous levels of auxin and cytokinin between different tissues, requirements for differentiation of explants were often extremely variable. A significant contribution to formulation of a defined growth medium suitable for a wide range of applications was made by Murashige & Skoog (1962). In their work to adapt tobacco callus cultures for use as a hormone bioassay system they evaluated many medium constituents to achieve optimal growth of calluses. In so doing, they improved upon existing

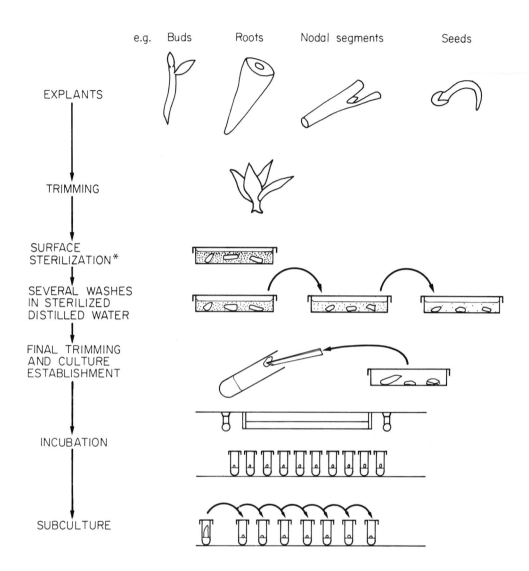

*See Appendix 4 for sterilizing agents

Fig. 5.1. Schematic outline of the basic procedure for establishing and maintaining plant tissue cultures. Suitable explants, e.g. buds, storage tissues, stem section or germinated seedlings, are trimmed before surface sterilization in a detergent solution (see Appendix 4). After washing in sterile distilled water, the explants are placed on suitable culture media of either a semi-solidified or liquid form. Subcultures are made at frequent intervals by subdividing single mother cultures into several daughter cultures.

types of plant tissue culture media to such an extent that their medium (the MS medium) has since proved to be one of the most widely used in plant tissue culture work.

The medium consists of the following major groups of ingredients:
    inorganic macronutrients (N, P, K, Ca, Mg, Fe content);
    inorganic micronutrients (Mn, Cu, Zn, B, Na, Cl, I, S, Mo, Co, Al,
    Ni content);
    vitamins (nicotinic acid, pyridoxine and thiamine);
    organic nitrogen sources (glycine and inositol);
    sugars (sucrose);
    growth regulators (e.g. auxin, cytokinin, gibberellic acid);
    optional organics (casein hydrolysate and yeast extract);
    optional gelling agent (0·5−1·0% agar).
    Details of the various minor modifications made to this medium and
of some alternative forms of plant tissue culture media are given in
Appendix 3 and further elaborated upon in excellent overviews such as
that by Gamborg *et al.* (1976).

Culture technique

Establishment of any plant tissue culture follows standard procedures
similar to the one outlined in Fig. 5.1. More details are provided in
specialist volumes.
    After the primary phase of development in plant tissue culture
technique in the pre-1960 era, the topic of *in vitro* culture of plant cells,
tissues and organs then diversified dramatically. Since it is the purpose
of this chapter to highlight those techniques and cultural tools which
have since developed and which are so well suited to application in plant
biotechnology, only the most significant techniques will be described. It
is intended that the necessary details of these be expounded upon in the
relevant areas of application treated in subsequent chapters of this book
and even then only in the exemplary manner.

Regeneration of plants

Numerous species ranging from algae to vascular plants can be induced
to form calluses in culture. In many cases, this callus material (Fig. 5.2)
can then be induced (though by no means in all cases) to differentiate
into whole plants by inclusion of appropriate growth regulators in media
and by the culture medium and culture environment.

Organogenesis and embryogenesis

With the discovery of the independent roles of auxin and cytokinin in
root and shoot induction in callus cultures, a process referred to as
organogenesis, Skoog & Miller (1957) established that one of the basic
regulatory mechanisms underlying it appeared to involve, amongst other
things, a balance between the relative levels of these two groups of

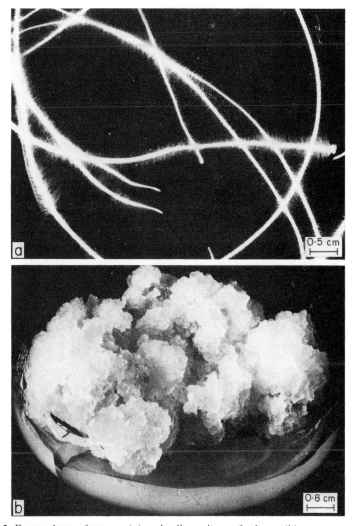

Fig. 5.2. Root culture of tomato (a) and callus culture of tobacco (b).

growth regulatory compounds present in the medium. In the tobacco
system with which they worked, a relatively high ratio of auxin to
cytokinin (IAA/kinetin) favours root formation, the reverse favours
shoot formation and intermediate ratios favour continued callus proliferation (Fig. 5.3). Plantlets arise through development of adventitious
roots on the shoot buds formed or through development of shoot buds
from tissues formed by proliferation at the base of rootlets. Alternatively, and most significantly, some callus cultures under certain
nutritional and hormonal conditions can be induced to develop bipolar
adventive embryoids. The development of such somatic embryoids from
somatic tissues follows a sequence through pro-embryoid, globular and

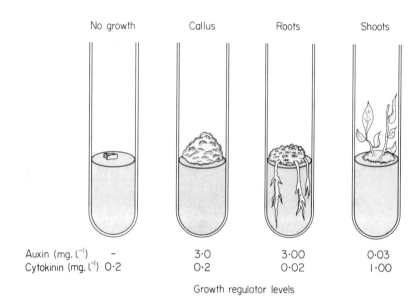

	No growth	Callus	Roots	Shoots
Auxin (mg. l^{-1})	–	3·0	3·00	0·03
Cytokinin (mg. l^{-1})	0·2	0·2	0·02	1·00

Growth regulator levels

Fig. 5.3. Effect of growth regulators auxin (IAA) and cytokinin (kinetin) on the proliferation and morphogenesis of tobacco pith explants.

torpedo stages referred to as somatic embryogenesis. This pattern of development is strikingly similar in some respects to those which occur in the differentiating zygotes after fertilization (Reinert *et al.*, 1977). Under appropriate cultural conditions, completely functional plants are formed. Embryogenic responses are stimulated particularly when 2,4-D is the auxin used to produce calluses and when these calluses are transferred to a 2,4-D-free medium supplemented with reduced forms of nitrogen (in the form of NH_4^+ salts or amino acids like glutamine as opposed to NO_3^-). Sequential manipulations of this type have proved most successful in the induction of useful levels of morphogenesis through either organogenesis or embryogenesis in plant tissue cultures. Tissue cultures of different species and genotype tend to have different requirements for induction of differentiation responses. Not all crop plant species can be manipulated as readily as the model systems of tobacco or carrot. One of the reasons why there is so much voluminous literature on tissue culture is the fact that different plant genotypes react differently to a standard set of cultural conditions. Much intensive study is still needed to optimize cultural conditions which support efficient organogenesis and embryogenesis in tissue cultures of several economically important crop plant species. Some of the modifications in technique and approaches being employed to overcome these so-called recalcitrance problems are discussed later in Chapter 6. The physiological condition of the explant is often a crucial factor in determining whether cultures eventually express morphogenesis or not. Certain

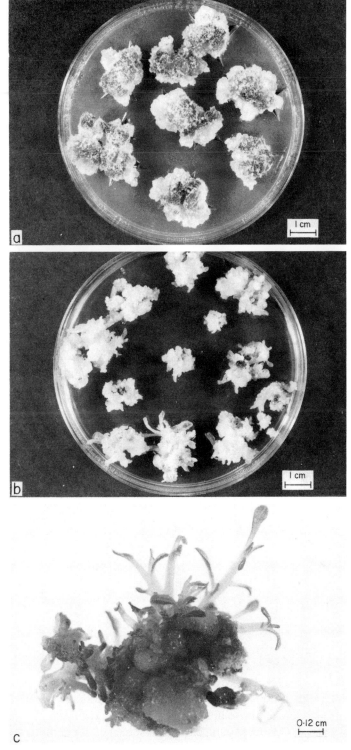

Fig. 5.4. Callus cultures of tobacco (a) after transfer to medium containing increasing proportions of cytokinin to auxin to induce organogenesis (b). Close-up view of callus developing shoots (c).

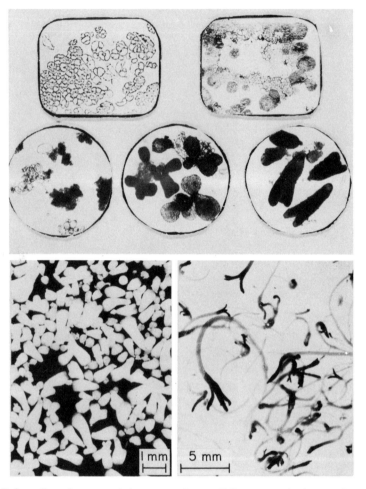

Fig. 5.5. Somatic embryogenesis in carrot cultures. Calluses are raised on semi-solidified medium containing 0·1 mg 1^{-1} 2,4-D (top left) and then placed on medium without 2,4-D (top right) to induce embryoidal masses. In liquid culture, a similar transfer induces embryoid formation through globular, heart-shaped and torpedo stages (left to right). Provided embryoids are transferred to fresh medium, torpedo embryoids elongate and form small plantlets which can then be transferred to soil and raised to produce plants which flower and set seed.

explants (e.g. various types of ovule or pollen materials) require no growth regulator induction treatments, whereas others only require one of the main types of growth regulators to be included in media for induction of either organogenesis or embryogenesis. Moreover, certain tissue explants such as epidermal strips, flower peduncles, leaf bases, petioles and midveins, because of their pre-existing physiological conditions can produce flowers, adventive embryos or adventitious shoots directly without passing through callus stages. One outcome of all this has been the exploitation and adaptation of natural asexual propagation processes and procedures on a miniature level, leading to the development of many of the valuable cloning and micro-propagation techniques described in Chapter 6. Figures 5.4 and 5.5 illustrate some of the commonest types of organogenesis and embryogenesis observed in plant tissue cultures obtained from a variety of explant sources.

Adaptation of microbiological techniques to plant tissue culture

About the time that whole plant regeneration was being achieved from tobacco tissue cultures, it was also discovered that when calluses are transferred from semi-solidified agar medium to liquid media of similar type but agitated on a shaker system, cell masses break up to yield suspensions of isolated cells and small clusters termed aggregates (Fig. 5.6). This type of situation is clearly far removed from the natural environment to which plant cells are exposed in the fully differentiated intact organism. Nevertheless, the ability to isolate discrete cells and to propagate the derived cell suspensions has led to some extremely important advances in manipulative technique.

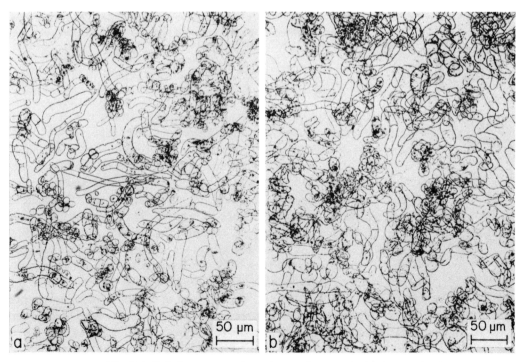

Fig. 5.6. Cells from suspension cultures of sycamore: (a) 3 days after inoculation of fresh medium; (b) 10 days after inoculation.

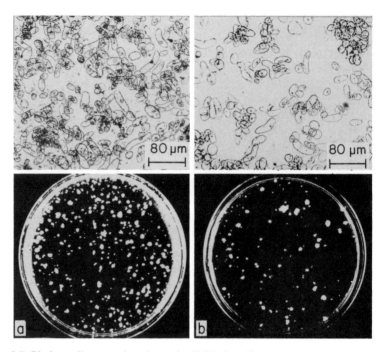

Fig. 5.7. Plating cell suspensions in semi-solidified medium at high (a) and low (b) density. The lower density would be more suitable for mutagenesis and selection work since cell colonies are discrete and can be removed to individual containers for further testing and eventually to act as a source of regenerated plants. Each discrete colony derived from a single cell is termed a calliclone.

Isolation and culture of single plant cells

Isolated single cells from cell suspension cultures when placed in micro-chambers were shown by Muir, Hildebrandt & Riker (1954) to be capable of division. Provided that cells were grown either in association with 'nurse' or 'feeder' callus cells, single cells could proliferate and divide to form calluses. When appropriate nutrient and hormonal conditions were met, calluses could regenerate new plants. This achievement presented practical evidence to support the concept of totipotency in somatic tissues of plants and, far more importantly, led to the ability to plate out single plant cells in a manner very much like that routinely used in microbial work (Fig. 5.7). This was possible only after it had been realized, just as with animal tissue culture manipulations, that certain conditioning factors are required in media in order to support initial divisions of cells cultured at low population densities. Subsequent studies (see Stuart & Street, 1971; Bergmann, 1977; Street, 1977) have identified certain essential amino acids such as glutamine and serine, gases like CO_2 and ethylene, and growth regulators like cytokinins as significant conditioning factors. Conditioned medium is prepared by

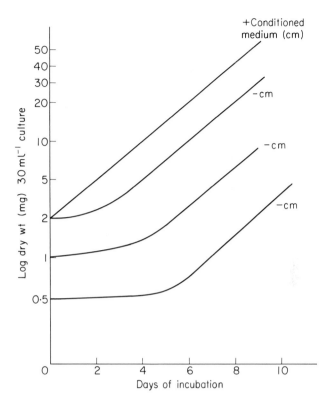

Fig. 5.8. Effect of initial cell inoculum size and the presence of conditioned medium on cell growth in tobacco cell suspension cultures (after Bergmann, 1977). Cultures were inoculated with washed cell suspensions and grown on MS medium. Note the pronounced lag in initial growth in low density populations in the absence of conditioned medium.

culturing high densities of cells of the same or different species in fresh medium for a short period (3–7 days). Cells are removed by filtration and then the medium is filter-sterilized rather than autoclaved to avoid loss of heat-labile components. Figure 5.8 illustrates the effects of initial cell inoculum size and the presence of conditioned medium on growth of cell cultures of tobacco. Similar effects are noted when suspended cells are plated out in a semi-solid medium. A replica plate method similar in principle to ones used in microbiological work has also been developed for use with plant cell cultures. Plated cell colonies are seeded from one petri dish to another by means of the transfer of cells attached to fibre mats. Over 90% transfer rates are possible using this method when suitable conditioned media are employed. The ability to plate plant cells and to induce calluses to express morphogenesis means that the isolation, characterization and utilization of deviant and mutant cell lines is now a routine procedure for several important crop species (Maliga, 1980). The regenerated plant lines from these mutant cell lines are proving to be a most valuable source of novel crop plants (see Chapter 7).

Culture of plant cells and tissues in bioreactors

Apart from being plated, plant cell suspensions can be maintained indefinitely by subculture along similar lines to those used for yeast or bacterial culture. It must be emphasized, however, that in the majority of cases, plant cell culture growth, genetic stability and rheological characteristics are markedly different from those of microbial systems. It must be realized that cell suspensions are made up of extremely heterogenous populations of single cells, small clusters of cells and larger cell aggregates. In the finest cell suspensions, aggregates can consist realistically of anything up to 200 cells. In general terms, callus tissues do not separate well to form ideal fine suspensions. There are, however, a few notable exceptions, particularly the friable calluses which have been reported for *Acer pseudoplatanus, Rosa* sp., *Glycine max, Haplopappus gracilis, Triticum monococcum, Nicotiana tabacum, Daucus carota* and *Saccharum* sp. (see King, 1980). Cell lines can be obtained from these species which are relatively homogenous and which can be cultivated in multilitre batch, chemostat and turbidostat bioreactors (see also Kato *et al.*, 1976; King & Street, 1977; Martin, 1980; Dougall, 1982; Fowler, 1983 and Chapter 8). Data has been obtained to show that it is even possible to maintain plant cells at steady growth rates (despite the restrictive levels of incomplete mixing present in plant cell cultures; Sahai & Shuler, 1982) similar to those mathematically defined previously by Monod (1950) for microbial fermentations (see Pirt, 1975). Steady states in plant cell suspension cultures have been characterized in terms of constancy in cell growth (parameters of which include cell dry weight, cell number and total cell protein), metabolic activities (particularly activities of enzymes of the pentose phosphate and Emden Meyerhof−Parnas pathways) and concentrations of nutrients in culture media. Such degrees of control of metabolic stability and relative homogeneity in culture make chemostat systems particularly valuable in fundamental studies on plant metabolism. However, their relative value as production systems for commercially important plant compounds are currently limited, although possibly somewhat underexploited as is discussed in Chapter 8. The most important point, however, is to realize the contrasting types of patterns of growth which can be generated in liquid culture systems using various types of medium withdrawal, fresh medium replacement and cell harvesting regimes. Such techniques allow the experimenter the ability to alter objectively the overall metabolic state of plant cells and the degree of synchrony in cultures. This is particularly important for inducing optimal conditons for the expression of plant metabolism involved in the biosynthesis and biotransformation

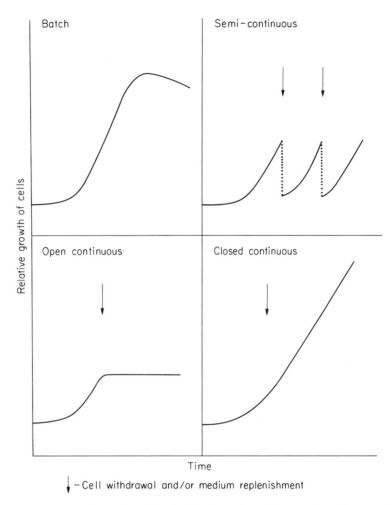

$\downarrow$ – Cell withdrawal and/or medium replenishment

Fig. 5.9. Patterns of growth produced in batch, semi-continuous and continuous plant cell cultures. A batch culture is one in which a finite volume of nutrient medium is present throughout the culture cycle and growth ceases when an essential nutrient is depleted. A semi-continuous culture is one in which the inflow of fresh medium is controlled manually at infrequent intervals by a 'drain-and-refill' process, such that the volume of culture removed is always replaced by an equivalent volume of fresh medium. A continuous culture is one which is supplied continuously with nutrients by the inflow of fresh medium. The culture volume is normally constant. In an open continuous culture, growth rate and cell density are held constant by a fixed rate of input of growth-limiting nutrient and removal of cells and spent medium while a closed continuous culture is one in which inflow of fresh medium is balanced by outflow of corresponding volumes of spent medium only. Cells are allowed to accumulate after separation from spent medium.

of compounds of commercial interest. Many of these compounds are secondary metabolites which are only produced in tissues expressing extensive degrees of differentiation. The main types of pattern of growth which can be induced in multilitre plant cell bioreactors are

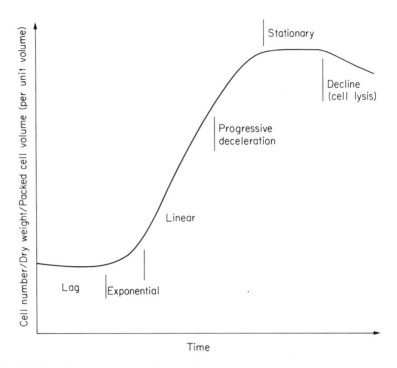

Fig. 5.10. Model growth curve of batch culture.

shown in generalized form in Fig. 5.9. In the batch culture system, typified by the growth pattern shown in Fig. 5.10, cells are grown in a finite volume of nutrient medium. Depending on various factors, particularly inoculum density, the growth of cells (usually measured as cell number, packed cell volume or cell weight per set volume of culture) is not always initiated immediately upon subculture so that a lag phase results which is terminated when cell division takes place. This leads to a phase of culture development known as exponential or logarithmic growth. During this phase, the rate of increase of biomass per unit of biomass concentration present in the culture at any given moment is constant and measureable. Theoretically, therefore, during a small period of time (dt) it would be expected that the increase in biomass (dx) would be proportional to the amount already present and to the time interval. Thus,

$$dx = \mu \cdot dt$$

i.e. $\dfrac{dx}{dt} = \mu x$

where μ = specific growth rate which is the rate of growth per unit amount of biomass. By rearrangement:

$$\mu = \frac{1}{x} \cdot \frac{dx}{dt}$$

As $\dfrac{d(\log_e x)}{dx} = \dfrac{1}{x}$, then $\dfrac{d(\log_e x)}{dt} = \mu$

$\therefore \mu = \dfrac{\log_e x - \log_e x_0}{t}$

where x_0 = initial cell density, x = final cell density after time, t. Since $\log_e x = \mu t + \log_e x_0$ then by plotting the values of t (abscissa) and $\log_e x$ (ordinate), a straight line is obtained for the exponential growth phase with slope of μ; by plotting $\log_{10} x$ against t, the slope is then represented by $\mu/2\cdot303$ (Fig. 5.11).

The time required for any given population of cultured cells to double is referred to as the doubling time (td).

Since $\log_e x = \mu t + \log_e x_0$, then after time, td

$\mu = \dfrac{\log_e^2}{td}$

$\therefore td = \dfrac{0\cdot693}{\mu}$

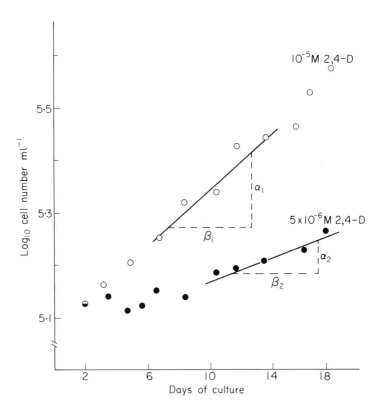

Fig. 5.11. Semi-logarithmic plot of typical exponential phase growth data of tobacco cells grown on media containing two levels of auxin. After calculation of slope value, specific growth rate, μ and doubling time, td can be determined mathematically,

i.e. Slope $= \dfrac{\mu}{2\cdot303}$ $\qquad td = \dfrac{0\cdot693}{\mu}$

This is the manner in which *td* values are calculated. Some typical doubling times of plant cell suspension cultures are 48, 36 and 24 hours for tobacco, rose and bean cell cultures, respectively, compared with *td* values within the range 20–120 minutes for microbial cultures.

As nutrients become exhausted in the culture medium and growth-limiting substances produced by the cells themselves accumulate, batch culture growth passes into the transient linear and progressive deceleration phases when the specific growth rate declines uniformly with time (linear) and then decreases more and more rapidly (progressive decerelation). The relative duration of these phases varies between cultures of different species and also depends greatly upon the components of the culture medium. The terminal phases of batch culture are the stationary and decline phases where no net synthesis of biomass increase in cell number is measurable. In an open continuous culture (Fig. 5.12), in which cells are constantly being washed out with the outflowing liquid medium, a situation of balanced growth is achieved, i.e. the majority of cells in the culture are in a similar metabolic state.

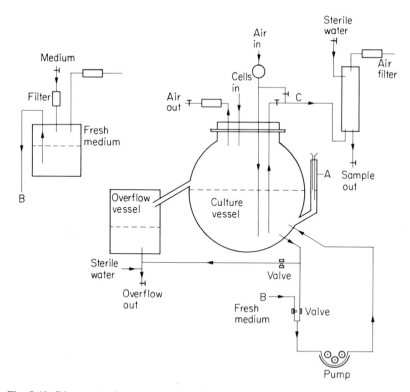

Fig. 5.12. Diagrammatic representation of an open continuous system for culture of plant cells (after Wilson *et al.*, 1971). Fresh medium is entered at a constant rate through B whenever the level probe A is activated. Because of increases in culture volume due to growth of the cell population, the state of cells in the culture vessel can be monitored by the sampling arm C.

Not only are cells of vascular plants capable of growth in bioreactors, they have been shown to divide and to remain viable for prolonged periods in inert matrices of the same types used in conventional and adapted systems of microbial cell immobilization. This opens up new horizons in the exploitation of immobilized plant cells, tissues and organs as systems for producing biochemicals. A review of immobilization of plant cells and tissues is given by Lindsey & Yeoman (1983) and the topic is discussed in Chapter 8.

Culture of specialized plant materials

Some of the more specialized techniques of plant tissue, cell and protoplast culture are now considered.

In contrast to the somatic tissues of vascular plants, pollen containing the male gametophyte or microspore stage is produced in small discrete units and in relatively large numbers. Pollen consists of not more than three cells in angiosperms and not more than five in

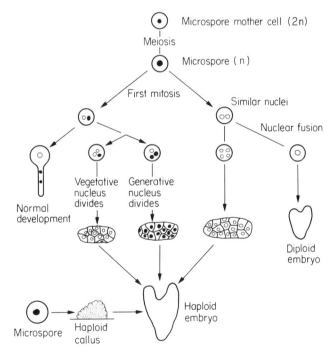

Fig. 5.13. Normal and abnormal patterns of pollen development. Development of pollen *in vivo* leads to the production of two generative nuclei and the formation of pollen tubes, whereas *in vitro* several types of development are possible. Either the generative or vegetative nucleus in each pollen grain divides repeatedly to produce a haploid embryoid or the first mitosis produces two similar nuclei, the repeated division of which also results in haploid embryoids formation. The identical nuclei, however, may also fuse in which case a diploid embryoid (far right) is produced.

gymnosperms. Most importantly though, each unit possesses a unique genome conferred upon it through meiosis by pairing and segregation of chromosomes and in the case of pollen from true diploid species (NB, some important crops like tobacco and potato are amphidiploids so that pollen of these plants contain two haploid chromosome complements), every gene is present as a single copy. Spontaneous haploid plant generation in natural breeding populations is a rare event. However, the development of pollen and/or anther culture now means that this unique genetic material can be incorporated directly into whole plants or cell lines which are invaluable to mutation research and plant breeding (Sunderland & Dunwell, 1977).

Culture of anthers and pollen

The first successful pollen cultures were made in the 1950s using mature pollen grains of several gymnosperms. It was observed that a small proportion of grains were switched from their normal determinate type of development, i.e. formation of pollen tubes and male gametes (see Fig. 5.13) into one of callus formation. Similar attempts to extend this type of approach to pollen of angiosperm species failed until Guha & Maheshwari (1964) discovered that pollen of *Datura innoxia* could be triggered into active growth by simply culturing the intact anthers containing developing pollen. Moreover, the type of growth produced resulted in the formation of embryoids directly from individual pollen grains. These embryoids could be induced to develop into whole plants which were subsequently shown by these workers to be true haploids (Guha & Maheshwari, 1967). Since that time, anthers containing immature pollen have been cultured successfully for a wide range of economically important species (see Table 5.2) and the major cultural procedures generally followed are outlined schematically in Fig. 5.14. There are three major approaches:

(a) culture of anthers on semi-solid media and the proliferation of pollen-derived embryos and plantlets through the dehiscence of mature anthers;

(b) culture of anthers on liquid media and the release of their pollen leading to the formation of embryos and plantlets directly from released pollen;

(c) *ab initio* culture of immature pollen extracted from developing anthers.

Critical determinates of successful culture and production of plants are the physiological condition of the donor plants (Table 5.3), the type of preculture treatment applied to excised flower buds (Table 5.4), the stage of pollen development reached when anthers are cultured, and the presence or absence of growth regulator supplements in media (for details see Sunderland & Dunwell, 1977).

Table 5.2. Important crop plants in which callus, embryoids or whole plants have been derived from cultures of anthers or pollen.

Species (name)	Response	References[*]
Aegilops	Callus/plantlets	Kimata & Sakamato (1972)
Arabidopsis spp.	Callus/plantlets	Scholl & Amos (1980)
Brassica campestris (turnip)	Embryoids/plantlets	Keller & Armstrong (1979)
B. napus (rapeseed)	Embryoids/plantlets	Keller & Armstrong (1978)
B. oleracea	Embryoids/plantlets	Quazi (1978)
Camellia sinensis (tea)	Callus	Iyer & Raina (1972)
Cajanus cajan (pigeon pea)	Callus	Bajaj *et al.* (1980)
Capsicum annuum (sweet pepper)	Embryoids/plantlets	Wang & Kuo (1978)
Festuca spp. (fescue)	Callus/plantlets	Kasperbauer *et al.* (1980)
Gossypium hirsutum (cotton)	Callus	Barrow *et al.* (1978)
Hordeum vulgare (barley)	Callus/plantlets	Clapham (1973)
	Embryoids	Wilson *et al.* (1978)
Lolium perenne (ryegrass)	Callus/plantlets	Clapham (1971)
Lycopersicon esculentum (tomato)	Callus/plantlets	Zamir *et al.* (1980)
Malus domestica (apple)	Embryoids	Milewska-Pawliczuk & Kubicki (1977)
Nicotiana tabacum (tobacco)	Embryoids/plantlets	Sunderland & Evans (1980)
Oryza sativa (rice)	Callus/plantlets	Rush & Shao (1980)
Oryza hybrids	Callus/plantlets	Woo & Huang (1980)
Phaseolus vulgaris (bean)	Callus	Peters *et al.* (1977)
Poncirus trifoliata (trifoliate orange)	Callus/embryoids/ plantlets	Hidaka *et al.* (1979)
Populus spp. (poplar)	Callus/plantlets	Lu *et al.* (1978)
Prunus avium	Embryoids/callus	Zenkteler *et al.* (1975)
Secale cereale (rye)	Embryoids/callus/ plantlets	Wenzel *et al.* (1977)
Solanum melongena (eggplant)	Callus/embryoids/ plantlets	Research Group of Plant Breeding (1978)
S. tuberosum (potato)	Callus/embryoids/ plantlets	Dunwell & Sunderland (1973) Sopory *et al.* (1979)
Triticum aestivum (wheat)	Callus/embryoids/ plantlets	De Buyser & Henry (1980) Chuang *et al.* (1978)
Triticale (rye × wheat)	Callus/embryoids/ plantlets	Bernard (1977) Vnuchkova (1979)
Vitis vinifera (grape)	Callus	Gresshoff & Doy (1974)
V. vinifera × rupestris	Callus/embryoids/ plantlets	Rajasekaran & Mullins (1979)

[*] Cited in Vasil *et al.* (1979) and Collins & Genovesi (1982).

Provided optimal conditions for donor plants and explants are supplied, the levels of haploid plant production can reach as high as 1–2% of the total pollen cultured inside intact anthers or as isolated grains. In species with anthers like those of tobacco, having an average pollen number of *c.* 40,000 in each, this can represent a haploid plant production level of 400–800 per cultured anther. However, it should be appreciated that differences in response of different genotypes, even

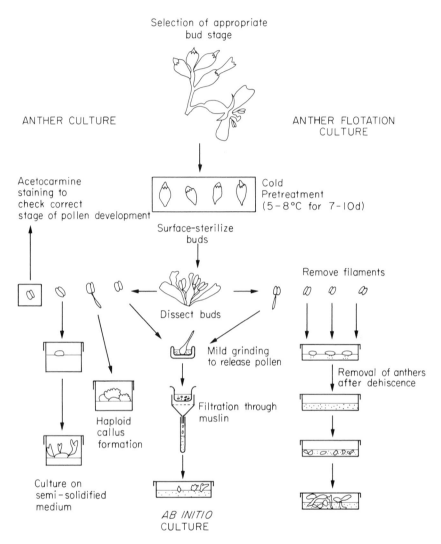

Fig. 5.14. Different cultural procedures that can be followed to establish anther and pollen cultures and from which embryoids and plantlets can be produced.

within the same crop variety or breeding line, mean that optimal conditions and pollen division synchrony are rarely coordinated sufficiently well to produce these high yields in a consistent fashion. The most usual stage of pollen development at which flower buds are excised is just on the point of the first mitotic division of the uninucleate microspore tetrads.

Some of the main culture media used to culture anthers and pollen are listed in Appendix 5. Species can be grouped into two major categories with respect to medium requirements for anther/pollen culture. In the first, a simple basal medium (minerals, vitamins and

Table 5.3. Influence of plant growth temperature of donor plants on the formation of pollen embryos and plantlets in anther cultures of *Nicotiana knightiana* (from data of Primo-Millo & Sunderland, cited in Sunderland & Dunwell, 1977).

| | Plant-growth temperature (°C) | | |
	14	20	28
Number of buds cultured	102	133	103
% cultures with plantlets	12·7*	24·7	26·2
% cultures with abortive embryos	9·8	24·0	37·8
% cultures induced	22·5	48·7	· 64·0

* Mean values obtained in cultures of anthers cultured at a single stage of pollen development and held at 25°C in light on a 16-hour (500 1x) photoperiod for 12 weeks. Four anthers from one bud were contained in each culture.

Table 5.4. Some of the anther and bud treatments used to raise levels of androgenesis in anther cultures of different species (after Collins & Genovesi, 1982).

Plant species	Pretreatment (days, °C)	References*
Brassica campestris (turnip)	3 d, 35°	
B. napus (rapeseed)	14 d, 30°	
Datura innoxia (jimson weed)	4 d, 4°	Tyagi *et al.* (1979)
D. metel	2 d, 0°	Gupta & Babbar (1980)
Festuca arundinacea (fescue)	25 d, 5°	Kasperbauer *et al.* (1980)
Hordeum vulgare (barley)	2 d, 3°	Bouharmont (1977)
	Cut flowers held 2 d in nutrient soln. without cold; *c.* 14 d, 7·5°	Sunderland *et al.* (1979)
Hyoscyamus albus	5 d, 15°	Sunderland & Wildon (1979)
H. niger (henbane)	5 d, 15°	Sunderland & Wildon (1979)
Nicotiana tabacum (tobacco)	12 d, 7/8°	Sunderland & Roberts (1979)
Oryza sativa (rice)	10 d, 13°	Genovesi & Magill (1979)
Petunia hybrida (petunia)	2 d, 6°	Malhotra & Maheshwari (1977)
Secale cereale (rye)	6−10 d, 6°	
Triticum aestivum (wheat)	2−8 d, 3°	Picard & De Buyser (1977)
	2−6, 7 d, 4−5°	Schaeffer *et al.* (1979)
T. aestivum × *S. cereale* (triticale)	7 d, 4°	Lukyanyuk *et al.* (1979)
	10−12 d, 4·5°	Vnuckkova (1979)
Vitis sp. hybrid (grape)	3 d, 4°	
Zea mays (corn)	14 d, 8°	
	7 d, 4° then 7 d, 8°	Genovesi & Collins (unpublished)

* As in Table 5.2 and as cited by Collins & Genovesi (1982).

Table 5.5. Species of plant which are requiring or non-requiring with respect to auxin/cytokinin inclusions in anther and pollen culture media.

Simple[*] (non-requiring)	Complex (requiring)
Datura innoxia	*Hordeum vulgare*
Hyoscyamus niger	*Oryza*
Nicotiana tabacum	*Triticum*
N. sylvestris	*Triticale*
N. knightiana	*Zea mays*
N. paniculata	*Asparagus officinalis*
Paeonia hybrida	*Brassica campestris*

[*] Inductive conditions presumed to be provided by the anther wall.

sugar) is all that is required for both inducing and sustaining growth of pollen to the plantlet or callus stage. In the second, requirements appear to be more complex and additional stimuli must be provided in media in the form of auxins, cytokinins or other growth factors and supplements like activated charcoal and amino acids, e.g. glutamine, serine and asparagine. Thus, Sunderland & Dunwell (1977) classified species according to whether they were hormone-independent or not (Table 5.5). Species of the first group are generally those with bicellular pollen, including *Nicotiana tabacum*, *N. sylvestris*, *N. knightiana*, *N. paniculata*, *Paeonia hybrida*, *Datura innoxia* and *Hyoscyamus niger*. For instance, in the case of *N. tabacum* and *D. innoxia*, growth of pollen can be induced simply by floating anthers on a 2% aqueous solution of sucrose. Species of the second group are generally those which produce pollens of either the bicellular or tricellular types. This group includes the cereals *Hordeum* (barley), *Oryza* (rice), *Triticum* (wheat) and *Triticale* (wheat/rye hybrids) that produce calluses from which haploid plants can be subsequently regenerated, and *Brassica* and *Asparagus* that produce embryos and haploid plantlets directly. This requirement for hormone in order to obtain successful anther and pollen culture is thought to be a reflection of the morphogenic competence of pollen in anthers of different species. Thus, in some cases there is an inherently high proportion (upwards of 50%) of variant pollen grains in every anther which is capable of abnormal embryo development leading to plantlet production directly *in vitro*. Variant grains are termed 'E' or 'S' (i.e. embryonic or small) and can be distinguished from normal types of pollens by differential staining techniques at an early stage of pollen development. Pollen dimorphism appears to be a common situation, albeit varying by degrees in different genotypes, and it has even been observed in morphogenic forms in non-excised anthers *in vivo*. The formation of multicellular embryo-like structures in non-excised anthers of some solanaceous hybrids (Horner & Street, 1978), and experimental cultures of anemone (Heberle-Bors & Reinert, 1980) are good examples of this phenomenon.

As shown in Fig. 5.14, pollen isolated from anthers and then cultured *in vitro* can lead to production of embryos and plantlets directly from pollen grains and the possibility of mixed somatic and pollen-derived plantlet production is avoided. This approach of *ab initio* pollen culture has been pioneered elegantly in *Nicotiana* and *Datura* systems by Nitsch and co-workers (see Nitsch, 1977). However, due to the absence of beneficial effects exerted by anther wall tissues, levels of haploid embryogenesis in isolated microspore cultures have often been disappointingly low as compared to anther culture techniques. More recently, however, it has been demonstrated convincingly that *ab initio* cultures can yield high numbers of haploid plantlets (in a *N. tabacum* cv. Badischer Burley system) provided that in addition to the usual pre-conditioning and pre-cultural treatments, embryogenic pollen is separated from non-embryogenic pollen grains by gentle density gradient centrifugation in percoll and sucrose (Rashid, 1982). Other improvements consist of raising initial pH of media from 5·6 to 6·5 (conditions which favour cell division at low cell densities) and incorporation of glutamine and asparagine in culture media. Also, pollen is taken from plants flowering at 18°C and excised buds are subjected to a cold treatment of 10°C for 10 days prior to isolation of pollen for culture. The mechanisms whereby the cold treatments bring about production of increased numbers of embryogenic pollen remain to be resolved but such stress conditions are known to induce relatively significant changes in the endogenous levels of growth regulatory substances, particularly abscisic acid (ABA) within pollen and the anther tissues themselves (Imamura & Harada, 1980). The advances made in anther and pollen culture since 1964 are most encouraging yet there remain several problems. Some of these are related to genetic stability and variability and are discussed later in this chapter. One of the major drawbacks is the high frequency of albinoism in pollen-derived plantlets of the Gramineae — the important taxonomic family which contains cereal and forage crops. The frequencies of albinos range from 5 to 90%, depending on cultivar and culture temperature employed. Raising temperature conditions during culture increases the frequency of albinoism (Chu, 1982). It remains an unsolved problem, though evidence at the present time points to the the condition being the result of variation in ctDNA, possibly induced or exacerbated by the cultural process, since it has been found that there is a lack of 23S and 16S RNA as well as large subunit of Fraction I protein in albinos. Causes of albinoism have been proposed; possibly albinos might originate from pollen with chromosome aberration or the customary reorganization of plastids fails following the regression of proplastids during meiotic development.

An alternative cultural method for haploid production is through culture of the female gametophyte. Haploid embryos and plants have been produced from ovules of gymnosperms and of angiosperms such as barley, tobacco, wheat and rice. Histological evidence indicates that plantlets originate from either the egg or antipodal cells. Plantlets have been obtained either directly by ovary culture in media with low levels of auxin or by regeneration of plantlets from calluses. Ovaries of the young embryo sac stage (at the point when pollen grains in anthers on the same flower are at late uninucleate or binucleate stages of development) usually give the best response for induction of haploid plants. Also, ovaries with attached receptacles and stamens always produce more haploid plants than those without these attached tissues (Yang & Zhou, 1982).

Culture of plant protoplasts

Out of the initial observation by Cocking (1960) that plant protoplasts (i.e. plasmalemma-bound vesicles released from plant cells as a result of mechanical disruption or enzymic degradation of their cellulose walls) could be released from root-tip cells using a fungal cellulase in 0·6 M sucrose, has sprung the revolutionary and potentially most exciting (yet technically specialized) branch of plant cell culture. Protoplasts are most useful materials for plant cell manipulations. The removal of cell walls, while simultaneously conserving the cytoplasmic and nuclear constituents of the cells necessary for subsequent cell wall deposition and cell division, leaves the plasmalemma membrane fully exposed as the only barrier between the external environment and the interior of the totipotent cell. This accessibility facilitates experiments designed to investigate and manipulate this membrane from the point of view of its physical and chemical properties and to follow the effect of the endocytosis of foreign particles, like DNA and RNA molecules, intact virus particles, microbes and organelles on daughter cells and subsequently regenerated plants. Moreover, the ability of plasmalemma membranes to fuse under certain conditions allows the fusion of similar and contrasting cell types through the process of somatic hybridization ultimately leading to the production of somatic hybrids and cybrids (see Fig. 7.2). The absence of cell walls on protoplasts makes them most amenable to mutagenesis by irradiation techniques and to cell separation and sorting by cell flow cytometry. These materials and methods create immense scope for genetic manipulation and breeding in plants, the details of which have already been alluded to in Chapter 4 and will later be expanded upon in Chapters 7 and 8.

Protoplast isolation can be carried out by means of many protocols designed for specific types of materials. The essentials though are always a good aseptic approach and aptitude for fine manipulations. Important components of the isolation procedure for plant protoplasts are the removal of the cell walls without causing irreversible damage to the released protoplasts (Evans & Cocking, 1977), and the maintenance of a suitable osmotic environment to stabilize the protoplasts. The technique of protoplast isolation has been approached in several different ways (Fig. 5.15). The mechanical method is dependent on preliminary plasmolysis of cells within tissues and the subsequent dissection of the tissue and deplasmolysis to release the preformed protoplasts. However, this method generally produces relatively low yields of viable protoplasts and the behaviour of these in subsequent culture is also affected by the presence of substances released from damaged cells. These techniques have been improved upon by the use of more gentle, less injurious enzymic methods for releasing protoplasts. By 1969, several potent and partially purified cell-wall-degrading enzymes were available such as one extracted from *Trichoderma viride*, a mixture of cellulase and a pectinase (Driselase) of basidiomycete origin and a macerozyme obtained

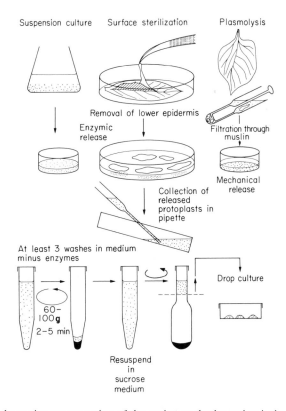

Fig. 5.15. Schematic representation of the major methods used to isolate plant protoplasts.

from *Rhizopus* spp. which is rich in pectinase. Although partial purification and further desalting of some of these enzymes are sometimes
necessary to avoid deleterious effects on viability of certain protoplasts,
most of the commercially available enzymes like 'Pectolyase Y-23',
'Onozuka R-10', 'Meicelase', 'Rhozyme' and 'Macerozyme R-10' are
desalted and are of sufficiently high quality to give rapid release and
high yields of protoplasts from most sources. Mesophyll cells of leaves
and cultured cell suspensions are the two most commonly used in
experimental work. Their relative usefulness is determined to a large
degree by the stringency required for genetic uniformity and for
morphogenic potential (by either organogenesis or embryogenesis) in
the isolated protoplasts. Occasionally, other tissues provide better
alternatives, especially with regard to the latter requirement. For
example, seedling cotyledons have proved excellent material for
isolating totipotent protoplasts in *Brassica oleracea*, *Datura innoxia* and
Medicago sativa (Lu *et al.*, 1982), roots of young seedlings have proved
convenient sources of totipotent protoplasts of *Brassica* spp. also (Xu *et
al.*, 1982) and flower petals have been efficient sources of protoplasts of
ornamental *Nicotiana* spp. (Flick & Evans, 1983).

Leaf mesophyll tissues of different genotypes vary in their requirements for protoplast release. In some species such as *Calystegia*,
Arachis, *Asparagus* and *Ipomoea* it is possible to obtain a preparation of
free cells by mechanical means as a first step to protoplast isolation.
Due to the physical structure of the leaves, shearing action in a glass
homogenizer is all that is needed to disrupt the tissue into separate
cells. After filtering through muslin to remove debris, protoplasts are
released using cellulase treatments. Recently, Bilkey & Cocking (1982)
have also used non-enzymatic methods to release particular types of
callus-derived protoplasts from tissues cultured on 2,4-D supplemented
media. The cells produced in the presence of this auxin have particularly
thin cell walls such that by simply teasing cells, large numbers of protoplasts can be released. In other cases, cells are first separated from
each other using pectinase then transferred to a second medium containing cellulase to degrade cell walls for protoplast release. This two-
step procedure is not necessary in most cases so that present day
methods employ a simultaneous degradation of pectin and cellulose cell
wall constituents in a single step. One eventuality which has to be
considered in the case of the one-step approach, however, is the
possibility that spontaneous fusion of protoplasts caused by fusion of
neighbouring cells still linked by plasmodesmatal strands may occur.
Another factor which should not be overlooked is the fact that the
sequential method most often leads to the production of protoplasts
predominantly from the palisade layer, whereas the mixed enzyme
method produces protoplasts from palisade, spongy and upper epidermal tissues. This means that protoplasts are often derived from leaf cells

Table 5.6. Examples of enzyme mixtures, osmotica and pH regimes used for protoplast isolation.

Species	Source	Enzyme mixture (w/v)	pH	Osmoticum	References
Nicotiana tabacum var. Xanthi	Leaf (mesophyll) Cell suspensions	4% Meicelase 0·4% Macerozyme 2% Driselase 2% Cellulase	5·8	13% Mannitol (0·71 M)	Evans & Cocking (1977)
	Leaf (mesophyll)	0·5% Macerozyme 2% Cellulase		Seawater	Nakata & Oshima (1982)
N. sylvestris	Leaf (mesophyll)	0·5% Macerozyme 0·1% Cellulase		Seawater	Nakata & Oshima (1982)
Solanum tuberosum cv. Bintje		0·02% Macerozyme	5·8	8% Mannitol (0·44 M)	Caboche (1980)
	Axenic shoots	1·5% Cellulase 0·3% Macerozyme	5·5	0·6 M Mannitol	Bokelmann & Roest (1983)
Macleaya spp.	Leaf (mesophyll)	0·2% PATE* 0·5% Cellulase	5·6	0·5 M Mannitol	Lang & Kohlenbach (1982)
Medicago spp.	Leaf (mesophyll)	2% Rhozyme 4% Meicelase 0·3% Macerozyme	5·6	13% Mannitol (0·71 M)	Arcioni et al. (1982)
Phaseolus aureus	Roots	2% Rhozyme 4% Meicelase 0·3% Macerozyme	5·6	13% Mannitol (0·71 M)	Xu et al. (1982)
Trigonella spp.	Cell suspensions	2% Rhozyme 4% Meicelase 0·3% Macerozyme	5·6	13% Mannitol (0·71 M)	Dos Santos et al. (1983)

* Pectin acid trans eliminase.

with divergent physiological and genetic characteristics, which may have an important bearing on their subsequent behaviour in culture and also on the genotypes regenerated. Enzyme mixtures used vary with species and materials being employed as sources of protoplasts. Examples of various enzyme mixtures in different osmotica used in protoplast isolation are shown in Table 5.6. Prolonged incubation in enzyme/ osmoticum mixtures at a stable temperature (20°C) overnight for up to 16 hours is adequate for protoplast release in most species. Before isolation, leaf tissues of suitable physiological age and condition (preferably obtained from young plants grown under optimal yet definable and reproducible environmental conditions in growth cabinets) are prepared in the manner illustrated in Fig. 5.15. After brief immersion in 70% ethanol, leaves are surface sterilized in a weak (2·5%) sodium hypochlorite solution for 15−30 minutes. After several thorough washes in sterile distilled water, large amounts of leaf material are dried between layers of sterile tissue paper. Prior to enzyme treatment, the lower epidermis of leaves is removed with fine forceps so that enzymes can penetrate into intercellular spaces. As an alternative to peeling — which is not practicable on small leaves of seedlings or for some types of leaf material obtained from plantlets propagated *in vitro* or on cotyledon material — tissue is 'feathered' into 1−2 mm strips and enzyme penetration achieved under vacuum.

Protoplasts obtained from suspension and callus cultures can be isolated without so much preparation although as Uchimiya & Murashige (1974) observed, the stage of growth of cell cultures is an extremely important factor when high yields of protoplasts are required. These workers found that in tobacco batch suspensions, cells at the 4 to 5-day stage of culture in a 14-day subculturing schedule are the most suitable for protoplast isolation and that enzyme mixtures in which Macerozyme R10 were included at 0·2% w/v gave optimal (30%) release of protoplasts.

Protoplasts can also be isolated, albeit at low levels, from immature pollen using lyophilized preparations of 'Helicase'. This enzyme is obtained from the guts of snails and is rich in the β1-3 glucanase activity required to degrade callose, the major constituent of immature pollen walls. Such protoplasts have potential as extremely useful sources of divergent haploid material.

After enzyme treatment, protoplast suspensions are collected by gentle centrifugation (60−100 g for 2−5 minutes) and then washed two to three times in fresh medium without enzyme. Separation of intact protoplasts (Fig. 5.16) from debris and non-viable protoplasts if desired can then be achieved, by flotation of protoplast preparations in similar medium in which the sugar alcohol (usually mannitol or sorbitol) is substituted for by an appropriate concentration of sugar, e.g. sucrose. After gentle centrifugation, viable protoplasts float on the top of the

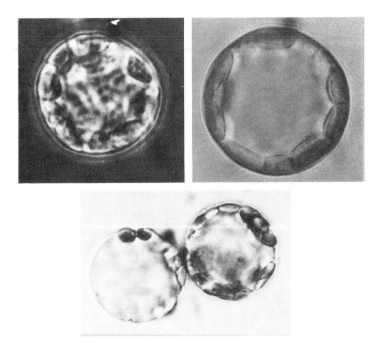

Fig. 5.16. Protoplasts of *Nicotiana* spp. shortly after release from mesophyll leaf tissue (top) and after treatment with fusogens (for details see Chapter 7).

mixture (Fig. 5.15). After adjusting densities within the range $10^4 - 10^7$ protoplasts/ml, protoplast suspensions are generally plated either in liquid or semisolid media solidified within agar or low melting-point agarose. All these methods have been reviewed and described in excellent detail in Evans & Cocking (1977), Eriksson (1977), Vasil & Vasil (1980) and Reinert & Yeoman (1982). In liquid form, higher plating efficiencies can often be obtained by holding protoplasts in small (0·5 µl) drops of medium dispensed on the base of petri dishes. After 5−10 days, protoplasts synthesize new cell walls and cell divisions are initiated. At this stage, the protoplast-derived cells can be diluted with fresh medium designed to sustain growth and division of cells at low density plating, such as the 'A' medium of Caboche (1980) designed for *Nicotiana sylvestris* protoplasts. The recovery of individual calluses derived from single protoplasts raised on defined media, and then plants via either organogenesis or embryogenesis, provides a powerful tool for plant recovery after genetic transformation of protoplasts by whatever technique (see Chapter 4 for details). An alternative to droplet plating is the feeder layer technique. Just like the nurse-raft feeder technique for culture of single cells devised earlier by Muir *et al.* (1954), single protoplasts at low density can be nurtured to produce calluses on filter paper or fibre mats placed on layers of feeder plant cells (Horsch & Jones, 1980).

Culture of plant microplasts and microcells

Worth noting are the recent advances which have been made in plant cell organelle isolation and in the transfer of intact organelles from cell to cell by microplast and protoplast technology in both plants and animal cell systems. Microcells containing individual chromosomes encapsulated in a cell membrane can be fused with recipient animal cells using routine somatic hybridization methods similar to those described in Chaper 7 (Wright *et al.*, 1980). Now that microplasts have been derived from protoplasts of cultured cells (Lörz *et al.*, 1981), the development of comparable microcell transfer systems in plants is available. Microplasts, surrounded by an inner membrane of the cell that is most probably derived from the tonoplasts which surround vacuoles, can be readily isolated by rupturing highly vacuolated thin-walled callus cells of several plant species grown in 2,4-D containing media (Bilkey *et al.*, 1982). The significance of these developments in gene transfer have already been considered in the last chapter.

Existing problems and limitations

Impressive as the tools and techniques may appear as regards value and potential, there still remain several problems which restrict their unlimited application in plant biotechnology. The two most important are (i) an inability to apply all of the cultural procedures described to diverse crop plant species because of so-called recalcitrance problems, and (ii) the high frequency of genetic and phenotypic variability in certain cultured materials and the subsequent influence of these on stability and constituents of the genomes of regenerated plants.

Recalcitrance

An indication of the scale of this problem is seen in the application of cell and protoplast culture techniques to forest tree crops (particularly economically important conifer species) and legumes and cereals. Plant regeneration *in vitro* in tissue cultures of these crops is often sporadic and transient, and in many cases only a few genotypes respond favourably to morphogenic conditions similar to those employed for tobacco or other solanaceous plants. In addition, cultures of these groups of plants rapidly lose their potential for regeneration (if at all inducible) after a few subcultures. Mesophyll protoplasts of cereals can be readily isolated using the conventional methods described earlier yet, even when isolated protoplasts can be induced to yield calluses, these invariably prove non-responsive to normal inductive treatments aimed at re-generating plants. Recently though, it has been demonstrated that some cereal leaf segments of important grain crops including *Panicum maximum* (millet), *Sorghum bicolor* and *Pennisetum purpureum* (pearl millet) form calluses which are responsive and which can form somatic embryos and plantlets (Vasil, 1982).

The successful induction of somatic embryogenesis and plantlet formation in protoplast-derived cell colonies of *Pennisetum americanum* has now also been reported (Vasil & Vasil, 1980).

Such breakthroughs are extremely encouraging and endorse the optimistic view that the regeneration *in vitro* of present day recalcitrant subjects will be accomplished in due course, especially with the imple-mentation of more objective cultural procedures. This temporal problem is only one side of the coin; the control of variability induced in plant tissue and cell cultures is a matter for some concern.

Variability in cultured tissues and cells

Although variation can be of great value when exploited in the breeding context (see Chapter 7), it is nevertheless a great disadvantage in the maintenance and multiplication of true-to-type plant lines or clones (see Chapter 6). Plant tissues and cells, like their animal counterparts, display more than the usual degree of genome irregularities when removed from the stabilizing and controlling influences exerted by an intact organism and into an unnatural environment inside the culture vessel (Sunderland, 1977). As highlighted in the introduction to this chapter, the many types of cells and tissues within a multicellular plant are under co-ordinated controls. Although the majority of somatic cells in a plant contain a representative somatic chromosome number, one consequence of natural developmental processes is altered ploidy levels induced in certain tissues through endoreduplication and endomitosis or even mutagenesis induced by solar sources of radiation. These processes yield cells with increased ploidy levels. If such cells are inadvertently present in high numbers in the original explants, this will lead to culture products which differ from the somatic type.

Some of the observed variations in tissue cultures are undoubtedly due to the development *in vitro* of totipotent aneuploid and polyploid cells present in the original explants (see Table 5.7). Also significant, are the effects of wounding and other physiological stresses incurred during the excision and preparation of explants for culture. Consider the tissue preparation, surface sterilization and cell wall removal procedures involved in isolation of protoplasts and the natural and artificial roles of callus induction. Callus is produced in the intact organism as a natural wound response and in only a few instances are root and shoot initials

Table 5.7. Variations in the ploidy of *Nicotiana tabacum* cv. Wisconsin 38 cells in freshly excised pith taken 3·5−10·5 vs. 15·5−22·5 cm from the shoot apex, and from pith-derived callus after either 1 or 6 years in culture (after Murashige & Nakano, 1967).

Cultured material	Metaphases examined	% distribution of ploidy levels			
		4x	8x	16x	Aneuploid
Fresh pith 3·5−10·5 cm	53	47·2	52·8	—	—
Fresh pith 15·5−22·5 cm	44	9·1	70·5	15·9	4·5
Pith callus 1 year	15	—	26.7	20.0	53.3
Pith callus 6 year	12	—	—	—	100.0

produced from the callus itself in the intact plant situation. Usually meristems which are induced as a consequence of wounding are produced within organized tissue at a location distal from the actual site of wounding and callus formation. By contrast, callusing is encouraged in tissue and cell cultures with deliberate use of growth regulators, e.g. auxin and cytokinin, and callus tissues form the basis of many important culture systems. Not surprisingly, therefore, organogenesis when expressed in calluses and cell suspension cultures may frequently lead to abnormal pathways of development. More often than not these have been associated either with changes in karyotype and chromosome number occurring in the nuclear genomes of dedifferentiated cells (which make up fast growing calluses) and of cells in adventitious meristems derived from dedifferentiated cells (see Skirvin, 1978) with changes in cytoplasmic genomes (see Pring *et al.*, 1981) or with alternations in the expression of genomes (so-called epigenetic changes) as described by Meins & Binns (1978).

The types of alteration to the nuclear genomes of cultured plant cells and their regenerants have been reviewed and described in great detail by D'Amato (1977), Bayliss (1980), Constantin (1981) and others. The extent and type of variations in chromosome numbers in plant tissue and cell cultures are exemplified in the following. Data shown in Table 5.7 demonstrate the effect of long-term tissue culture on chromosome number, Fig. 5.17 shows how nuclear changes can occur during the first few weeks of culture and Table 5.8 shows the changes which occur in karyotype during prolonged suspension culture. Figure 5.18 illustrates the type of gross karyotypic changes which can occur on individual sets of chromosomes during protracted suspension culture, particularly in the presence of cytokinins like BAP in culture media.

Observed nuclear changes therefore include polyploidy, aneuploidy,

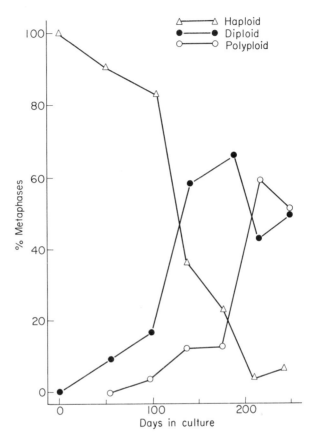

Fig. 5.17. Changes in chromosome number and karyotype in haploid cells and tissues following culture initiation (from Bayliss, 1980). Cultures of *Nicotiana sylvestris* were grown on MS medium containing 2,4-D and subcultured at 35-day intervals.

i.e. the presence of cells containing chromosomal numbers other than those in the polyploid series, structural changes such as the frequent occurrence of chromosomal bridges at anaphase and mitotic aberrations such as multipolar spindles, lagging chromosomes, fragments and unequal separation of chromatids. Polyploidy in cultured cells is thought to arise by processes such as endomitosis and endoreduplication which are either already occurring in the explant or have been induced by the culture processes. Aneuploidy on the other hand probably occurs mainly *in vitro*, although the precise mechanisms for its induction are not clearly understood. Both polyploidy and aneuploidy may also arise as a direct result of the use of synthetic auxins like NAA and 2,4-D in culture media. These compounds are known to induce spindle failure and other abnormalities of mitosis in intact plants. Associated with these growth factor effects, is the loss of morphogenic capabilities of cell lines which have been cultured for protracted periods.

Table 5.8. Types and frequencies of chromosomal changes which occur in celery suspension culture (after Murata & Orton, 1982).

Ploidy levels	% cells observed[*]	% cells with fusions	translocations
Hypodiploid ($2n = 17-21$)	42·1	36·3	5.0
Diploid ($2n = 22$)	49·6	5·0	2·9
Hyperdiploid ($2n = 23$)	0·4	0·0	0·0
Hypotetraploid ($2n = 38-43$)	5·4	4·6	0·8
Tetraploid ($2n = 44$)	2·5	0·8	0·4
Totals	100·0	46·7	9·2

[*] Cell line retained regeneration capability. The most frequent aberrations in chromosomes were fusions between two or more chromosomes and these fusions occurred at random among all chromosomes in a cell. Short arms of acrocentric chromosomes were more frequently involved in fusions. Aberrations resulting from fusions could be transferred into regenerated plants since plants with decreased chromosome number were regenerated from tissue and cell cultures.

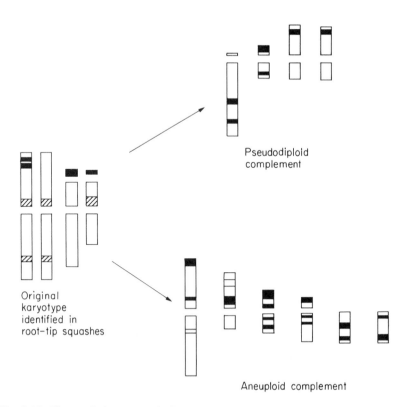

Pseudodiploid complement

Original karyotype identified in root-tip squashes

Aneuploid complement

Fig. 5.18. Changes in karyotype during culture as determined by Giemsa C-banding patterns. The $2n = 4$ karyotype of *Brachycome dichromosomatica* was followed in non-regenerable cell suspension cultures containing cells in which all four chromosomes are separately identifiable by banding patterns (after Gould, 1982).

With increased study of the cytoplasmic genomes of plants (Chapter 2), evidence is accumulating on the variation of these in cultured tissues and cells and in the plants regenerated from tissue cultures. For example, evidence for the recovery of extranuclear variation from maize tissue cultures has been obtained in several separate studies (Pring *et al.*, 1981). These were carried out with tissue cultures of Texas cytoplasm (T) maize that were capable of plant regeneration. Calluses of these cultures were exposed to the fungal pathotoxin of *Helminthosporium maydis* race T and from these were regenerated some resistant and susceptible (wild type) plants. The mitochondrial DNA of these was isolated from representative plant lines and compared by restriction endonuclease fragment analyses (Gengenbach *et al.*, 1981). Besides extranuclear variation in plants regenerated from T cytoplasm maize tissue cultures, variability in mt DNA was also detected in plants regenerated from wild type calluses. Random alterations in the mt DNA restriction fragment patterns of cells derived from protoplasts of other species have also recently been reported, and it is likely that additional examples of extranuclear variation will be obtained as more plant tissue culture systems are characterized and reported, *viz.* Galun *et al.* (1982) and Shepard *et al.* (1983).

Some tissues gradually lose their dependence for inclusion of growth factors in the medium, while certain others acquire this ability after transformation by fully competent T-DNA of tumorogenic or teratoma-inducing strains of *Agrobacterium tumefaciens* (see Chapter 4).

In the former case of habituation, tissue cultures have not lost their requirement for growth factors as such but, rather, have acquired the ability to produce them in amounts sufficient to promote growth and cell division (Meins & Binns, 1978). The basis of this change is epigenetic as indicated by experimental evidence (Binns, 1981) which shows that habituated phenotypes are stably inherited and are induced at frequencies much higher than those expected for induction of somatic mutation and yet still retain totipotency. It is postulated that cytokinin habituation (i.e. the ability of tissues to proliferate by cell division in the absence of this growth factor) is due to a stable activation of certain biosynthetic systems which are normally repressed in the original explant and in the primary culture. Mechanisms possibly involved are biostability, transposable genetic elements, gene amplification, DNA methylation and 'gene determination', all of which are discussed in great detail by Meins (1986). Cytokinin habituation is inducible in pith cells of tobacco by either 35°C treatment or brief exposure to cytokinin, and the incidence of this type of habituation in pith cultures is influenced by the position on the plant from which the original pith explant is taken (Meins *et al.*, 1980). Such habituation occurs in the absence of any detectable changes in the chromosome number of cells in the culture (Binns & Meins, 1980). The occurrence of habituation in tissue cultures is important from the point of view that with continuing culture, growth regulator-inducible organogenesis or embryogenesis will be affected. This means that the behaviour of certain cells or tissues held under a defined set of cultural conditions is likely to alter over extended culture periods.

After transfer of integral T-DNA into plant protoplasts or cells via gene vector systems or natural infection of cells and tissues susceptible to tumoregenic strains of *Agrobacterium tumefaciens* (for details of their molecular biology see Chapter 4), transformed cells are capable of growing in the absence of growth regulators auxin and cytokinin *in vitro*. Transformed cell cultures of this type are easily obtained by culturing gall tissues on media containing suitable antibiotic supplements, e.g. 50 µg ml^{-1} tetracycline, which are toxic to the bacterium but not detrimental to cytoplasmic DNA replication in the transformed cells. Neoplastic growth is also displayed by callus cultures of certain tumour-inducing interspecific hybrids of *Nicotiana*, e.g. *N. glauca* × *N. langsdorffii*. The applications and significance of these types of neoplastic development in cultured cells is later discussed in Chapter 7 in the context of the genetic engineering of plants.

Cryopreservation and germplasm storage

There are clearly many difficulties to be dealt with in long-term culture of calluses or cell suspensions, such as losses in regenerative ability and increases in genetic instability. Where instability is a problem, there is need for methods of preserving useful genotypes and phenotypes before these are lost as a consequence of maintaining the cultures by repeated subculture. The method of greatest value is cryopreservation and recent overviews by Kartha (1982) and Withers (1983) have dealt with the technique in depth, as it relates to the storage of various forms of plant tissue cell and protoplast culture materials. Alternatively, some cultures albeit mainly of an organized, differentiated type such as shoot-tip cultures, can be maintained satisfactorily for periods of up to 1 year before subculturing is required by growing these under growth-limiting conditions.

Cryopreservation (Gr., Kryos = frost) is literally 'preservation in the frozen state'. In practice, this is generally taken to mean storage at very low temperatures over solid carbon dioxide ($-79°C$), in low temperature deep freezers ($-80°C$ or below), in vapour phase (*c.* $-150°C$) or in liquid nitrogen ($-196°C$). The object of storage at very low temperatures like these is to slow down considerably, or even to halt, metabolic processes and biological deterioration. In addition, cryopreserved materials remain genetically stable and the situations of genetic drift such as those described in the last section are avoided. Cryopreservation also brings considerable savings in the costs of equipment and personnel and reduces the risk of losing valuable material through contamination, human error or equipment failure.

Principles of freezing living cells

Two major considerations have to be taken into account when freezing living specimens. These are the susceptibility or degree of freeze tolerance displayed by a given genotype to reduced temperatures and the formation of ice crystals within the cells which may puncture the membrane systems (James, 1983). Because most plant cells have rigid cell walls, any rise in the external solute concentration leads to plasmolysis, i.e. shrinkage of the protoplast away from the cell wall. Under some conditions, ice can form in the space between the cell wall and the protoplast which can cause severe disruption of the cell structure. Preceding cryopreservation, the freeze tolerance of a culture can be improved by timing the harvest of cultures when the majority of cells or tissues are at a most amenable stage of growth. Experience has shown that the degree of vacuolation is important in determining the degree of susceptibility of cells to freezing. Stationary-phase cells are generally more susceptible than exponential-phase cells (Withers & Street, 1977). In fact very few plant materials other than orthodox seeds have any intrinsic freeze tolerance to the low temperatures required for cryopreservation. Therefore, both chemical cryoprotection and optimization of the freezing and thawing rates used are essential if cells are to survive the cryopreservation procedures.

The theoretical aim of these is to use a cooling rate which is slow enough to allow the cells to dehydrate in order to avoid intracellular ice formation but fast enough to prevent damage from the increased solute concentrations formed as a result of the removal of water from cells. An intermediate cooling rate — the optimum — rarely leads to 100% survival. Shortly before preservation, various cryoprotectants can be applied. These substances are a heterogenous group of compounds which appear to act by a variety of different mechanisms to enhance the survival of cryopreserved cells. Cryoprotectants depress both the freezing point and the supercooling point of water, i.e. the temperature at which the homogenous nucleation of ice occurs. They help reduce the amount of water removed from solution in the form of ice at any given temperature, help reduce the concentrations of any other dissolved solutes, and retard the growth of ice crystals. In the case of plant cells, the most widely used cryoprotectants are 5–10% w/v or v/v levels of DMSO, sucrose, glycerol or 1 M proline, or complex mixtures of these compounds. Culture specimens are exposed gradually to increasing concentrations of the cryoprotectants and then placed aseptically into suitable containers such as shatterproof polypropylene ampoules or in aluminium foil envelopes. These containers allow expansion processes which accompany freezing and so prevent undue pressure on the tissues during freezing and thawing.

Cooling rates range widely from very slow $(1-2°C \ min^{-1})$ for cell suspensions, calluses and various organized cultures to very rapid $(50-1,000°C \ min^{-1})$ for the entire cooling of some specimens such as shoot tips and for the final quenching of initially slowly frozen specimens. During storage, temperatures are kept low to ensure stability. A liquid nitrogen refrigerator runing at $-150°C$ or $-196°C$ (in the vapour or liquid phases, respectively) is ideal for this purpose.

Thawing is usually carried out rapidly using a warm water bath $(35-40°C)$ although on occasions, specimens are thawed slowly by exposure to air at room temperature. It is necessary to avoid excessive damage to the fragile thawed tissues or cells by minimizing the amount of handling at the pregrowth stage.

In excess of eighty species of plant have been successfully maintained by means of cryopreservation of cultured embryos, tissues, cells or protoplasts (Withers, 1983). Of particular significance is the discovery that zygotic embryos or embryoid materials from cultures in which somatic embryogenesis or androgenesis have been induced are suitable for dry cryopreservation in aluminium foil containers (Withers, 1982). These materials store well and recover after thawing by the formation of secondary embryoids and plantlets directly without passing through undesirable callus stages.

Versatility of cultural tools and technique

The potential which current plant biotechnology now enjoys is due to the many lines of experimentation opened up by plant cell and tissue cultural tools and techniques. To conclude this chapter a summary of the major routes of *in vitro* manipulation possible in plants is given in Fig. 5.19. It should be recognized after the highlighting of some of the existing problems and limitations of technique in the last section that the ploidy and genetic stability of some materials cannot be guaranteed using particular routes of manipulation. This applies particularly to cells and tissue materials derived from calluses or cell suspensions. Such matters are at the core of topics dealt with in the next chapter on cloning of plants.

Further reading

Bhojwani S.S. & Razdan M.K. (1983). *Plant Tissue Culture: Theory and Practice*. Elsevier, Amsterdam.

Dodds J.H. (1983) (Ed.) *Tissue Culture of Trees*. Croom Helm, London.

Dodds J.H. & Roberts L.W. (1982). *Experiments in Plant Tissue Culture*. Cambridge University Press, Cambridge.

Reinert J. & Yeoman M.M. (1982). *Plant Tissue Culture*: *a Laboratory Manual*. Springer Verlag, Berlin.

Thorpe T.A. (1981) (Ed.) *Plant Tissue Culture. Methods and Applications in Agriculture*. Academic Press, New York.

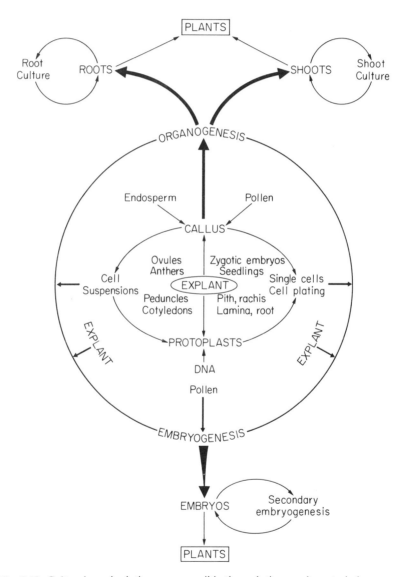

Fig. 5.19. Cultural manipulations now possible through tissue culture technique.

6 Rapid Clonal Propagation

Crop improvement has two important components. These are: (i) the generation of useful types of genetic and epigenetic based variation by breeding, and (ii) the selection, maintenance and bulking of desirable traits by sexual (seed) and asexual (vegetative) propagation methods. The cultural tools and technique of plant cell and tissue culture described in the last chapter, together with the recent advances in recombinant DNA technology have obvious implications and applications to both components of crop improvement.

The demands of both crop breeding and selection require the widespread use of reliable true-to-type propagation methods, firstly, to maintain the sources of germplasm upon which breeding operations are based and secondly, to rapidly proliferate the material selected to sufficient levels for adequate exploitation in the various scales of agriculture, horticulture and forestry practised worldwide. In this general context, the types of propagation required will vary immensely. The individual species being propagated, the multiplication rates desired, the level of uniformity which is demanded in daughter generations from a particular propagation method and the types of material which must be produced to suit the needs of individual production systems are all important considerations. The purpose of this chapter is not to describe all the ranges of vegetative propagation available in plants but to examine the principles of rapid cloning as these relate to propagation of crop plants, and to describe how various methods of *in vitro* plant propagation technique are proving so suitable for application to rapid plant cloning.

Definitions and scope of clonal propagation

Some higher plants can be multiplied or propagated exclusively by vegetative means, e.g. by division, cuttings, budding or grafting (see Hartmann & Kester, 1983). In the case of crop species, cultivated plants will either be lost or will revert to less desirable forms unless they are propagated under controlled conditions (i.e. by directed inbreeding or by vegetative propagation) that preserve the unique characteristics which make these plants useful. The word 'clone' was first used by Webber (1903) to apply to cultivated plants that were propagated vegetatively. The word is derived from Greek (clon = twig, spray or a slip, like those broken off as propagules for multiplication). It provides a means of signifying that plants grown from such vegetative parts are not individuals in the ordinary sense, but are simply transplanted parts of the same individual and that such plants are identical. Shull (1912) narrowed down this term 'clone' to encompass all groups of genotypically identical individuals (of both plants and animals) that arise by asexual reproduction of any sort, including apogamy. This brings up the crux of the whole matter as far as the issue of cloning is concerned since this definition would infer that the products of any somatic mutation should strictly be identified and defined as a discrete clone. Such a definition, however, would be extremely difficult to implement in a practical manner and Stout (1940) tried to resolve the issue by arguing that a 'clone' should be regarded as an artificial unit and that it should be a collective term for a genetically uniform assemblage of individuals (which may be even chimeral in nature, i.e. cells of more than one genotype being present in a single plant), derived originally from a single individual by asexual propagation. This, therefore, includes such widely used methods of artificial propagation as grafting and budding, which are examples of asexual or clonal multiplication but which are at the same time extreme cases of chimeral development. Since current techniques of single cell and protoplast culture enable many thousands of plants to be derived ultimately from a single cell in a comparatively short space of time, the products of this rapid vegetative propagation should by definition be considered a single clone. However, such a notion is clearly not acceptable in practical terms since, as the last chapter showed, the products of callus and cell suspension cultures may consist of many abnormal and deviant idiotypes. This situation stresses the fact that a high level of fidelity, i.e. uniformity, in regenerants of tissue cultures needs to be clearly established before an *in vitro* propagation method can be used in any true-to-type clonal propagation situation. It therefore must not be forgotten that the objective of rapid cloning of plants using *in vitro* methods must be to reproduce asexually, at a reliable and defined level of fidelity, a designated individual plant genotype. This individual genotype can be viewed in the broad sense to include plants (from immature zygotic embryos to mature plants), plant parts which may be genotypically different from the rest of the plant (such as bud sports and chimeras), primary and secondary somatic embryos and single cells (including protoplasts, immature pollen and cell suspensions). The problems of genetic instability and variability frequently associated with some of the last types of culture materials dictate to a large degree their relative usefulness in clonal propagation. Currently, protoplast, callus and cell suspension materials are of greater value to the breeding and the selection sides of crop improvement work, particularly because they generate novel types of genetic and epigenetic variation referred to collectively as somaclonal variation, details of which are covered in the next chapter. However, there are one or two noticeable exceptions to this rule. These will be discussed along with the most widely used methods of clonal propagation which rely on the proliferation and induction of axillary and apical shoot meristems (each meristem being a potential plant). These techniques are in effect extensions of conventional propagation techniques (see Hartmann & Kester, 1983) carried out on a miniature scale under aseptic conditions. For this reason, clonal propagation *in vitro* is called micropropagation.

Micropropagation techniques

Suitable explants from well over 350 species of vascular plants, which include angiosperms, gymnosperms and ferns, can be cultured *in vitro* and induced to form adventitious buds, shoots, embryoids or whole plants (for lists see Vasil & Vasil, 1980 and Conger, 1981). The major stages involved in micropropagation are outlined in Fig. 6.1. They usually comprise three stages designated Stages I, II and III by

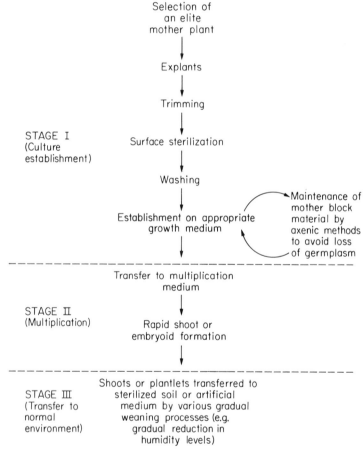

Fig. 6.1. Major stages of micropropagation. Stage I involves preparation of the explant for culture and its subsequent establishment on a suitable culture medium. Once the culture is established and growth initiated in the form of either callus development or of axillary or adventitious bud formation, the culture is subdivided and transferred to a Stage II medium designed to stimulate maximum proliferation through which optimal multiplication can be achieved. Stage II takes up the bulk of the micropropagation activity although no less important is the establishment of Stage III. This involves the hardening and preconditioning of plantlets, or the production of suitable propagules like minitubers or minicorms, which can be established directly in soil or in suitable potting mixtures.

Murashige (1974). These consist of:

Stage I   selection of suitable explants, their sterilization and transfer
            to nutrient media;

Stage II   proliferation of shoots on multiplication medium;

Stage III   transfer of shoots to a rooting (or storage) medium followed
            later by planting into soil or some suitable compost mixture.

A further stage, Stage IV is sometimes also included in cases where
establishment of plantlets in soil is particularly elaborate.

Not all crop species need to be propagated *in vitro* by means of all
three stages. These have been designed to help describe micropropagation processes and to facilitate ease of comparison between two or
more systems.

Micropropagation can be achieved in any one of four ways (see Fig.
6.2) as part of Stages I and II:

(a) by multiplication of existing meristems within axillary shoots which
proliferate on explants after removal from the parent plant;

(b) by multiplication through growth and proliferation of existing apical
shoots excised from the parent plant;

(c) by multiplication through induction of adventitious meristems
through either processes of organogenesis or somatic embryogenesis
directly on explants;

(d) by multiplication of calluses derived either from organs, tissues, cells
or protoplasts and their subsequent expression of either organogenesis
or somatic embryogenesis in serial subcultures. Shoots obtained can be
further subdivided using the principles of multiplication used in either
(a), (b) or (c) above.

Multiplication by apical and axillary shoots

Axillary shoots are those that emerge from their normal positions on the
plant in the leaf axils while apical shoots are those that occupy the
growing tip of shoots. Both axillary and apical shoots contain quiescent
or active meristems depending on the physiological state of the plant.
Most vascular plants have an indeterminate mode of growth in which
the leaf axils contain subsidiary meristems, each of which is capable of
growing into a shoot that is identical to the main axis. Depending on the
degree of branching displayed by a particular species (a feature which is
also influenced to a certain degree by the environment), only a limited
number of axillary meristems develop, the majority being inhibited by
apical dominance. Although the mechanism of apical dominance has
been demonstrated to be under the control of various growth regulators,
in many plants the outgrowth of axillary shoots appears to depend on
the supply of cytokinin to their meristem. Thus, shoot tips cultured on
basal medium containing no growth regulators typically develop into
single seedling-like shoots with strong apical dominance. However,
when the shoots of the same explant material are grown on media

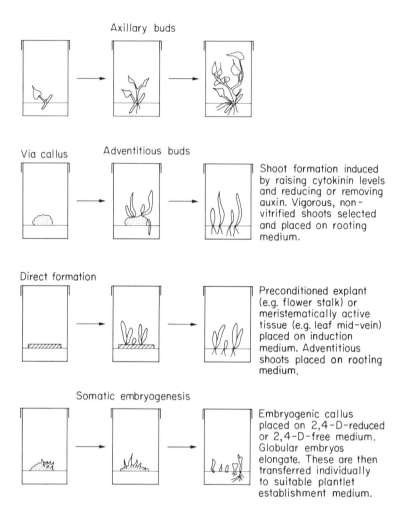

Axillary buds

Via callus   Adventitious buds

Shoot formation induced by raising cytokinin levels and reducing or removing auxin. Vigorous, non-vitrified shoots selected and placed on rooting medium.

Direct formation

Preconditioned explant (e.g. flower stalk) or meristematically active tissue (e.g. leaf mid-vein) placed on induction medium. Adventitious shoots placed on rooting medium.

Somatic embryogenesis

Embryogenic callus placed on 2,4-D-reduced or 2,4-D-free medium. Globular embryos elongate. These are then transferred individually to suitable plantlet establishment medium.

Fig. 6.2. Schematic diagram of some important ways of achieving micropropagation through the induction of growth of axillary buds, the formation of adventitious buds either on calluses or on original explant tissues or by the induction of somatic embryogenesis from calluses derived from explants.

containing cytokinin, axillary shoots often develop prematurely. This results in precocious branching which leads to the development of secondary, then tertiary etc. shoots in a proliferating cluster (see Fig. 6.3). Once such clusters have developed, these can be subdivided into smaller clumps of shoots or separate shoots which will in turn form similar clusters when subcultured on fresh medium (Fig. 6.4). Provided the basic nutrient formulation is adequate for normal growth, this subdivision process can be continued indefinitely. For example, proliferating shoots of many species have been maintained for up to 10–15 years with no apparent deterioration (Hussey, 1983). The multiplication

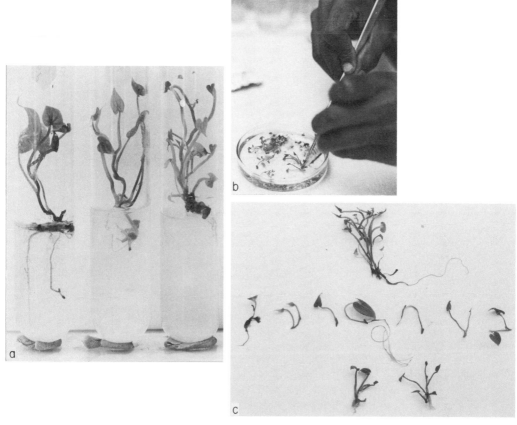

Fig. 6.3. Proliferation of axillary shoots. *Dioscorea* yams derived from single nodal explants (a). The shoots are subdivided (b) to produce several daughter cultures (c) and these can be regularly subdivided every 4−6 weeks to produce many thousands of plantlets (see also Fig. 6.4).

rates possible through axillary shoot proliferation obviously vary with genotype and reflect the relative ability of a genotype to form leaves. However, if optimum levels of cytokinin are employed (generally in the range 0·5−10 mg l^{-1}) and optimal conditions of culture maintained (see later), 5−10 × multiplication rates can be achieved on a regular 4−8 week micropropagation cycle. This may lead to potential rapid multiplication levels in the range of 0·1−3·0 × 10^6 within 1 year. Since all cultural operations are undertaken within the confines of artificial environments, these levels of propagation can be maintained throughout the year and are therefore more independent of seasonal effects normally associated with conventional clonal propagation methods. In general, the technique of proliferation by axillary shoots is applicable to any plant that produces regular axillary shoots and responds to cytokinins such as

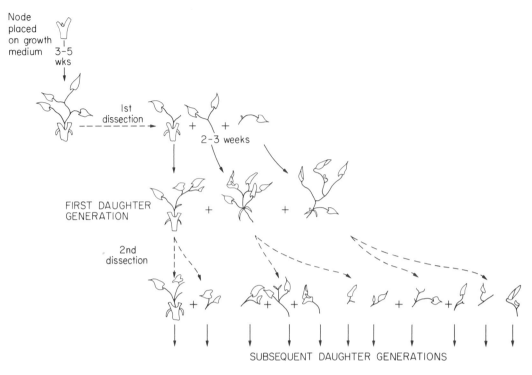

Node
placed
on growth
medium   3–5
wks

1st
dissection

2–3 weeks

FIRST DAUGHTER
GENERATION

2nd
dissection

SUBSEQUENT DAUGHTER GENERATIONS

Fig. 6.4. Diagrammatic representation of the early stages of the multiplication of nodal segment cultures using a simple axillary bud proliferation technique (after Mantell *et al.*, 1978).

BAP, 2iP and zeatin. This includes an increasing number of woody species, especially forest and orchard trees (see Jones, 1983) for which there are clearly great advantages in having systems of rapid clonal propagation. many tree species are propagated vegetatively by means of woody cuttings or special organs, e.g. the lignotubers of *Eucalyptus* sp., and occasionally by specialized layering operations. These are usually quite slow and labour-intensive procedures and since many forest trees and orchard crops are also managed on a 20–25 year rotation, rapid multiplication of elite clonal materials is especially desirable. Juvenility is of major significance in relation to the vegetative propagation of trees by conventional and *in vitro* methods. The stage of growth of seedlings following germination is described as the juvenile phase. This is a phase of very active growth, frequently characterized by morphological features such as unique leaf shape and the presence of spines and by a period of development when the tree does not initiate flowers and when vegetative propagation is achieved readily by traditional methods. With this in mind, explants of axillary and apical buds and shoots are generally taken for culture during this phase of growth in young trees. In the case of maturer specimens, the rejuvenated types of growth described can be induced by treatments such as the grafting of shoots onto seedlings, shoot pruning, the maintenance of high fertilizer levels, or spraying with cytokinins.

Apical shoots (normally 1–5 mm in size) are cultured on media containing mixtures of auxin and cytokinin e.g. 0·01–0·1 and 0·05–0·5 mg l^{-1}, respectively. The level of cytokinin is generally raised in subsequent subcultures in order to achieve an acceptable rate of proliferation while at the same time not inducing yellowing or distortion of the shoots. If callus is induced by presence of auxin, levels of this growth regulator are usually decreased in order to avoid the possibility of regenerating shoots from this material. Since the presence of cytokinin in the medium inhibits root development, cultured material is often transferred in Stage III to a rooting medium which contains reduced levels of cytokinin. This latter situation is particularly so in the case of many monocotyledons, where root formation and proliferation is concomitant with subculture on a medium containing no cytokinin. The use of extremely small shoot tips or apical meristems which include only a few leaf primordia as explants is an extension of this type of micropropagation and forms the basis of many successful virus elimination procedures, details of which are given later in a subsequent section.

Multiplication by adventitious shoots

Adventitious shoots are stem and leaf structures that arise naturally on plant tissues located in sites other than at the normal leaf axil regions. The structures in question include stems, bulbs, corms, tubers and rhizomes amongst others. Almost every one of these organs can be used as a cutting in the conventional propagation context. For instance, leaves of *Begonia* and some other ornamentals produce shoots on certain of their leaves or scale leaves, respectively. Similar types of adventitious shoot development can be induced either by manipulation of cytokinin levels in media or preconditioning the parent plants and explants. Care has to be taken not to create conditions which lead to extensive callusing. Successful methods of this type of micropropagation have been devised for many ornamental species (see Table 6.1). Bulbs and corms grow from meristems at the bases of leaves and scales where they join the basal plate. Such meristematic regions will regenerate shoots in all genera. Scale and leaf base explants form multiple shoots on medium containing both cytokinin and auxin. Buds, bulbils or cormels under these conditions form adventitious shoots around the swollen base tissues. Sections of young flower stems within a bulb or the ensheathing leaves of a corm respond to auxin- or auxin plus cytokinin-supplemented media. Levels of fidelity in propagated material of these species are generally quite high and this is probably due to the fact that adventitious shoots arise from only one or two layers of cells or

Table 6.1. Micropropagation of some economically important ornamental and horticultural species via adventitious shoot cultures.

Group	Species	Explant
Bulbs and corms	*Allium*	Scale leaves, leaf bases, stems, flower parts[*]
	Lilium	Scale leaves, leaf bases, stems, flower parts
	Tulipa	Scale leaves, leaf bases, stems, flower parts
	Narcissus	Scale leaves, leaf bases, stems, flower parts
	Nerine	Scale leaves, stems
	Iris	Scale leaves, stems, inflorescences
	Gladiolus	Corms, stems
	Freesia	Corms, leaf bases, stems, inflorescences, flower parts[*]
House plants	*Saintpaulia ionantha*	2-mm thick petiole sections
	Petunia hybrida	Small leaf pieces
	Kalanchoe blossfeldiana	Stem pieces
	Begonia × *hiemalis*	Petioles and leaf lamina
	Gloxinia spp.	Petioles and leaf lamina
Orchard crops	*Malus domestica*	Root pieces
Conifers	*Picea abies*	Needles from the upper half of the buds

[*] Flower pedicels, ovaries, petals or anther filaments.

in some cases only single epidermal cells, e.g. adventitious shoots produced from stems of *Tulipa* (Wright & Alderson, 1980). For bulbous species, annual rates of multiplication through conventional propagation techniques are generally below × 5 whereas by micropropagation, levels of shoot multiplication are achieved which are ×10 to ×10^3. When comparing conventional with micropropagation methods of bulb production (see Hussey, 1982), micropropagation results in overall multiplication levels of ×5 to ×10 per annum. This estimation takes into account the fact that at least 3 years are required to develop bulbs large enough for field planting purposes from the cultured shoots.

Continuous propagation by adventitious shoot proliferation is possible with many species that form bulbs or corms. Shoot bases, 10 mm high and split vertically into two pieces, will regenerate clusters of shoots from around the abaxial surfaces of the developing leaves and scales (Fig. 6.5a). Senescence and dormancy which is often expressed in such cultured materials can be prevented by *in vitro* trimming of shoots to within 2−3 mm of the basal plate (Fig. 6.5b). In this way, continuously productive cultures of *Iris*, *Lilium* and some *Tulipa* hybrids can be maintained for indefinite periods. In bulbs with strong apical dominance, e.g. *Narcissus*, *Nerine*, *Allium* and *Hyacinthus*, it is necessary also to destory the main apex. Hussey (1983) achieved this most efficiently by making two shallow vertical cuts at right angles to each other to the level of the basal plate (Fig. 6.5c). When large enough, the regenerating shoots are in turn cut down and cross-cut to obtain repeated cycles of regeneration (Fig. 6.5d).

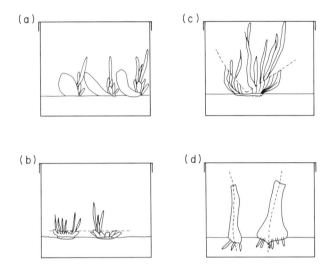

Fig. 6.5. Schematic representation of some approaches which have been used for achieving micropropagation of bulbs and corms: (a) regeneration of shoot clusters, (b) trimming of shoots to within 2−3 mm of basal plate, (c) vertical cuts at right angles to each other to remove dominance of main axis and (d) cross cutting minicorms and bulbils to obtain repeated cyles of propagation *in vitro*. Dotted lines indicate orientation of cuts and subdivisions.

Just as shoots and roots can be induced on explants, in an adventitious manner, so too can somatic embryos. Adventitious embryo formation is distinct from that type of embryo formation which occurs via a callus stage. Adventitous embryos can be formed directly from groups of cells within the original explant, e.g. pollen (microspores) and mesophyll cells of the leaf, or from individual cells within the original explant, e.g. the epidermal cells of leaf bases or of primary embryoids. Embryoids are in fact formed *in vivo* from diverse tissues and organs in many species. For instance, the orchid *Malaxis paludosa* produces a large number of embryoids at the tips of its leaves and many species and cultivars of *Citrus* and *Mangifera* (mango) exhibit polyembryony in which nucellar cells lining the micropylar end of the embryo sac give rise to embryoids, which push their way into developing endosperm tissue for nutrition and further growth. The nucellar embryoids which develop are diploid and have often been used as traditional sources of clonal material of these fruit trees. In cultures, direct embryogenesis can be induced on certain explants. For instance, leaf pieces of *Arabusta* coffee trees can be induced to form embryos directly when cultured on a basal MS medium containing high levels of cytokinin, and when devoid of auxin (Dublin, 1981).

Multiplication through callus culture

As described earlier, tissue and cell cultures in which callusing is produced tend to be of low value as a means of micropropagation through the induction of organogenesis or embryogenesis. This is due to the relatively high incidence of aneuploidy and polyploidy sometimes associated with the tissues and regenerated plants obtained from meristems or meristemoids, i.e. meristematic centres consisting of a spherical mass of small isodiametric cells with dense cytoplasm and a high nucleo-cytoplasmic ratio (Torrey, 1966) formed on calluses. This is not to say that micropropagation via a callus intermediary is still not capable of producing regenerants of uniform type. In certain cases the propagator can visibly distinguish aberrant regenerants at the first step of the multiplication procedure, i.e. when shoots are dissected away from calluses. Sometimes aberrant shoots are distinguishable by their vitrified or glassy appearance so that these can be eliminated from any further propagation steps. However, such an approach is not sufficient guarantee against the inadvertent multiplication of chimeric shoots or mutants. Notwithstanding this, *in vitro* propagation via organogenic or embryogenic calluses is unavoidable in the case of certain economically important species, particularly some of those in the cereals, forage legumes, forest trees and tropical palms. Also, any plant regeneration from protoplasts requires passage through at least one callus stage. This operation is of course an essential element of the procedures used to derive genetically engineered regenerants from transformed or manipulated protoplasts as described in Chapter 4.

The production of many thousands of plantlets from calluses either derived from cell suspensions or protoplasts isolated from a single leaf constitutes unique cases of cloning. Skirvin & Janick (1976) used the term 'calliclones' to describe regenerants of individual callus lines and several workers (e.g. Shepard *et al.*, 1980) have more recently coined the term 'protoclones' to describe regenerants of individual protoplast-derived callus lines when these materials are derived from single donor plants. In both these cases, somaclonal-based variation in the regenerants is a common occurrence (*viz* Barbier & Dulieu, 1983) and clearly callus-based cloning methods require special consideration in the context of the definition of the term 'cloning' alluded to earlier in this chapter.

Over and above such technicalities, there are also an increasing number of reports in the literature on the establishment of stable regenerative calluses either by chance or, in some cases, by deliberate selection of organogenic or embryogenic sectors of callus cultures. This has led to increased regeneration potentials in cultures of some traditionally recalcitrant types. For instance, Heyser & Nabors (1982) successfully regenerated plants in a consistent manner from secondary calluses of oats (*Avena sativa*) using this approach. Also, calluses have been obtained which can regenerate genotypically uniform plants for up to 10–14 years. These stable calluses have been described for genera such as *Lilium* (Sheridan, 1968), *Freesia* (Davies, 1972), *Chrysanthemum* (Earle & Langhans, 1974), tomato (De Langhe & De Bruijne, 1976) and *Hemerocallus* (Krikorian *et al.*, 1981). In these types of callus materials, it appears that the slowly growing meristematic cells from which shoots and embryoids are derived are situated on the periphery of highly vacuolated inner cells. The diploid cells making up the meristematic layers express totipotency while the inner layers made up of mixoploid cells do not. These types of calluses when obtained are of great value since they can be suitably subdivided by random dissection or by placing in a homogenizer to produce many thousands of propagules in a single operation. They are, therefore, ideal for some semi-mechanized and large-scale forms of rapid clonal propagation (see later under 'Mass propagation', p.154).

Factors affecting morphogenesis and proliferation rate

The commercial use of plant tissue cultures for clonal plant propagation requires a quantitative approach which leads to an optimization of the conditions associated with vegetative plant propagation. The effects of various factors on morphogenesis and proliferation rate are measured in terms of their influence on the relative incidence of organogenesis or embryogenesis scored, and the number of propagules which can be regenerated per given amount of culture over a given period of time or a single culture generation. There are five major factors which influence the expression of morphogenesis and proliferation rates in micropropagation systems. These are:
(a) physiological status of the explants and donor plants;
(b) composition of culture media;
(c) culture environment inside and outside the culture vessel;
(d) genotypes being propagated;
(e) various technical problems associated with persistent contamination by bacteria or viruses and with the continued stability of regenerative capacity of cultures.

Physiological status of the donor plant and explant

As discussed earlier, the most suitable explants for tissue culture are those in which there is a large proportion of either meristematic tissue present or cells which retain an ability to express totipotency. Successful cultures are rarely obtained from senescing tissues. In tree species, the regeneration potential of tissue culture diminishes with each year of plant maturation, even though in some cases juvenile characteristics are apparently maintained (Cheng, 1975). Tissues excised from the more recently produced parts of a herbaceous plant are also more regenerative than those from older regions. Also, embryogenesis in somatic cells has been generally associated with cultures established from embryo explants rather than maturer, non-embryonic tissues. In this respect the season and stage of growth of the parent plant may be critical in determining the behaviour of the explant in culture. There are many examples of this. For instance, Litz & Conover (1981) found that optimum conditions for the establishment of papaya tissue cultures occurred during the hot summer months and also during the transitional months of April and November under the Florida climatic regime. Flower stem explants of *Tulipa* give rise to shoots only when excised during the dry storage (dormant) phase; once elongation of stems has commenced following dormancy, the capacity for these explants to regenerate is lost (Wright & Alderson, 1980). Similarly, nodal explants of *Dioscorea alata* yams only produce axillary shoot growth when excised from donor plants growing under a 16-hour photoperiod, conditions which induce active vegetative growth. Under 12-hour photoperiods, donor plants give explants which show either no growth or prolific callus development (Mantell *et al.*, 1978).

Familiarity with a plant's natural propagation mechanism is frequently helpful in determining the more suitable explant sources. Thus, sections of leaves are most suitably employed in cases where plants normally regenerate from leaves while sections of bulb, root, stem, flower, ovary, nucellus, cotyledon and other structures may have applicability with certain species. Appendix 6 shows typical examples of explants used in successful cases of micropropagation in a wide range of important herbaceous and woody crop species.

Composition of the culture media

The importance of the culture medium on the growth and proliferation rate of plant tissue cultures needs no emphasis since, as described in Chapter 5, many components of the medium dictate the pathways of development taken by a culture.

In general, a suitable growth medium is adequate for achieving both Stages I and II, with modifications only being necessary for Stage III of micropropagation. However, the type and relative proportion of growth regulating substances present in the initial culture medium will largely determine the regeneration potential of a culture system. Appendix 8 shows examples of the various growth regulator treatments used to achieve micropropagation of a wide range of crops. Within any given culture system, the level and type of growth regulator mixtures as well as those of carbon, potassium, phosphate and nitrogen sources, and the medium pH and buffers used, if any, will affect its overall propagation performance.

For instance, the capacity of cell cultures to utilize NH_4^+ as sole nitrogen sources depends on maintaining the medium pH above 5·0 (Dougall & Verma, 1978). The availability of NH_4^+ as opposed to NO_3^- as sources of nitrogen to a tissue is particularly important as regards the development of somatic embryogenesis in a culture. The levels of phosphate present in media can influence the number and size of shoots produced in shoot tip cultures of tropical foliage plants (Miller & Murashige, 1976). The relative levels of potassium influence the number of embryos produced in wild carrot suspension cultures; while embryo productivity is maximal at 10−50 mM potassium, growth is maximal at 1 mM (Brown *et al.*, 1976). Many other examples of how these factors effect the growth and proliferation of plant tissue cultures are provided in the reviews listed at the end of this chapter.

Culture environment

Just as certain environmental conditions such as light, temperature and gas phases influence the growth of plants *in vivo*, so these factors can be expected to have significant effects on plant materials held in micropropagation systems. Plant cells, tissues and organs cultured on media containing a readily available source of energy such as sucrose would be expected to be less dependent on photosynthesis. However, several studies have indicated that light apparently absorbed by photosynthetic pigments, plays an important role in inducing morphogenesis in cultured tissues. For instance, the incidence of *Asparagus* spear production is increased in the light (Hasegawa *et al.*, 1973). Kato (1978) showed that bud induction in excised leaf segments of the lily *Heloniopsis orientalis* is controlled to a certain extent by a photosynthetic system. This was concluded after the photosynthetic inhibitors DCMU and AT were found to inhibit bud formation in the light while morphactin, which has a stimulatory effect on carbohydrate synthesis, stimulated bud formation in the dark. Light quality effects have been registered *in vitro* in both the red and blue ends of the visible spectrum. Seibert (1973) found that blue light in the region of 467 nm was effective in inducing bud formation in tobacco callus cultures and Kadkade & Seibert (1977) later showed that adventitious shoot formation in lettuce is regulated by phytochrome. As little as 5 min of 660 nm light at 2·5 W m^2 each day during the second week of culture led to a doubling in the number of shoots produced. There are also reports that red light stimulates induction of flower buds on thin layer epidermal sections of tobacco and that far-red light treatments stimulate root production (Tran Thanh Van, 1977). Several micropropagation systems have now been described in which morphogenesis is induced by appropriate red/far-red light treatments. This aleviates to a certain extent the need for the addition of growth regulators to the culture medium, and thus reduces the risk of genetic abnormalities occurring in the micropropagation Stages I and II. For most cultured plants, a 660 nm light treatment stimulates shoots while 740 nm light stimulates roots. The intensity of light required for most micropropagation purposes is around 1,000 lux. However, higher light intensities of up to 10,000 lux have been found to be beneficial, particularly during Stage III of micropropagation. This illustrates the importance of optimizing cultural conditions for each particular species under propagation. Photoperiod effects as would be expected often reflect the relative sensitivity of the individual species being propagated. For example, tobacco has an optimum photoperiod of 16 hours (Murashige & Nakano, 1968) while cauliflower has one of 9 hours (Margara, 1969).

Apart from light, another obvious environmental influence is temperature. Plants in culture are most often grown at 25°C for convenience. However, there are species of plants that have temperature optima for morphogenesis which contrast with this arbitrary regime. For instance, cultures of *Begonia* × *cheimantha* hybrids produced greatest numbers of shoots on petiole segments at 18°C (Fonnesbech, 1974) while shoot tip cultures of *Asparagus officinalis* grew best at 27°C (Hasegawa *et al.*, 1973).

A third factor of the culture environment affecting the performance of tissue cultures is the constitution of the gas phase within the culture vessels. Gases which are metabolically active and could have possible effects on morphogenesis include ethylene, oxygen, carbon dioxide, ethanol and acetaldehyde. In general, ethylene is antagonistic to morphogenesis and promotes unorganized growth of cells (i.e. callus formation). Of significance here is the fact that the levels of ethylene and other volatiles may be influenced by the types of closures used and the practice of flaming flasks with alcohol or gas burners for sterilization purposes. Beasley & Eaks (1979) have found that this practice introduces variable levels of ethylene into flasks. Although most of the gas diffused out of flasks in the first 2 hours, in cases where flasks are tightly closed high levels of ethylene can persist for substantial periods. These workers noticed significant differences in the growth and proliferation of excised ovules of cotton when these were grown in sealed incubators as compared to others that were grown in ones that were opened regularly. Clearly, the type of closure used on culture vessels needs to be checked in the wake of these observations, especially since ethanol and acetaldehyde have now also been implicated as potent inhibitors both of organogenesis and embryogenesis (Thomas & Murashige, 1979). Raised levels of carbon dioxide in the absence of ethylene are known to lead to enhanced greening in some cell culture systems. However, the interaction of all these gases is undoubtedly complex and more detailed studies need to be carried out to ascertain real effects of the gas phase on micropropagation systems. It is one component of the micropropagation environment which should not be overlooked any longer.

Genotype being propagated

Certain genotypes lend themselves more than others to vegetative propagation. Different genotypes can, therefore, be expected to react differently *in vitro* to a given set of cultural conditions designed to promote proliferation of a given species of plant. Examples of the different *in vitro* responses of quite closely related genotypes are frequent in the literature. For example, tissue culture initiation and plant regeneration was examined by Rines & McCoy (1981) for several genotypes from three hexaploid oat species. These were the cultivated oat, *Avena sativa*, and two wild oats, *A. sterilis* and *A. fatua*. Various types of tissue cultures were initiated from immature embryos with so-called 'regenerable' cultures being characterized by organized chlorophyllous primordia present in compact, yellowish-white, highly lobed callus. Apart from other factors, such as the pre-conditioning of donor plants, embryo size and 2,4-D concentrations used in the culture initiation medium, there was a strong effect of genotype on the frequency with which regenerable type cultures were produced. Among twenty-three *A. sativa* cultivars tested cv. Lodi and two related lines gave the highest frequencies (up to 80%) of regenerable type cultures. Of sixteen *A. sterilis* lines tested, only three produced regenerable type cultures at frequencies of less than 20%. Seven out of thirty-two *A. fatua* lines tested produced regenerable type cultures at frequencies greater than 45%. In all three species there were tissue cultures capable of plant regeneration after more than 12 months in culture (equivalent to 9–10 subcultures). This work has led to the suggestion that since genotype influences culture initiation frequency and culture type, screening of genotypes and selection among segregating populations might prove a fruitful approach in the improvement of micropropagation capabilities in oats and indeed in other more recalcitrant cereals. This approach of purposefully breeding or selecting more suitable genotypes which lend themselves to micropropagation techniques was first attempted by Bingham *et al*. (1975) whereby lines of alfalfa were intentionally bred and selected for their regeneration ability *in vitro*. Similar marked influences of genotype are observed in the types of morphogenesis obtained in particular types of tobacco explants. Tran Thanh Van (1980) has described how different genotypes and species of *Nicotiana* determine the regenerating ability of thin cell layers of tobacco in culture. Table

Table 6.2. The effect of genotype on the regeneration ability of thin cell layers of *Nicotiana* spp. (from Tran Thanh Van, 1980).

Species, cultivars or cross	Photoperiodic requirement	% explants with flowers (f) or floral shoots (fs)	Other organogenesis
N. tabacum cv. W38	Day neutral	100 (f)	+[*]
cv. Samsun	Day neutral	100 (f)	+
N. sylvestris	Long day	0	+
N. tomentosiformis	Short day	0	+
F_1: *N. sylvestris* ×			
N. tomentosiformis	Long day	30 (fs)	+
N. tabacum cv. Samsun × F_1	Long day	30 (fs)	+
N. tabacum cv. Samsun ×			
N. sylvestris	Day neutral	60 (fs)	+
N. rustica	Day neutral	0	Callus

[*] Buds, roots and calluses formed also.

6.2 summarizes some of the results of experiments in which thin layer explants of stem tissue (1 × 1 or 1 × 10 mm), composed of one to six layers of epidermal and subepidermal cells, were cultured on simple nutrient media. Provided appropriate photoperiod treatments were applied to donor plants, morphogenesis was expressed in these specialized explants. However, explants of *N. sylvestris* and *N. tomentosiformis* were unable to form *de novo* flower buds except when these two genotypes were combined in an F_1 cross. Similar effects of genotype on morphogenic response were obtained after combination of *N. tabacum* cv. Samsun germplasm with that of *N. sylvestris*. The 100% flower induction frequency of the former species was reduced to 60% after combination of germplasm from *N. sylvestris*, a non-inductive genotype. Genotypic effects of this nature are frequent and it only serves to underline the fact that a micropropagation system developed for one particular cultivar will not automatically be applicable to another within the same species.

Technical problems

An occasional and often serious problem encountered during large scale micropropagation of some plants is the persistence of certain types of slow-growing saprophytic or pathogenic bacteria that survive the initial decontamination procedures. Such contaminants, e.g. *Pseudomonas* spp., *Erwinia* spp. and *Bacillus* spp., can persist for many culture generations without being noticed. Under some conditions species such as *E. carotovora* can cause considerable reductions in vigour and can cause chlorosis in the propagated plantlets (Knauss & Miller, 1978). A

Pseudomonas infection severely limited proliferation rates in tissue cultures of papaya initiated from field grown plants by Litz & Conover (1981). In extreme cases, effects of these types of infections may be reduced by the use of appropriate levels of antibiotics incorporated in culture media. An associated problem is the inadvertant propagation of plants which are infected with latent or symptomless types of viruses or mycoplasmas which may markedly reduce the vigour and proliferation rates of cultures. This is discussed later in greater detail in a subsequent section dealing with the application of micropropagation to the production of disease-free crop plants.

A further problem more frequently associated with micropropagation of tree species is the accumulation of inhibitory substances in the growth medium during initiation of cultures. Explants of these species often produce excessive amounts of phenolic substances, the oxidation products of which often strongly inhibit growth. Where the problem is confined to the reaction of the initial explant, it may be prevented by dissecting tissues for culture under the surface of liquids or by incorporating ascorbic acid or citric acid in culture media. In the case of teak tissue cultures, polyvinyl polypyrrolidone has proved an effective amendment to culture media (Gupta *et al.*, 1980). By contrast, some phenolics have been used to great advantage. Phloroglucinol incorporated in media supporting apple shoot tip cultures of M.7 rootstocks produced a two- to three-fold increase in shoot proliferation and rooting. Various other beneficial effects of this and other phenolics on rejuvenation *in vitro* have now been recorded on apple and some other fruit tree crops (Jones, 1983).

Activated charcoal when added at levels of 1–2% (w/v) in media can sometimes be beneficial by adsorbing inhibitory concentrations of growth regulatory substances such as ABA, which might be present in the original explant or produced by proliferating tissues.

It is not uncommon in callus cultures to find that the regenerative capacity of some cultures declines over prolonged subculture. There may be several reasons for this, one of which may be the development of habituation in some of the cell population. As a result of epigenetic changes brought on by the cultural process, sectors of the culture may become non-competent whilst others retain their competence for morphogenesis. Experience with culture of embryogenic calluses of grasses and cerals has shown that early recognition and physical separation of embryogenic sectors is critical if stable embryogenic tissue cultures are to be developed and then maintained (Vasil, 1982).

The applications of micropropagation

Apart from the ability to rapidly multiply plants, micropropagation also offers a means for circumvention of many crop diseases. This is due to the eradication of pathogenic agents either as part of the decontamination phase of explant preparation during Stage I, or as the result of culturing small enough explants which contain few or none of the infective agents. Further propagation and disease testing of regenerated plants kept under the controlled and protected conditions well away from vectors or any potential pathways of reinfection, mean that valuable nuclear stocks of disease-free plant materials can be maintained conveniently at reduced cost and with less effort. Subsequent bulking by conventional means can then be carried out as and when the need arises. The small size of micropropagules and their ability to proliferate in a soil-free environment, facilitate the convenient storage, handling and rapid dissemination of propagated materials by air transport across international phytosanitary barriers (Roca *et al.*, 1979). Linked with these benefits of micropropagation is the suitability of tissue cultures for storage of germplasm either by cryopreservation or by limited culture growth. Using these methods, stocks of germplasm can be maintained in a stable condition for many years.

The major applications of micropropagation are listed in Table 6.3 and each of these is discussed in outline below.

Small-scale cloning

In breeding work, micropropagation is particularly useful for the main-

Table 6.3. Major uses of micropropagation and the required specification for each of these (after Lawrence, 1981).

Cloning application	Levels of multiplication	Specifications required		Cost tolerance
		Phenotype fidelity	Genetic conservativeness	
Small scale				
Breeding and genotype rescue	10^3	High	Absolute	High
Mutation introduction	10^3	Moderate to high	Absolute	High
Production of pathogen-free plants				
Production and maintenance	10^3	High	Absolute	High
Germplasm storage				
Limited growth and cryopreservation	10^3	High	Absolute	Moderate
Seed production				
Parental propagation	$10^3 - 10^6$	Moderate	Very high	Low to moderate
Large scale				
Ornamentals	$10^3 - 10^6$	High	Moderate	Low to moderate
Tree crops	$10^5 - 10^6$	High	Moderate to high	Low
Vegetable crops	$10^6 - 10^8$	Very high	Moderate	Very low

tenance and multiplication of modest numbers of special genotypes or potential new cultivars including any products of genetic engineering involving *in vitro* procedures. In these cases, propagation by means of axillary or apical shoot development is desirable because genetic conservativeness must be absolute. However, since these procedures involve handling individual shoots, the work is labour intensive and therefore generally quite costly.

Production of pathogen-free plants

This is a specialized area of micropropagation which is based on general aseptic culture procedures and meristem-tip and shoot-tip culture techniques (see Ingram & Helgeson, 1980 for details). Diseases of crop plants caused by pathogens such as viruses, viroids, fungi, nematodes, bacteria and mycoplasma reduce the yield, quality and vigour of crops. Virus diseases like potato leaf roll virus (PLRV) or potato virus Y (PVY) for example, can cause up to 95% reductions in the tuber yield of potato crops, and potato virus X (PVX) infections can lead to reductions in tuber yields of between 5 and 75% depending on the virus strains involved, the cultivar of potato infected, the environmental influences exerted and the types of latent virus infections also present. Since many virus diseases and other pathogens like nematodes, bacteria and mycoplasma are transmitted by vegetative propagation procedures, there is frequently an essential need to eradicate pathogens from certain elite lines of plant material. With nematode infestation and the majority of bacterial infections, this can be achieved most effectively by culturing explants removed from pathogen-free parts of a plant. However, since the majority of viruses infect plants in a systemic manner this type of approach is not sufficient and more specialized methods are required to achieve the elimination of virus infections. These are the regeneration of plants from:

(a) cultures of small growing tips of shoots — the apical meristems consisting of less than 0·5 mm apical dome and one to three leaf primordia;

(b) cultures of larger shoot tips excised from donor plants or dormant propagules which have been exposed to hot-air treatments of 30–37°C for 10–14 days or hot water treatments of 50–60°C for 5–10 minutes designed to reduce the levels of virus replication in the explants;

(c) cultures of (a) or (b) materials grown on media containing anti-viral compounds such as malachite green or thiouracil.

As shown in Fig. 6.6, meristem tips are carefully dissected away from the apical or lateral shoot buds with the aid of a binocular microscope. Provided trimming and dissection procedures are carried out under aseptic conditions, most meristems can be placed directly into culture without surface sterilization. Meristem-tips can be cultured on

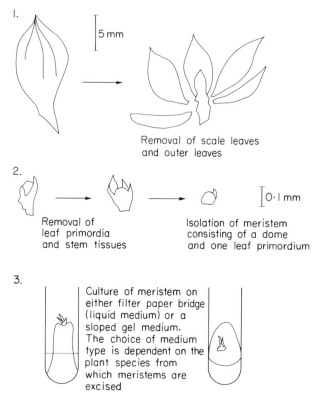

1.

|5 mm

Removal of scale leaves
and outer leaves

2.

Removal of
leaf primordia
and stem tissues

Isolation of meristem
consisting of a dome
and one leaf primordium

|0·1 mm

3.

Culture of meristem on
either filter paper bridge
(liquid medium) or a
sloped gel medium.
The choice of medium
type is dependent on the
plant species from
which meristems are
excised

Fig. 6.6. Diagrammatic representation of the principal stages of apical meristem tip culture. After removal of the growing shoot tip (5–10 mm in length) the apical meristem is dissected out from its protective sheath of young leaves and primordia with the aid of sterile scalpels or fine needles and placed directly onto a suitable growth medium. Under favourable conditions, plantlets can be regenerated directly from the meristematic dome often in the absence of excessive callus development.

either liquid or semi-solidified nutrient media (for details see Quak, 1977) supplemented with growth regulators which induce plantlet regeneration. Culture media are generally those based on modified White's media. Growth regulators used vary within the range 0·1–2·0 mg l^{-1}. In the cases of potato shoot tips, presoaking in 10 mg l^{-1} GA is beneficial as this treatment breaks dormancy in the tuber sprouts.

After a period of between 50 and 100 days, the few plantlets or adventitious shoots obtained can be further micropropagated and the regenerants tested for the presence of viruses or other pathogens, if appropriate. Disease testing is an essential component of pathogen-free production schemes. Recent improvements in the techniques of PAGE and ELISA allow early and sensitive detection of viroid and virus infections, respectively. More conventional types of indicator host indexing methods can also be used but these lack specificity.

Meristem-tip culture, either with or without heat therapy, has been used for the elimination of viruses from well over thirty species (Walkey, 1978) and the benefits of this are well recognized. Rhubarb crops freed of virus yield 60–90% more stem weight than infected stocks. Chrysanthemum, narcissus, carnations and other flower crops freed of major virus diseases produce both improved size of blooms and increased number of blooms per plant. In other cut flower crops like *Pelargonium*, 20–30% more cuttings are produced per plant and rooting capacity is also improved in virus-freed material. Particularly impressive have been the effects of freeing tuber crops of viruses on tuber yield and quality. When potatoes are freed of potato viruses, 40–50% higher fresh weight yields of tubers and haulms and a greater number of marketable tubers per plant are produced.

The combination of meristem-tip culture with small-scale and large-scale cloning of plant material has allowed the successful integration of pathogen-tested crop lines into commercial scale production systems (see for instance Fig. 6.7). In the case of some fruit crops, particularly *Citrus* and *Prunus*, advantage has been taken of *in vitro* grafting. Grafted plants are desirable for a number of reasons, including the fact that they possess vigorous characteristics normally associated with seedlings of nucellar or zygotic origin, yet they mature and fruit sooner. Besides this, many cultivars have been commercially propagated by grafting for many years. Micrografting of virus-free shoot tips directly onto appropriate root stock seedlings *in vitro* has been found effective procedure for *Citrus* (Navarro *et al.*, 1975; Yontsey, 1978), *Prunus* (Martinez *et al.*, 1979) and apple (Huth, 1978). Little is known about the behaviour of scion and root interactions on plant size, disease and pest responses and cold-hardiness, although such matters are under investigation (Jones, 1983).

The success of meristem-tip culture can depend on many factors. One of the most important is the relative distribution of viruses in the growing tip of donor plants. Some viruses are less tenacious than others, depending on their relative rates of replication in actively growing tissues in which there is high meristematic activity. Some viruses are present in the very tip of a growing shoot. For example, PVX infections could not be totally eradicated from potato plants raised from meristems as small as 0·12 mm in length and which had only a single leaf primordium attached. An estimated 52% of the plantlets obtained from such material still contained PVX infections. Other potato viruses are less tenacious. In a group of slightly larger meristems 0·2 mm in length and containing a single leaf primordium, the regenerants were 100% free of PLRV and 70–80% free of PVA and PYV. Of these not more than 10% were free of PVX. Therefore, the type of virus infection will determine the size of meristem which must be taken before complete eradication of virus can reasonably be expected.

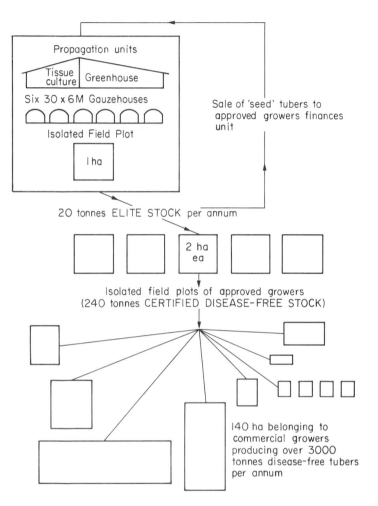

Fig. 6.7. A 'seed' tuber propagation scheme based on a nucleus of micropropagated disease-free stock held and multiplied in a tissue culture unit. Plantlets produced by the unit are hardened in a greenhouse area under mist irrigation. Tubers are then produced, either in protected gauzehouses or in isolated field plots in which plantlets or small tubers obtained from greenhouse-raised plants are used as planting material. Elite, certified stock is then released to approved growers only after strict virus-testing procedures have been carried out. The approved growers who are registered as being competent to handle important reserves of valuable planting material, produce further tubers which can then be released following certification to commercial growers. Sale of certified 'seed' tubers to approved growers can often finance a tissue culture unit and its ancillary facilities.

Germplasm storage

Plant breeding programmes rely heavily on locally adapted ancient plant varieties and their wild relatives as sources of germplasm. Until fairly recently, these varieties had been preserved either in primitive agricultural systems or in their natural habitats. Within the last 20 years it has been recognized that this supply is becoming supplanted by highly bred modern varieties that have been produced by plant breeders working in association with internationally co-ordinated programmes of agricultural improvement (Henshaw & O'Hara, 1983). With increased pressures for land use, some of the natural germplasm is being eroded away to such an extent that many authorities fear that unless some moves are made soon, potentially valuable germplasm could be irretrievably lost and future breeding programmes could suffer as a consequence (Frankel & Hawkes, 1975).

Even in view of the limitations of genetic stability and regenerative ability of plant tissue cultures, micropropagation has great value as a potential system of germplasm storage, either as sources of material for cryopreservation or as materials for maintaining for protracted periods under growth-limiting conditions.

The principles of cryopreservation were discussed in outline in the last chapter. These techniques have an obvious value in preserving valuable tissue culture materials used in plant biotechnology such as protoplasts, pollen embryos, callus and cell suspension cultures, somatic embryos and shoot-tip cultures (see Withers, 1983). For the germplasm storage of crop species, however, it would seem that shoot tips, meristems and embryos are the best types of material for cryopreserving since, after thawing, high levels of survivability and regneration can be achieved. For example, data in Table 6.4 shows levels of regeneration obtained from pea and strawberry meristems following various periods of storage in liquid nitrogen ($-196°C$). Also, these materials have the

Table 6.4. Frequency of plant regeneration from pea and strawberry meristems after various periods of storage in liquid nitrogen (after Kartha, 1982).

Storage duration (weeks)	% plant regeneration Pea	Strawberry
1	68	95
2		50
4		57
5	65	
6		64
7	63	
8		56
26	61	
52	60	
80		75

Meristems were precultured for 2 days on agar-solidified medium containing 5% DMSO to $-40°C$ and stored in liquid N_2. Thawing was carried out at 37°C for 90 seconds.

best chances of producing genetically stable regenerants, since little callus development occurs during their proliferation although there have been cases of an increased tendency for meristems to form calluses after thawing (e.g. Grout *et al.*, 1978).

There are clearly many more technical details to perfect with cryopreservation but it is proving to be a promising method for long-term storage of valuable germplasm (see Appendix 8).

Growth limitation is also proving to be a reliable and cost-effective method of maintaining stable germplasm. Using low temperatures and media containing osmotic or hormonal inhibitors under oxygen limitation, shoot-tip cultures can be maintained satisfactorily without transfer for periods of up to 1 year (Withers, 1983).

Potato shoot-tip cultures can survive passage lengths as long as 1 year (Westcott, 1981) either by adopting a regime of alternating low temperatures (12°C day, 16°C night) or by maintaining temperature at 10°C together with increasing sucrose levels in media (8% w/v). Incorporation of growth retardants like ABA or osmotic agents like mannitol in media can also have beneficial effects on reducing growth rates and increasing subculture intervals.

Seed production

For seed production from cloned parents, a major limiting factor is the high degree of genetic conservation that is required (Table 6.3). This restricts the type of micropropagation used to axillary bud multiplication which is usually at levels of less than $\times 10^3$. There are therefore a few applications which can currently be made under this category. They include the production of F_1 hybrid seed lines in crops like cauliflower, where individual parent clones can be bulked for the production of more uniform seed (Crisp & Walkey, 1974); the production of male sterile lines of onion by micropropagation to provide an alternative to difficult back-crossing methods, and the production of asparagus for producing high quality supermale and female homozygous lines, from which desirable all-male hybrids can be produced. The latter material is of high quality and produces higher yields of spears than pistillate plants (Harney, 1982).

Mass propagation

The most reliable types of micropropagation are achieved through axillary shoot proliferation. However, a much larger number of plants can be produced from a given amount of explant material within a short period of time when adventitious shoots or embryos are induced in callus or cell suspension cultures. If a large proportion of the cultured cell population is made up of totipotent cells of cell clusters, extremely

high numbers (10^5-10^6) of plants can be produced from a few 100 ml
cultures within a single culture generation. This type of mass propagation can best be achieved using liquid culture media for Stage II of
micropropagation. It has been demonstrated on both the laboratory and
commercial scales of operation for the mass propagation of ornamental
species (Fig. 6.8) and for vegetables like celery and carrot which form
somatic embryos readily in liquid culture. There are not many species
which can be induced to form somatic embryos under appropriate conditions on semi-solid media and which also respond well under the liquid
culture conditions. Therefore, the concept of producing large quantities
of plants via somatic embryogenesis on a large scale is not yet practically

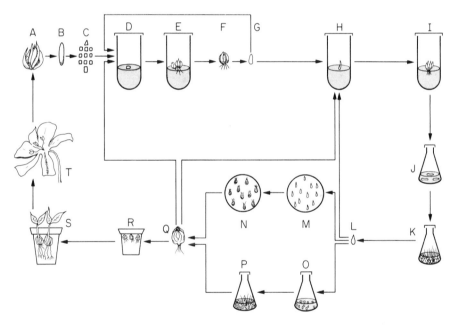

Fig. 6.8. Mass propagation of ornamentals, e.g. Lily (after Takayama & Misawa,
1982). A bulb of a mother plant grown in soil (A) is washed and surface sterilized
(B) and then subdivided into small pieces ($0.5-1$ cm^2). Each piece is then transferred into a 25×125 mm test tube containing MS agar medium containing
0.1 mg l^{-1} NAA and cultured at 25°C under 2.5 W m^{-2} of continuous irradiance. A
bulb scale (G) dissected from a minibulb produced *in vitro* (F) is then transferred to
MS agar medium containing high concentrations ($3-10$ mg l^{-1}) of cytokinin which
induces numerous primordia-like multiple adventitious bulbscales (I). These are
grown on shake culture (J,K). This leads to the production of numerous secondary
bulbscales (L) which are then used as the materials for minibulb formation on agar
(M,N) or in liquid media using a shake flask or a larger vessel (O,P). The minibulbs
produced through *in vitro* technique (Q) can be established in soil (R) and induced to
develop into normal plants (S and T). Dormancy of minibulbs is broken by low
temperature (5°C) treatment. Rapid multiplication is achieved by recycling at H, I, J,
K and L. Maintenance is best achieved by recycling at D, E, F and G. Pathological
and genotype checks can be carried out most conveniently at S and T.

feasible for those crops which would benefit most, such as plantation crops and forest trees. The moderate propagation rates achievable for some of these species by adventitious embryo and shoot formation have led to the ability to clonally propagate crops which would otherwise only be propagated by seed. This is particularly true for some of the mono-cotyledonous tropical palm crops such as coconut, oil and date palm. Embryogenic cultures have been obtained and are being used to produce 'clonal' plant material for subsequent assessment in field trials (Branton & Blake, 1983). Several large-scale clonal propagation programmes are under way in which elite specimens of these plantation crops are being micropropagated. Unilever Ltd has been undertaking the planting of cloned oil palms in Malaysia since 1977 and these plantings have now been extended to 12,000 palms from thirty clones. Assessments have yet to be completed on the range of variability in the yields of these trees (Jones, 1983). Forest trees have also been propagated traditionally by seeds. Although propagation *in vitro* from seeds and seedlings is more amenable and has certain applications mainly to increase output from species that are low in seed production, the most important application is in the mass production of elite adult trees, and this is expected to produce dramatic improvements in forest productivity (Bonga & Durzan, 1982).

In addition to the exploitation of somatic embryogenesis as a means of producing large numbers of cloned plants, there are several other areas of potentially useful mass propagation methods using micropropagation. These include the induction of minitubers and other dormant propagules in multiple shoot cultures. For instance, axillary shoot cultures of potato in the presence of suitable levels of cytokinin and GA form small tubers (or minitubers) in quite large numbers (Hussey, 1983). This makes convenient and easily transportable material and in some cases might lend itself to mechanization in the field establishment phases of propagation of seed stocks. Similar minitubers may be produced by tropical tuber crops like *Dioscorea alata* (White Lisbon yam) when grown in culture and could form the basis of very efficient multiplication and tuber bulking programmes since they would be planted directly into the field and their use would avoid some of the rotting problems associated with field planting of small tuber setts. Table 6.5 illustrates the potential propagation levels achievable through use of minitubers as against those already achieved by conventional sett propagation methods.

Also of potential at some stage in the future is the use of embryoids produced either through somatic embryogenesis, pollen embryogenesis or secondary embryogenesis for sowing directly in the field by fluid drilling. Encapsulation of somatic or haploid embryoids at a suitable stage of development (globular, torpedo or cotyledon stages) protected by gels or other suitable matrices, which prevent premature desiccation

Table 6.5. Production of tubers from a 100 g tuber by traditional and tissue culture methods of propagation over two growing seasons.

	Traditional	Micropropagation	
Year 1	100 g tuber ↓ One mature plant	100 g tuber ↓ One preconditioned plant* ↓ 10 nodal cultures ↓	
	1600 g tubers ↓	Shoot multiplication ↓	
	--------------------	650,000 minitubers	Dormant
Year 2	16 mature plants ↓	617,500 plants* ↓	Season
	16 × 600 g tubers = 25·6 kg	617,500 × 500 mg tubers = 308.7 kg	

* Grown under 16-h photoperiod for 12 weeks (Mantell *et al.*, 1978).
† Assuming 5% losses on establishment in soil.

of embryoids and which also contain growth regulatory compounds to control development of the encapsulated embryoids, is being sought. Suitable encapsulation matrices include those in which gels are mixed with peat. It is likely that satisfactory encapsulation of mass-produced embryoid materials for direct drilling will become a feasible method of large-scale clonal planting or as a method for field planting of haploid materials to use directly in field selection trials carried out under specialized cropping or environmental stress conditions.

Further reading

Bonga J.M. & Durzan D.J. (1982) (Eds) *Tissue Culture in Forestry*. Nijhoff/Junk, The Hague.

Hartmann H.T. & Kester D.E. (1983) *Plant Propagation Principles and Practices*, 4th edn. Prentice Hall, Englewood Cliffs.

Vasil I.K. & Vasil V. (1980) Clonal propagation. In *Perspectives in Plant Cell and Tissue Culture*. Int. Rev. Cytol. Suppl. 11A, (Ed. I.K. Vasil) pp. 145–174, Academic Press, New York.

7 Crop Breeding

Conventional types of plant breeding have had remarkable success this century in improving the yield and quality traits of a wide range of crops (Bingham, 1981). Most notable of these have been cereal and tuber crops in which about half of the increases in yields can be attributed to positive breeding and selection of lines that are resistant to pests and diseases and that are also tolerant of many stressful environmental conditions. The remainder of these increases is attributable to general improvements in agronomic practices and in the more widespread use of sophisticated agrochemicals. Continual need for satisfying food demands and for developing crop plants which can make best use of changing environments necessitates the further improvement of breeding techniques and crop lines.

Scope and applications of *in vitro* technologies to breeding

It is often desirable to make sexual crosses between wild or crop species that are sexually incompatible: in these cases, crosses are not possible and germplasm flow is impeded. Certain *in vitro* techniques now provide solutions to such problems and allow rapid generation of many useful plant types which would normally be obtained only after many years of intensive breeding cycles. The alternatives include certain parasexual methods by which genetic transformations are achieved and by which mutants are obtained using tissue culture selection procedures (somatic cell genetics). In addition, new alternatives are being developed. These include the production of completely novel types of variants as a consequence of tissue culture (variations collectively referred to as somaclonal variation) and the exciting prospect that defined plant genes might be transferred from one plant to another by means of gene vectors (see Chapter 4). In addition, tissue culture methods provide a means of controlled fertilization and recovery of plants from fertilized ovules and developing embryos which would otherwise not have developed due to various incompatability mechanisms; these operate in certain combinations of sexual partners in crosses between certain species and genera. Furthermore, tissue culture methods enable some valuable types of breeding materials, e.g. haploids, aneuploids and polyploids, to be generated in extremely short periods of time and in some cases with minimal effort. It is important to realize that some of these methods are finding practical use already (such as in the breeding of rice, barley and tobacco through large-scale application of anther and/or pollen culture techniques) whilst others, particularly single gene transfers, have been demonstrated in only experimental systems and therefore will not be exploited at the practical level for several years to come. Attempts to establish genetic engineering as a practical facet of plant breeding are also complicated by the fact that the majority of genes which encode for some of the more important phenotypes in crop plants have not as yet even been identified and characterized themselves. Some of the practical applications of single gene transfer technology in crop plants and the isolation and characterization of genes responsible for valuable traits are discussed later in this chapter; they relate to such diverse areas as improvement of plant nutritional quality, decreased need for nitrogen fertilizers and the continuing requirements for increased resistance to environmental stresses and pathogens. Before this is done, however, examples of technologies which are of more immediate application to breeding are discussed.

Somatic hybridization

Plant protoplasts isolated according to the techniques described in Chapter 5 can be induced to fuse with each other by various methods. The non-specific fusion of protoplasts from the same or different species of plant can be achieved using the following two methods:

By use of chemical fusogens. Protoplasts with similar osmotic properties can be fused in the presence of salts like sodium nitrate. This fusogen produces at best 25% fusions (Vasil, 1976) while others like high molecular weight polyvinyl alcohol, dextran, poly-L-ornithine or polyethylene glycol (PEG) in the presence of high Ca^{++} and high pH (8−10) induce a wide range of levels of fusion. These levels can vary from 1 to 100% depending on the operator and the materials used. Fusion of protoplasts occurs upon dilution of the fusogens from the medium (Kao & Michayluk, 1974) as represented in Fig. 7.1.

By electrical depolarization (electro-fusion). Surface charges on plasmalemma membranes of protoplasts are altered with short pulses of direct current which, unlike chemical fusogens, have relatively little effect on protoplast viability. This method has now been demonstrated to give high frequencies of fusions generally in the region of 50–100% (Zimmerman & Scheurich, 1981; Vienken *et al.*, 1983; Jacob *et al.*, 1983).

Upon fusion of protoplasts, there is a coalescence of the cytoplasm. The course of development and hybridization which follows may vary with the protoplast materials being fused and the application of treatments such as irradiation prior to fusion. Figure 7.2 summarizes the various products which may result as a consequence to protoplast and nuclear fusions.

Somatic hybridization has important potential in the following areas.
(a) Production of fertile amphidiploid somatic hybrids of sexually incompatible species.
(b) Production of heterozygous lines within a single species which normally could only be propagated by vegetative means, e.g. potato and other tuber and root crops.
(c) Transfer of limited parts of the genome from one species to another

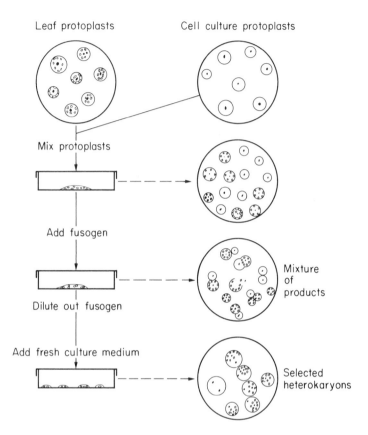

Leaf protoplasts   Cell culture protoplasts

Mix protoplasts

Add fusogen

Dilute out fusogen

Add fresh culture medium

Mixture
of
products

Selected
heterokaryons

Fig. 7.1. The basic protocol for achieving protoplast fusions through the use of chemical fusogens.

by the formation of heterokaryons in which unidirectional sorting of cytoplasmic elements occurs. This enables hybrids with a mixed nuclear component to be obtained against a common cytoplasmic background. Conversely, the irradiation (X-rays at 20–100 Krads) of one of the partners enables the selective loss of one nuclear genome and the combination of single nuclear genomes against a segregated cytoplasmic background as in cybrid formation (Fig. 7.2).

(d) Production of novel interspecific and intergeneric crosses between plants that are difficult or impossible to hybridize conventionally, e.g. fusions between protoplasts of *Lycopersicon esculentum* (tomato) and *Solanum tuberosum* (potato) created the 'pomato' first achieved by Melchers *et al.* (1978). Many others have followed, e.g. fusions between protoplasts of *Datura innoxia* and and *Atropa belladonna* (Krumbiegel & Schieder, 1979), *Arabidopsis thaliana* and *Brassica campestris* (Gleba & Hoffman, 1979) and *Petunia parodii* and *P. parviflora* (Power *et al.*, 1980). There are limitations, however, to these types of somatic

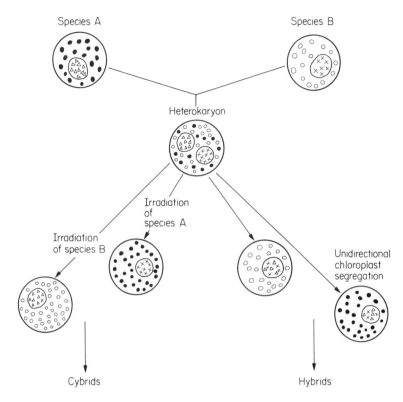

Fig. 7.2. The various combinations of cell products which can be obtained through protoplast fusions (after Cocking, 1981) particularly as far as the segregations of nuclear and chloroplast genomes are concerned.

hybridizations since plants regenerated from some combinations are not always fertile and do not produce viable seed. Experience now indicates that the main opportunities for use of somatic hybridization is likely to be more successful if centred around hybridization within the same genus or between closely related genera (Shepard *et al.*, 1983).

Obviously, within a population of fusing protoplasts there will exist many combinations of products. There are several ways of selecting out the desired products of protoplast fusion. One of the most direct methods is by visual selection. Colourless protoplasts obtained from cells grown in cell suspension cultures, from albino donor plants or from leaves of plants previously treated with certain herbicides can be fused with green mesophyll protoplasts and the white/green fusion products readily identified and then isolated using micromanipulation techniques. Somatic hybrids of *Glycine max* × *Nicotiana glauca*, *Arabidopsis thaliana* × *Brassica campestris* and *N. knightiana* × *N. sylvestris* have been produced in this way. Another successful method of direct visible selection is based on the use of specific non-toxic fluorescent markers

(Patnaik *et al.,* 1981) in which one of the fusion partners can be tagged prior to fusion. The alternative to the use of these visible selection techniques is the use of specific auxotrophic or autotrophic mutants which confer certain predictable characteristics on complemented fusion partners. These biochemical complementation/selection methods tend, however, to lead to the preferential recovery of amphidiploid somatic hybrids to the possible exclusion of other potentially valuable plant types. Cocking *et al.* (1981) have pointed out that plant hybrids such as those possessing one complete genome with only a few chromosomes of the other parent are most likely lost during the process of selection, since they are either slower growing or are not able to survive the strong selection conditions invariably used. Availability of nitrate-reductase-deficient (NR^-) lines of true haploids of *Nicotiana* lines and of *Hyoscyamus*, the protoplasts of which are capable of regeneration (e.g. Pental *et al.*, 1982 and Lazar *et al.*, 1983, respectively) has facilitated the recovery of so-called complementation hybrids occurring at very low frequencies. Nitrate reductase is the key enzyme in the reduction of NO_3^- to NO_2^- and then NH_4^+. Because NR^- cells are unable to utilize NO_3^- as a sole nitrogen source, their growth is dependent on the availability in the medium of amino acids or urea as a nitrogen source. Partial or full NR^- mutants can be isolated by plating wild type cells on media containing toxic levels of chlorate (an analogue of NO_3^-) as for example those used by Marton *et al.* (1982) for *N. plumbaginifolia*. Resistant cells are NR^- to various degrees. In so-called *cnx* lines, nitrate reductase activity is thought to be impaired in the synthesis of the molybdenum co-factor necessary for NR activity while in others known as *nia* lines, deficiency in nitrate reductase enzyme results from defects in the NR apoprotein. In mixed extracts of fully deficient *cnx* and *nia* lines, NR activity can be detected. Also, fusion of protoplasts of *cnx* and *nia* lines restores NR activity so that these hybrids can grow in the presence of NO_3^- as sole nitrogen source and can regenerate normal plants. Other complementation selection systems have been successfully used such as those which confer antibiotic (e.g. methotrexate or chloramphenicol) resistance on susceptible wild type cells and those which restore photoautotrophy to an albino mutant with defective plastids as, for example, those described for *Nicotiana* (Glimelius & Bonnett, 1981) and for *N. plumbaginifolia* (Sidorov & Maliga, 1982).

The transfer of limited parts of a genome between two different cell populations by somatic hybridization is of broad significance to plant breeding, particularly with reference to the transfer of cytoplasmic genomic components. The cytoplasmic genomes are important determinants of yield in crops such as hexaploid triticale (wheat × rye hybrids). However, while it is relatively simple to bring together two plastid genotypes in a common cytoplasm by protoplast fusion, it has been frequently difficult to keep them together especially through meiosis (McKenzie, 1979). The use of restriction enzyme fragment 'finger printing' has shown that somatic segregation generally occurs following somatic hybridization so that just one species type of chloroplast DNA remains in a protoplast hybrid between two sexually compatible *Nicotiana* species (Belliard *et al.*, 1978). Therefore, opportunities for increasing cytoplasmic variability by protoplast fusions appear to be greater with mitochondria than with chloroplasts (e.g. Galun *et al.*, 1982). Belliard *et al.* (1979) have obtained evidence to indicate that mitochondrial recombination occurs in cytoplasmic hybrids of *N. tabacum* by protoplast fusion, and that the mt DNAs present in the cybrids were different from those in the parents and from the expected mixture of the two. An important phenotype under cytoplasmic control and which is of immediate breeding and agronomic interest is cytoplasmic male sterility (see Chapter 4). Transfer of CMS from *N. tabacum* to *N. sylvestris* by protoplast fusion was first reported by Zelcer *et al.* (1978). By irradiating *N. tabacum* protoplasts with X-rays, functional nuclei were eliminated and CMS-controlling elements transferred following somatic fusion and integration and recombination of mt DNA from both parents. Figure 7.3 illustrates the CMS phenotype which is now proving a most useful phenotypic marker in combination with herbicide and antibiotic resistance marker systems (see later). An alternative method to X-ray irradiation for elimination of the nuclear component of one of the partners in somatic fusion is by the production of enucleate microplasts (see Chapter 5). This avoids irradiation treatments which are relatively non-specific and which could possibly also be causing undetected changes in the cytoplasmic genomes.

Resistance of plants to the herbicide, atrazine has been reported to have been transferred from bird's rape (*Brassica campestris*) to cultivated oilseed rape (*B. napus*) via fractionated protoplast (i.e. subprotoplast) fusions (Beversdorf *et al.*, 1980). Herbicide resistance of this type is maternally inherited since the genes responsible for resistance are located in the chloroplast genome. Since conventional sexual hybrids contain and express only maternally-derived cytoplasmic genes, the value of protoplast fusions for transfer of cytoplasmic inherited genes of both parents is of major significance to crop breeding; opportunities are created to generate completely novel types of cytoplasmic mixtures not previously available through conventional sexual crosses.

The role of these types of protoplast technology in specific gene transfer using alternative gene vector systems requires emphasis here, particularly since it is techniques of protoplast fusion which now permit the controlled transfer and uptake of foreign DNA encapsulated in either liposomes, microplasts or microcell vehicles through a combination of the techniques elaborated upon in Chapter 4 and in this chapter.

Fig. 7.3. Normal (a) and cytoplasmic male sterile (b) forms of *Nicotiana tabacum cv*. Smyrna flowers.

Cell mutants of value to crop improvement

In a breeding context, mutation is a permanent, hereditable change in the primary structure of the genetic material making up the total genome of a cell or a plant. These alterations include the deletion or addition of DNA material or the rearrangement of chromosomes by means of inversion or translocation of DNA. A change in the primary structure of DNA may result in an altered phenotype called the mutation phenotype and this has four characteristics:

(a) it remains stable through consecutive cell generations;

Table 7.1. Examples of mutations recovered from cell cultures (after Henke, 1981).

Plant species	Variant phenotype resistant to:	Inheritance pattern
Tobacco	Methionine sulphoximine	Semidominant, two recessive loci with additive effects
	Streptomycin	Uniparental
	5-Bromodeoxyuridine	Semidominant
	Valine	Dominant, semidominant
	Chlorate	Recessive
	Picloram (herbicide)	Dominant and semidominant
	Carboxin	Dominant
	Isonicotinic acid hydrazide	Dominant
Corn	*Helminthosporium* toxin	Maternal
	Lysine + threonine	Dominant
Rice	S-(2-aminoethyl)-cysteine	Dominant

Table 7.2. Mutagenesis treatments applied to cell cultures and the recovery of spontaneous and induced mutants (after Maliga, 1980).

Species	Mutagenic treatment	Cell survival (%)	Phenotype selected	Frequency Spontaneous	Induced
Suspension cultures					
Carrot	EMS (2·5%, 2 h)[*]	10	Cycloheximide Res.	$5·4 \times 10^{-8}$	$7·7 \times 10^{-7}$
	NG (100 µg ml^{-1}, 14 h)	1	Cycloheximide Res.	$5·4 \times 10^{-8}$	$4·4 \times 10^{-6}$
Tobacco	NEU (25 mM, until decay)	—	Chlorate Res.	$6·6 \times 10^{-8}$	2×10^{-7}
Protoplasts					
Datura	X-rays (1000 R)	50	Altered pigments	10^{-5}	4×10^{-4}
	NG (10 µg ml^{-1}, 0·5 h)	50	Altered pigments	10^{-5}	2×10^{-4}
Tobacco	UV (1000 erg mm^{-2})	40−60	Valine Res.	$2·2 \times 10^{-6}$	$1·4 \times 10^{-5}$

[*] See Glossary.

(b) it occurs at relatively low frequency, i.e. 10^{-6} to 10^{-10}, the levels of which can be raised by mutagenesis;

(c) it should where possible be correlated with specific gene products and, most importantly,

(d) it should be transmitted in sexual crosses.

As described in Chapter 5, plant protoplasts and cells of many species can be plated in much the same way as microbes. It has been found possible, therefore, to mutagenize groups of protoplasts or single cells suitably dispersed in appropriate semi-solid media and then to recover cell lines and to regenerate plants from these cells which express particular mutant phenotypes (Table 7.1). Figure 7.4 illustrates the basic

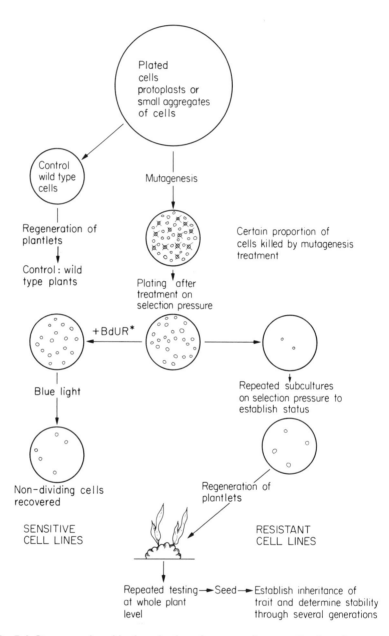

Fig. 7.4. Stages employed in the selection of a mutant from a cell culture line.
*5-Bromodeoxyuridine is an analogue of thymine. Dividing cells incorporate the
analogue in their DNA and these cells are killed on subsequent exposure to
fluorescent light. Non-dividing (sensitive) cells survive and can be rescued.

protocol used in the development of plant cell mutants and Table 7.2
lists examples of the types of mutagens used to raise the frequency of
mutations and thus the number of mutants recovered from cultured

cells. Single cell and protoplast culture systems have proved to be valuable for mutagenesis, since the presence of discrete cells in these avoids the development of excessive numbers of chimeral mixtures of cells that are often obtained when multicellular tissues or organs are exposed to mutagens. Protoplasts are particularly suitable in this regard since they have less tendency to form aggregates; complications of chimeral formations and of possible cross-feeding can thus be avoided. This does not preclude the use of complex tissues, however, to recover plant mutants since some of these approaches have yielded potentially useful agronomically important traits. For example, immature or mature embryos of cereals (in which recalcitrance is a major consideration) have proved useful starting materials from which to obtain herbicide and pathotoxin-resistant mutants (Gengenbach et al., 1977; Brettell et al., 1980) and amino acid accumulators (Hibberd et al., 1980; Henke, 1981; Bright et al., 1983). The latter mutants are resistant to amino acid analogues such as S-(2-aminoethyl)-cysteine (AEC), an analogue of lysine. In the case of those crops where seed is readily available and is of a convenient size (i.e. a kilo contains $> 10^5$ seeds), mutagenesis with sodium azide or ethylmethanesulphonate (EMS) treatments, followed by screening in the presence of defined selection pressures can provide sufficiently adequate means for obtaining useful traits for direct use in any breeding programme. However, these types of mutant selection and screening protocols require a great deal of space and labour to achieve. Cell cultures have a distinct advantage in that many thousands of cells within a few cultures can be exposed uniformly to a selection pressure, either incorporated in the medium or imposed on the culture externally, and many putative mutants quickly and efficiently recovered. Provided cultures can be induced to express morphogenesis and can produce regenerants which can flower and set seed, the inheritance of characterized materials can be tested. One important limitation to remember though, is that phenotypes such as resistance to physiological stresses imposed by high salt (NaCl), heavy metals, high osmotica, specific pathotoxins of fungal or bacterial pathogens and high and low temperature may be expressed at the cellular level while not necessarily being expressed at the whole plant level. In all cases, therefore, putative mutants which are identified in cell cultures need further testing at the regenerated plant level and, what is more, extensive work is then needed to clarify the genetic bases for the selected traits. Yet tissue culture materials possess so many potential advantages that these far outweigh the limitations mentioned. Since some of the agronomically important traits can be recessive in character, it is generally considered best to recover mutants from haploid materials because these will contain single gene complements. Tissue culture technique provides an extremely versatile way of providing these materials through pollen and anther culture (see Chapter 5). Use of haploid cell cultures has led to the recovery of several useful auxotrophs (mutants requiring specific compounds for their growth) and other potentially useful mutants for fundamental biochemical studies (Maliga *et al.*, 1982). The isolation of auxotrophic plant cell lines is now playing a significant role in successful selection of somatic hybrids (e.g. Lazar *et al.*, 1983; Evola *et al.*, 1983) and both herbicide and antibiotic resistance traits are used for this purpose. From the agronomic point of view, cell cultures have been used successfully to obtain plants of many crop species, e.g. alfalfa, rice, tobacco and pepper, with tolerance to excessively high salinity conditions which occur in both arid and maritime situations. Nabors *et al.* (1980) have shown that tobacco plants regenerated from salt-tolerant tobacco cells had a higher survival rate in the presence of salt. Although these plants were shown to transmit tolerance to subsequent seed generations, it has been suggested by these workers and others (e.g. Croughan *et al.*, 1981) that perhaps this tolerance may not be due to genetic changes but due rather to physiological changes connected with ionic transport mechanisms. Whichever the case, the materials generated have important uses in agriculture. Other types of resistance such as those to heavy salts, e.g. aluminium, and to toxic substances like $HgCl_2$ have been successfully selected for in cell cultures of tomato and petunia and this augers well for the possibility of developing crops for growing in areas in which heavy salts and environmental pollutants are particular problems.

Somaclonal variation

Somaclonal variation is a term coined by Larkin & Scowcroft (1981) to cover all those types of variations which occur in plants regenerated from cultured cells or tissues. This variation has already been exploited to great advantage in such crops as sugar-cane, tobacco, potato, rice, maize and *Pelargonium*. In sugar-cane, for example, calliclones from tissue cultures produce plant lines which differ significantly in their response to Fiji disease (caused by a leaf hopper-transmitted virus), downy mildew and *Helminthosporium sacchari*. This wide variation in disease response also includes classes of plant which are highly tolerant and in some cases resistant to these particular diseases (Heinz *et al.*, 1977). Use of a special bioassay similar to one developed to quantify the sensitivity of leaves to fungal toxins administered at a standardized concentration known to induce leaf damage, enabled a large number of somaclones of Australian varieties of sugar-cane to be screened. Many of these somaclones proved to be resistant or essentially immune to the effects of the toxin. But most importantly, the resistant somaclones retained their resistance through subsequent cane generations although there were some individual plants which transgressed toward susceptibility in some later generation somaclones (Scowcroft & Larkin, 1982).

Similar beneficial selections have been obtained concurrently in sugar callus cloning work carried out in Taiwan. The independent nature of these results indicates that cell culture should now become an integral part of sugar-cane improvement programmes. Not only is tissue culture cloning of value to improving sugar yields, therefore, but it may also produce novel types of sugar-cane, especially useful for animal feedstock or for substrates in alcohol fermentations (see Chapter 8). In other crops like tobacco, somaclonal variation in pollen and protoplast-derived plants is providing extended opportunities for breeders of air-cured, flue-cured and burley types of tobacco, since any sources of variation in such highly inbred crops are welcomed as avenues through which improved varieties can be developed. Dihaploids of all three types of tobacco derived from anther culture display extensive variations in leaf yield, days to flowering, plant height, leaf number, leaf length, leaf width, total alkaloids and reducing sugar content. An example of somaclonal variation in this crop can be seen in the leaf-shape and plant-height phenotypes displayed in *N. tabacum* cv. Smyrna plants regenerated from protoclones obtained from protoplasts of a single dihaploid leaf (Fig. 7.5). In the case of potato, Shepard *et al.* (1980) screened over 1,000 protoclones produced from leaf protoplasts of the established variety Russet Burbank and found significant yet quite stable variation in compactness of growth habit, maturity date, tuber uniformity, tuber skin colour, photoperiod requirements and fruit production. Some of these characteristics, e.g. greater tuber uniformity and early onset of tuberization, were far better than in the parent variety itself. Of even greater significance is the fact that some protoclones were recovered that were more resistant to early blight (caused by *Alternaria solani*) and that this phenotype was retained through several vegetative generations. Examples of these types of extremely valuable somaclonal variation can be found in an increasing number of crops extending through fruit, tuber, ornamental, forage and cereal crops (Table 7.3).

Several mechanisms may be responsible for induction of somaclonal variation. These include the gross karyotypic changes which accompany *in vitro* culture via calluses as previously discussed in Chapter 5, cryptic chromosomal rearrangements, somatic crossing-over with sister chromatid exchange, transposable elements, gene amplification or diminution or perhaps various combinations of these processes. Different types of cryptic chromosomal arrangements are well described aspects of the meiotic behaviour of chromosomes in plants regenerated from cell cultures. They include reciprocal locations, deletions, inversions, non-homologous translocations and acentric and centric fragment formations. Such rearrangements probably cause losses of genetic material or at the very least realignment and transportation of chromosomal material. This can lead to expression of previously silent genes, especially where loss or switching off of a dominant allele has

Fig. 7.5. Plants (top) regenerated from protoclones (middle) derived from protoplasts obtained from a single leaf of *N. tabacum* cv. Smyrna. Wide ranges of somaclonal variation are often exhibited in plant height, plant form, the earliness in flowering and the shape of leaves (top and bottom) in plants regenerated from these types of calluses.

Table 7.3. Examples of somaclonal variation in crop species (after Scowcroft & Larkin, 1982).

Species	Somaclonal variant characters
Oats	Plant height, heading date, leaf striping, twin culms, awn morphology, heteromorphic bivalents, ring chromosomes
Maize	Pollen fertility
Barley	Plant height, tillering, fertility
Sorghum	Fertility, leaf morphology, growth habit
Onion	Bulb size and shape, clove no., aerial bulbil germination
Rape	Flowering time, glucosinolate content, growth habit
Lettuce	Leaf weight, length, width, flatness and colour, bud number
Pelargonium	Leaf shape, size and form, flower morphology, plant height, fasciation, pubescence, anthocyanin pigmentation, essential oil composition

occurred. The tissue culture environment may enhance the frequency of somatic crossing-over, and if a proportion of such exchanges were asymmetric or between non-homologous chromosomes then genetic variants could be generated as a consequence. It is known that the frequency of sister chromatid exchange in plants is quite high (*c.* 20% per cell division has been observed in barley). Transposable elements (see Chapters 2 and 4) may be responsible for certain types of genetic instability in cell cultures and it may well be that such elements contribute significantly to somaclonal variation. As described in Chapter 2, plant cells like those of other eukaryotes can increase or decrease the quantity of a specific gene product by differential gene amplification or diminution, respectively. For instance, ribosomal RNA gene amplification and diminution are now known to be widespread in wheat, rye and tobacco and in flax, ribosomal DNA is known to alter directly in response to environmental and cultural pressures (Cullis & Goldsborough, 1980).

In vitro *fertilization and embryo rescue*

Various methods of mechanical pollination have traditionally been used in crop breeding. These can circumvent natural incompatability mechanisms often associated with (i) the differential timing of pollen and ovule development within single flowers or within flowers on a single plant, or (ii) the occurrence of the dioecious habit in certain species. In some cases, however, application of pollen to stigmas *in vivo* is not always effective at bringing about desired fertilization events due to incompatability mechanisms present in the pistil and/or the stigma which effect pollen tube development or induce abortion of the fertilized egg and/or young embryo. In these cases, ovules can be cultured *in vitro* and fertilized *in vitro* and this measure has been found to be effective for interspecific crosses, e.g. those of corn (*Zea mays* × *Z. mexicana*). Styles of individual ovules are removed to expose a section of each ovule and the application of pollen onto the exposed surface leads to successful fertilization and seed development (Dhaliwal & King, 1978). By far the most commonly used technique of *in vitro* fertilization in interspecific crosses is the culture of pistils with part or all of the ovary wall removed. Pollen is placed on the exposed placenta or on the ovules themselves (Stewart, 1981). Table 7.4 shows some examples of success- ful seed production from wide crosses made with the aid of *in vitro* pollination and fertilization techniques.

In some cases, fertilization occurs in wide crosses but embryos abort early on in their development. This is due to various factors. A major one is failure of the endosperm to develop properly due to suppression of its nutrient supply. By aseptically removing immature embryos and placing these on suitable culture media, plants can be recovered for breeding purposes. Successful recovery has been reported from inter- specific hybrids in cotton, barley, tomato, rice and jute, and from intergeneric hybrids of *Hordeum* × *Secale* (Barley × Rye), *Hordeum* × *Hordelymus*, *Triticum* × *Secale* and *Tripsacum* × *Zea* (Raghavan, 1977). In these crosses, progeny were obtained with desirable traits of pest and disease resistance and tolerance to extreme environmental conditions. *In vitro* embryo culture also has application in the recovery of embryos from species in which self-sterility mechanisms operate (Table 7.5). Some tropical species, e.g. *Musa bulbisiana* (wild banana) and *Colocasia*, produce seed but this has proved impossible to ger- minate and so utilize progeny for breeding purposes. Removal of embryos from these seeds and their culture *in vitro* now allows recovery of plants from seed of these species.

Production of useful breeding materials

Haploid plant production using pollen and anther culture techniques is an obvious benefit derived from tissue culture application and has been dealt with at great length in recent reviews by Chu (1982) and Collins & Genovesi (1982). In the breeding context, haploids are most useful as sources of homozygous lines. By conventional inbreeding and back- crossing over at least five generations, pure breeding lines can be obtained through a so-called pedigree method. Now, by tissue culture, haploids can be produced in a matter of months in large amounts and haploid chromosome complements of the haploids produced doubled (using colchicine or other chemical treatments) to generate the homozygous lines necessary for breeding. There are obvious advantages with the *in vitro* approach but also some reservations, e.g. (i) the high

Table 7.4. Examples of species in which seed was obtained from ovules pollinated and fertilized by *in vitro* techniques.

Family	Species	Pollination method	Result
Amaryllidaceae	*Narcissus pseudonarcissus*	Pollen placed on ovules and placenta *in vitro*	Some mature seed
Cruciferae	*Brassica oleracea*	Pollen placed on gelatin film near ovules treated with CaCl₂	3% mature seed develop
Gramineae	*Zea mays*	Stigmatic pollination of caryopses on cultured sections of scope	0·5% development to mature seed
Liliaceae	*Tulipa gesneriana*	Pollen placed on cultured ovules with placenta	Occasional mature seed
Papaveraceae	*Papaver somniferum*	Pollen placed on cultured ovules with placenta	Seed produced
Scrophulariaceae	*Antirrhinum majus*	Stigmatic pollination of cultured complete pistil	Mature, viable seed
Solanaceae	*Nicotiana tabacum*	Pollen placed on cultured ovules with placenta	Mature seed
	Petunia hybrida	Pollen placed on cultured ovules with placenta	Mature seed

level of management and expertise required to operate the tissue culture production of haploids, (ii) the relatively high incidence of albinoism in some types of anther and pollen cultures (particularly of the cereals) and, most importantly, (iii) the lack of selection of traits during the derivation of haploid material. In the pedigree method, selection of elite traits is possible at each stage of the backcrossing and inbreeding procedures. An alternative to both these methods of haploid production in cereals and in some other crops like tobacco is the

Table 7.5. Examples of interspecific crosses of forage legumes in which *in vitro* embryo culture has proven an effective method for obtaining progeny.

Crosses achieved	Phenotypes required
Trifolium ambiguum (4n) × *T. repens*	Virus resistance and vigour of stoloniferous habit
T. ambiguum (4n) × *T. hybridum* (2n	Virus resistance and spreading habit
T. repens × *T. uniflorum*	Deeper rooting habit and resistance to root-chewing insects
Lotus pedunculatus × *L. corniculatus*	Tolerance to soils of low fertility and acid soils. Increase foliar tannins to prevent bloat in grazing animals
Ornithopus sativus × *0. compressus*	Consistency under heavy grazing
O. pinnatus × *O. sativus*	Increase foliar tannins and high productivity

exploitation of chromosome elimination. Barley (*Hordeum vulgare*) is an open pollinator and a related species, *H. bulbosum* can readily be used to pollinate and induce fertilization in crosses with it. By means of an obscure mechanism, chromosome elimination occurs in the *H. bulbosum* complement with the result that haploid embryos of *H. vulgare* are produced. Normally, such embryos would not develop further, but by using the embryo culture methods described in the last section, embryos can be rescued and allowed to form haploid plants (Fig. 7.6). This forms the basis of a method for producing stable haploids of barley, thus providing an alternative to haploid production from haploid calluses derived from cultured anthers. Similarly, crosses between *Nicotiana tabacum* and *N. africana*, *Solanum tuberosum* and *S.*

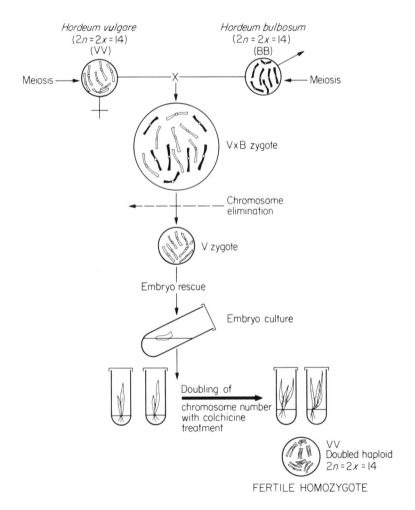

Fig. 7.6. The production of haploid barley by crossing maternal *Hordeum bulbosum* with other species of barley.

phurjea, Medicago sativa and *M. falcata* and *Triticum aestivum* cv. Salmon and *Aegilops* are also ways of inducing haploids in the former species by chromosome elimination procedures.

Flower induction *in vitro* through culture of thin cell layers of epidermal tissues excised from flowering stems, appears to be a promising method for chromosome reduction in some amphidiploid species like tobacco and potato. Thin cell layers cultured from dihaploid plants under appropriate conditions produce flowers *in vitro* (Fig. 7.7). These

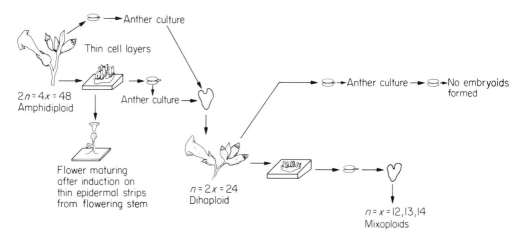

Fig. 7.7. A comparison of the types of dihaploid and mixoploid materials which can be obtained from neoformed flower structures produced on thin cell layers of tobacco with those which can be obtained from conventional flowers (after Tran Thanh Van, 1977).

contain anthers which produce pollen that can be induced to form embryos and mixoploid plants. Tobacco plants produced contain chromosome numbers of between 3 and 24, the majority containing 12, 13 and 14 chromosomes per cell (Tran Thanh Van, 1977). This technique has significance since flowers borne on dihaploid tobacco normally do not produce viable pollen, let alone material which can be induced to form embryoids and plants. A satisfactory explanation for the success of neoformed flower material and not of *in vivo* flowers can not yet be given.

Potential applications of recombinant DNA technology to breeding

The basis of crop breeding is the transfer of genetic information between plants in order to develop desired phenotypes. Recombinant DNA technology allows directed and highly specific manipulation of the genetic material. Once applied and developed to a sufficient degree, it promises ulimately to provide a powerful additional tool to the plant breeders. Above all, the technology broadens the possibilities of transferring genes between unrelated organisms, and creating novel genetic information by the specific alteration of cloned genes. It must be emphasized, however, that recombinant DNA technology has not yet been perfected to a sufficient level to allow it to be used routinely as a tool in plant breeding, but it is likely to become so within the next few decades. The types of breeding situation in which recombinant DNA could be of most value are those involving transfer of a single or small group of genes from one organism to an unrelated organism, where such transfer cannot be achieved by conventional means. A wide range of such situations can be envisaged in plant breeding; a few examples are presented here.

Development of disease-resistant varieties

Substantial crop losses occur each year due to attacks by insect pests or microbial pathogens. The former are largely controlled by spraying crops with large quantities of agrochemicals, which is not only expensive but can also have detrimental effects on ecosystems. For example, the build up of insecticides in animals higher up the food chain is one aspect of topical concern. Many cultivars of crop species already exhibit resistance to pests and diseases to some extent, but there would obviously be a good market for cultivars resistant to a wider range.

With regard to resistance to *Lepidoptera* infestation, transfer of a microbial gene to crop plants may be of particular significance. *Bacillus thuringiensis* contains a glycoprotein which is particularly toxic to *Lepidoptera*. In its native state, this glycoprotein exists as a crystalline protoxin of 134,000 molecular weight which is solubilized and activated following ingestion by a susceptible insect. The protein is stable for many months at room temperature. The gene encoding this polypeptide has been cloned and partially characterized (Miller *et al.*, 1983), and is a candidate for transferring to plants. Its insertion in, for example, brassicas could dramatically reduce the build-up of high populations of caterpillars (e.g. cabbage white butterfly) on these crops. Before producing such plants, it would be important to ensure that the *B. thuringiensis* polypeptide is not also toxic to the final consumers, when encoded against a brassica genomic background.

Cloning of plant genes responsible for pest and disease resistance will firstly help in elucidating some of the biological mechanisms of resistance, which at the moment are poorly understood, particularly with regard to those operating at the molecular level. Transfer of specific genes from one species to another may be of great value in exploiting resistance mechanisms more fully.

Development of increased photosynthetic efficiency in crop plants

The most important process carried out by plants is photosynthesis, as this is the major mechanism available for capturing the sun's energy within the biosphere. However, even the most efficient of crop plants can only utilize about 3−4% of full sunlight. Is there any way of improving this level of photosynthetic efficiency, in order to increase biomass and crop yields? The first enzyme in carbon fixation, ribulose bisphosphate carboxylase (RuBPCase), is an extremely inefficient catalyst. Under certain environmental conditions it also catalyses a competing reaction, i.e. the addition of oxygen to ribulose bisphosphate. This latter reaction is the first in the pathway known as photorespiration, in which CO_2 and ammonia are liberated. Photorespiration therefore reduces the effective levels of photosynthetic efficiency. Some important crop species, known as 'C$_4$-plants' (e.g. maize), have a natural mechanism for overcoming this competing reaction by maintaining high carbon dioxide and low oxygen levels at the site of carbon fixation. Carbon dioxide can then compete effectively for RuBPCase; unfortunately, most temperate crops do not exhibit this phenomenon. Many workers have suggested that it may be possible to engineer RuBPCase, by recombinant DNA technology, to improve the efficiency of catalysis or reduce the competitive oxygenase function. It will probably not be possible to totally separate the carboxylase function from the oxygenase function, but site-directed mutagenesis (coincidental with investigations to determine whether catalytic properties are altered) may yield enzymes which have a higher affinity for CO_2 and a lower affinity for oxygen. The presence of such an enzyme in a plant may lead to improvements in overall photosynthetic efficiency.

Alongside this approach, useful variants may possibly be produced by combining in one species the genes coding for large and small subunits of the enzyme from different species. Two methods of achieving this might be envisaged: (i) specific transfer of small subunit genes from one species to the nuclear genome of another species; (ii) bringing together, within a single cell, chloroplast and nuclear genomes from different species by means of protoplast fusion; hence, different combinations of large and small subunit would also be generated. There is no guarantee that these types of manipulation would improve overall photosynthetic efficiency in the crop, but, until they are prepared and analysed the possibility cannot be overlooked.

Development of nitrogen-fixing cultivars in non-leguminous crops

Yields of many crops, particularly cereals, have been increased over the years by the application of large quantities of nitrogen fertilizers. Indeed many cultivars (e.g. 'green-revolution' wheats) have been specifically selected to give high yields in response to fertilizer application. This practice is expensive and leads to the eventual contamination of waterways with high levels of nitrates.

The natural supply of nitrogen to certain plants is achieved by close associations between them and nitrogen-fixing micro-organisms. Of the important crop species, only the legumes exhibit this phenomenon; nitrogen-fixing nodules are formed on their roots due to a symbiotic relationship with *Rhizobium spp.* Nodule formation depends on recognition between the appropriate bacterial strain and the legume host (e.g. *R. leguminosarum* and peas). A series of biochemical and morphological changes then takes place, resulting in the formation of effective nodules in which the *Rhizobium* bacteroids convert gaseous nitrogen to ammonia, using photosynthate from the plant as an energy source. The fixed nitrogen is then made available to the plant. Could this natural phenomenon be exploited for a wider range of crop species? The feasibility of transferring the capacity to fix nitrogen or the capability of forming nodules from legumes to cereals has been discussed at length in the literature (e.g. Barton & Brill, 1983; Earl & Ausubel, 1983), and this is now considered.

The formation of effective nodules requires a number of changes in gene expression in both the bacteria and the plants. In the bacteria, certain genes (*Sym* genes) are required for the interaction with the plant to be successful, and the nitrogen-fixation function is specified by a separate set of *nif* genes. *Rhizobium* spp. carry these genes on large 500 kbp plasmids. There are seventeen *nif* genes carried in eight, closely-linked operons. These code for synthesis of the three polypeptides of the nitrogenase, cofactors, electron transfer components and for the synthesis of products controlling the expression of nitrogenase. Initial studies on *nif* genes were carried out in the free-living nitrogen-fixer *Klebsiella pneumoniae* but have recently been extended to *Rhizobium*. The structure and control of the *nif* genes is reasonably well characterized (Drummond *et al.*, 1983; Sundaresan *et al.*, 1983), and is outlined in Fig. 7.8. The plant responds to bacterial invasion by producing a variety of proteins, one group of which, known as nodulins, is poorly characterized but is essential for nodule formation. One component of this group, a 35,000 molecular weight polypeptide (nodulin-35), is nodule-specific and can make up 4% of soluble protein of the nodule. However, the function of this protein is unknown. In addition to nodulins, the plant synthesizes large quantities of leghemoglobin which serves the vital function of protecting the bacterial nitrogenase complex from oxygen. The heme moiety of leghemoglobin is supplied to the plant by the bacteria. Protection from oxygen is vital as one component of the nitrogenase has a half-life of only 45 seconds in the presence of oxygen. Leghemoglobin can account for 25–30% of the soluble proteins in the nodule. A number of leghemoglobin and nodulin genes have been cloned and characterized (e.g. Verma *et al.*, 1983), but the control of synthesis is not well understood.

Would it be possible to extend the host range of *Rhizobium* spp. to include cereals and forage grasses? The interaction between plant and

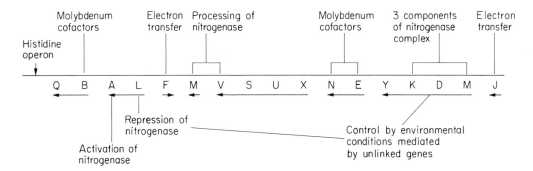

Fig. 7.8. *Nif* genes of *Klebsiella pneumoniae*. *Nif* genes have been more extensively analysed in the free-living nitrogen-fixer *K. pneumoniae* than in *Rhizobium*. However, the *nif* genes from the two organisms appear to be very similar. In *K. pneumoniae* the synthesis of nitrogenase is controlled by ammonia, certain amino acids, oxygen and temperature, whereas in *Rhizobium* the synthesis of nitrogenase is dependent upon the establishment of symbiosis. In spite of the different conditions involved in regulation, some similarities in the mechanism of regulation have been observed (Sundaresan *et al.*, 1983). The seventeen *nif* genes are designated by capital letters, and the eight operons and their direction of transcription are indicated by arrows. The function of some of the genes has been defined, including those giving rise to the essential molybdenum-containing cofactors, and those involved in the supply of electrons (reducing power). The *K. pneumoniae* genes are carried on the bacterial chromosome, but are located on a large plasmid in most *Rhizobium* species.

bacterium is extraordinarily complex, and the molecular and genetic details are far from being fully understood. Broadening the host range would certainly require changes in the recognition system between plant and bacterium. In addition, the plant genes required for the establishment of symbiosis may well be unique to legumes and, if this were the case, these genes would have to be transferred to the new cereal host.

Recent advances in the understanding of bacterial *nif* genes have offered the prospect of transfering nitrogen-fixing ability to the plants themselves. The *nif* genes of *Klebsiella pneumoniae* have long ago been transferred to another bacterium, *E. coli*, converting it into a nitrogen-fixer (Dixon & Postgate, 1971). Transforming a plant cell into a nitrogen-fixer is a completely different problem. Even assuming that the technical difficulties (outlined in Chapter 4) of placing genes into cereals can be overcome. there are other difficulties to be considered. The *nif* genes are prokaryotic in nature, so that eukaryotic promotors and other control sequences would have to be spliced into the operons to ensure expression in plant cells, unless the *nif* genes were located in the chloroplast which has a prokaryotic-type genetic system. If the genes were expressed, the plant would have to supply reducing power and ATP (17 moles of ATP per mole of N_2 fixed), and maintain the nitrogenase in an oxygen-depleted environment. Sceptics have argued that the drain on the plant brought about by the ATP and reducing power requirements would be too great, and could contribute to lowering rather than raising yields. However, since the plant expends a great deal of energy extracting nitrate from the soil anyway, this energy deficit may not prove to be too deleterious to yield. Recent calculations (Schubert, 1982) have suggested that maize is actually more capable of compensating for this energy cost than is soybean, which under normal growing conditions has to supply energy to nitrogen-fixing nodules.

Protecting nitrogenase from oxygen may be a much more difficult problem to solve. Plant cells are naturally oxygen-rich but, nevertheless, contain oxygen-sensitive molecules such as cytochromes. Natural mechanisms exist, therefore, for the protection of a protein from oxygen within cells. Unfortunately, the problem of oxygen protection will not really be studied in detail until earlier steps in the transfer of *nif* genes have been achieved.

The chloroplast has been suggested as a possible target for the transfer of the nitrogen-fixing genes (Earl & Ausubel, 1983). Use of this target would solve a number of problems: (i) the genome of chloroplasts is a prokaryotic type and could therefore be expected to cope better with introduced prokaryotic genes, consequently requiring a minimum amount of manipulation of the *nif* genes; (ii) in the chloroplast ATP would be readily available; (iii) ammonia generated by any nitrogen-fixation would be unlikely to cause a toxicity problem as this organelle is the site of the conversion of nitrate to ammonia in the plant cell. The major drawback of the chloroplast as a target for nitrogen-fixing genes is the presence of a high-oxygen environment; this need not necessarily be a problem as the chloroplast contains oxygen-sensitive cytochromes.

As the cost of producing artificial fertilizers will probably continue to rise, it is an attractive proposition to produce agronomically desirable cultivars with the partial or total ability to fix atmospheric nitrogen. Such plants could make use of the readily available resource of gaseous nitrogen. Before this can be achieved, considerably more information must be obtained about the molecular mechanisms of nitrogen fixation and symbiosis. The difficulty of these tasks should not be underestimated at this time.

Improvement of nutritional quality by manipulation of genes encoding seed storage proteins

Seed crops play important roles in human and animal nutrition worldwide. Eight species of cereal contribute over 50% of total world food calories; seven species of grain legume make a smaller total contribution but are important in certain geographical areas. In addition to carbohydrate, these seed crops supply a large proportion of the protein required by man and animals. The nutritional problem with cereals and legumes is that they contain limited amounts of certain amino acids which are essential to man and monogastric animals. Most cereals are deficient in lysine and to a lesser extent threonine, while legumes are deficient in sulphur amino acids. Some seed crops, notably rice, have low overall protein levels, but a somewhat better amino acid balance.

Over hundreds of years these crops have been bred for increased yields, protein levels, improvement in specific characteristics (such as the baking quality of wheat and malting quality of barley), and to a certain extent for nutritional quality. While there has been only limited progress in the area of nutritional quality, other characteristics have been improved dramatically.

The proteins of seeds have been studied for a considerable time. At the turn of the century Thomas Osborn reported the fractionation of proteins from seeds on the basis of solubility, and current methods are still based on the fractionations he devised. The four major categories of seed proteins are:
(a) albumins, soluble in water;
(b) globulins, soluble in salt solutions;
(c) prolamins, soluble in aqueous alcohol;
(d) glutelins, soluble in dilute acid or alkali.
Although the classification is fairly crude it provides a useful basis of reference. At one time, there was often confusion between prolamins and glutelins due to inefficient separations, but current techniques now give better separations, by utilizing hot aqueous alcohol with the addition of a reducing agent such as 2-mercaptoethanol.

The major storage proteins of cereals (i.e. those utilized during germination to provide nitrogen to the developing seedling) generally fall into the prolamin category. They are deficient in lysine, rich in proline, glutamine and asparagine, and highly hydrophobic. Legumes, on the other hand, principally store globulins which are deficient in methionine and are much less hydrophobic. The nomenclature and properties of the major storage proteins of some important seed crops are summarized in Table 7.6. There is clearly some deviation from the general groupings given above. The main storage proteins of rice fall into the glutelin category, making the grain less deficient in lysine. An endosperm globulin forms the principal nitrogen store in oats.

There have been a variety of approaches to improving nutritional quality. Early attempts concentrated on screening existing cultivars for unusual amino acid compositions (using dye-binding assays), and using these in breeding programmes. The high-lysine barley 'Hiproly' was utilized in this way but failed to give rise to any commercial varieties. An extension of this approach has been to screen plants grown from mutagenized seed or young excised embryos for overproduction of certain free amino acids (Bright *et al.*, 1983) or for unusual protein patterns. A mutant of barley, Risø 1508, produced in this way has a very high lysine content due to severe depletion of the storage protein,

Table 7.6. Properties of seed storage proteins from some major crop species.

Species	Proteins	Protein type	Subunit (MW × 10⁻³)	Lys (%)	Met (%)	Pro+Glx (%)	Approximate proportion of total protein (%)
Wheat (*Triticum aestivum*)	Gliadin	Prolamin	30–70	0·6	1·4	49	40
	Glutenin	Glutelin	up to 133	1·5	1·4	48·8	
Barley (*Hordeum vulgare*)	Hordein	Prolamin	30–55	0·5	0·6	34·2	55
Maize (*Zea mays*)	Zein	Prolamin	15–21	0·3	0·1	63	52
French bean (*Phaseolus vulgaris*)	Phaseolin (G1)	Globulin	45·5–51	7·6	0·5	22·4	50
Soybean (*Glycine max*)	Glycinin (11s)	Globulin	20,40	3·9	1·0	27·9	
	β-Conglycinin (7s)		44–90	7·0	0·3	24·8	60–80
Pea (*Pisum sativum*)	Legumin (11s)	Globulin	20,40	4·4	0·5	26	
	Vicillin (7s)		30–70	7·9	0·2	22·8	80
Rice (*Oryza sativa*)	γ-Globulin	Globulin	33–70	3·3	0·9	20·3	10
	Glutelin	Glutelin	16–38	4·8	0·9	24·2	80
Oat (*Avena sativa*)	Endosperm globulin	Globulin	21·7, 31·7	2·6	N	26·7	56

Most data in this table are taken from Payne & Rhodes (1982) and Derbyshire *et al.*, 1976. There is variation in amino acid composition of these proteins between cultivars.
N = not determined.

hordein (Doll *et al.*, 1974). The mutation is pleiotrophic and is not linked to the storage protein loci. In addition to the inhibition of storage protein synthesis, there are also effects on endosperm structure, starch metabolism, and ribonuclease and amylase levels. The grains of Risø 1508 are shrunken and give a poor yield. The variety has therefore never been grown commercially, nor the character incorporated into any agronomically viable line.

Legume breeding has led to the production of some cultivars with extremely high protein contents. Some nutritional improvement has also been achieved through breeding for an altered balance between the two groups (7s and 11s; see Table 7.6) of storage proteins. The 11s-type proteins have a higher methionine content, and hence an increase in these at the expense of the 7s-type proteins would improve the amino acid balance of the whole seed. However, to date there have been no dramatic improvements in nutritional quality of commercially grown cultivars of seed crops.

Can recombinant DNA technology be used to overcome some of these problems? The genes coding for a number of these storage proteins have now been cloned (see Table 3.2) and extensively characterized. A considerable amount is known about the structure of the genes but, as yet, it is not understood how their expression is regulated in the seed. It has been suggested that nutritional improvement could be achieved by using site-directed mutagenesis with the objective of introducing more lysine or methionine codons into the gene sequences. The engineered gene would then be replaced in the plant and, when expressed in the seed, should considerably increase the levels of the deficient amino acids. However, such an approach would still entail an extensive programme of breeding and testing, since this would be essential in order to ensure the production of an acceptable cultivar.

These aims are currently far from being fulfilled although some steps have been achieved. The genes have been cloned and methods are available for engineering the appropriate changes in them. To date this is as far as the story goes. As yet, there have been no reports of successful replacement of a storage protein gene into a crop plant, with the exception of one recent report indicating that a gene encoding the french bean protein, phaseolin, has been expressed in sunflower tissue culture. The gene had been inserted into the sunflower cells via an *Agrobacterium* plasmid (Murai *et al.*, 1983). Rapid progress in the area of plant gene vectors will probably make this type of manipulation possible in a wider range of dicotyledenous plants in the near future. There are still problems however for cereal crops as, except for controlling elements, there are no natural vector systems available. Liposome-mediated DNA transfer may be possible. To produce a plant in which all cells carry the engineered genes, the vector must be used to place the gene into protoplasts which can be regenerated somatically to produce whole plants. Unfortunately, many crop plants, particularly cereals, have proved recalcitrant as regards this type of manipulation, although some progress has now been made in regenerating cereals from embryogenic callus cultures, and in a few cases from protoplasts (see Chapter 5).

The problems outlined so far are purely physical ones of achieving the placement of an engineered gene into a plant, but there are many more factors to be considered. Firstly, the regulation of these genes is tightly controlled in the plant and it is essential that this control be maintained over the inserted genes. Production of these storage proteins in other tissues would be of little value, and could even be detrimental to plant development. The second consideration is that storage proteins are usually encoded in multigene families, so the introduction of one engineered gene may have little effect on the overall amino acid composition. Finally, assuming it is possible to introduce large amounts of an engineered protein into the seed there may be associated detrimental effects. For instance, if a legume seed requires a larger supply of sulphur-containing amino acids, from which source are these going to be supplied? In the case of cereals, the storage proteins are packaged into endoplasmic reticulum associated protein bodies by virtue of the hydrophobicity of the proteins themselves (Miflin *et al.*, 1981). The presence of extra lysine residues in the storage proteins may reduce their hydrophobicity and interfere with their packaging. Such interference may alter subsequent processes involved in seed maturation. Inefficient packaging is unlikely to be conducive to the production of a well filled grain. Until these types of specific gene transfers have been achieved, we can only guess at the biological consequences for any given crop species.

The idea of using recombinant DNA technology to improve seed crops is attractive in that it may allow very specific and controlled changes to be carried out. It can be argued that this approach is more likely to achieve improved nutritional quality along with the production of well filled grains, because the aim is to subtly alter the nature of the proteins while maintaining the balance between the different types of protein in the seed. Most mutant lines selected so far have an altered amino acid composition by virtue of an overall reduction in storage protein synthesis, more often than not resulting in small grains.

The time-scale for the use of recombinant DNA to improve seed proteins is impossible to predict, although some workers suggested that it could be achieved over a period as short as 3−5 years. It is likely that such approaches will take longer than that as, even if some of the current technical difficulties can be resolved, breeding and testing the new cultivars at the field level will take the usual passage of several seasons. The grower, as well as the molecular biologist, must be convinced that any new cultivar produced is of a superior and reliable quality.

Further reading

Barton K.A. & Brill W.J. (1983). Prospects in plant genetic engineering. *Science*, **219**, 671–675.

Borlaug N.E. (1983). Contributions of conventional plant breeding to food production. *Science*, **219**, 689–693.

Owens L.D. (1983) (Ed.) *Genetic Engineering: Applications to Agriculture*. Beltsville Symposia in Agricultural Research Vol. 7. Granada Publishing, London.

Sen S.K. Giles K.L. (1982) (Eds) *Plant Cell Culture in Crop Improvement*. Plenum Press, New York.

Sneep J. & Hendriksen A.J.J. (1979) (Eds) *Plant Breeding Perspectives*. Centre for Agricultural Publishing and Documentation, Wageningen.

8 Industrial Plant Products

Introduction: use of plants as energy, chemical and genetic resource

Plant-derived biomass provides as much as 15% of the world's energy needs (Hall, 1979). This biomass production involves the use of fast-growing plants to provide raw materials which can be converted by various processes to a range of energy-rich materials. Typical of the industrial use of biomass is the conversion of plant materials such as lignocellulose to alcohols, and on a smaller scale to biogas (carbon dioxide and methane). It has been argued that the production of ethanol for use in combination with petroleum may help to satisfy demands for fuel and so avert a total reliance on fossil fuels. However, this policy of producing ethanol for fuel and feedstock for the chemical industry, in order to alleviate the oil import burden, can have its problems. For example, in Kenya the switching of 400,000 hectares from food to sugarcane production has in turn led to an undesirable increase in food imports. An alternative programme of ethanol production based on forestry resources is totally impracticable for that country, particularly since the markets for the chemicals produced, i.e. acetic and citric acids, are small. On the other hand the policies, and practicalities, regarding ethanol production in other countries, such as Brazil and Zimbabwe, have so far resulted in no food shortages.

For centuries, plants have been a valuable source of chemicals and they are currently seen as a source of high added value, low volume, chemicals of great value to the pharmaceutical, perfume and fine chemicals industries. This is emphasized by the fact that even today 25% of all drugs prescribed are derived from plants; quinine, codeine, diosgenin and digoxin being the most notable examples. The developing technologies of fermentor production of some of these chemicals in batch and continuous culture systems is examined, as are the current applications and uses of plant-derived enzymes. Such plant products are likely to find increasing uses in the future, as evidenced by the fact that 1,500 new plant compounds are reported in the literature every year. Some 20% of these usually have biological activity.

The potential of plants as a genetic resource is all too obvious, especially in view of the fact that increasing attention and concern is now being focused on the dwindling natural vegetation, particularly in the tropics and subtropics, and on the narrow genetic bases of a large number of the world's staple food crops. In the latter part of this chapter a different aspect of the genetic potential of plants is examined. The techniques and methodologies are now at hand to begin the manipulation of plant genes in micro-organisms, with a view to firstly achieving the production of plant proteins in microbial systems, and secondly, to the transfer of altered plant genetic material back into the parent plant, in order to effect a beneficial change, for example, in a single enzyme or polypeptide.

Energy resource

There are several ways in which plant material may be used as a substrate for the production of energy. Products of agricultural crops, of course, supply the major proportion of food for man and animals, in addition to certain raw materials. In this respect, it is worth noting that the total food materials produced on cultivated lands has been estimated to account for only 6% of the total biomass derived from primary photosynthesis. The major proportion of the global primary photosynthetic production occurs in woodland and forest (44%), and this is converted to usable energy by direct burning either to obtain heat, or to produce steam to drive machines and turbines which produce electricity. Other alternatives include the conversion or extraction of fuels and chemicals from primary products. Energy is also generated by the feeding of animals on grassland and then by the utilization of these to perform work. The move towards the use of biomass-derived fuels and chemicals has come about because unlike the fossil fuels such as petroleum and natural gas, biomass is, in the long term at least, completely renewable.

The useful components of biomass are sugars, starch and lignocellulose. Plants producing high levels of sugars include sugar-cane, sugar-beet and millet. These are perhaps the most suitable and readily available to be used as substrates in a wide variety of processes, especially those geared to the production of alcohol.

Plant products containing starch include the grain crops, particularly maize, rice and wheat, as well as potatoes and other root crops like sweet potato and cassava. Starch, however, must be first broken down by digestion or hydrolysis to mono- and oligosaccharides, if it is to be used in fermentation processes.

These two sources of biomass represent a relatively small proportion of that available for use in chemical or energy fuel production programmes, competing as they do with demand as food sources. One exception to this situation is found in Brazil where sugar-cane is specifically grown as a substrate for gasohol. It is likely that this approach may eventually be adopted by other countries.

Undoubtedly, the major source of biomass for the various biotechnological processes will come from lignocellulose derived from the agriculture and forestry industries. Lignocellulose contains three major chemical components; lignin, α-cellulose and a collection of polysaccharides collectively known as hemicellulose. The latter two are capable of comparatively slow fermentation by anaerobic bacteria, whereas lignin is not. Moreover, lignin surrounds many plant-derived polymers rendering them unavailable to processing by micro-organisms. Expensive and energy demanding pretreatments are often required to obtain a substrate from lignocellulose which is then suitable for microbial degradation. However, recent research aimed at using recombinant DNA techniques to manipulate the cellulase genes of a thermophilic actinomycete, *Thermomonospora*, which grows rapidly at 65°C and has one of the most active cellulase complexes yet found, represents an important start to work aimed at producing cellulose from lignocellulose substrates (Faber, 1983).

There are several energy conversion systems available for dealing with lignocellulose biomass substrates. Like coal, biomass can be burned directly to yield energy or can be subjected to pyrolysis or gasification. These processes yield mainly methane, or with the necessary additional synthetic steps methanol. Although representing an important conversion technology, this method does not preserve important, high-value intermediate products such as glucose and xylose. An alternative conversion system would be the fermentation of lignocellulose by a range of micro-organisms. However, as previously mentioned, treatment of lignocellulose is necessary to dissociate lignin from other polysaccharides. The operations involved in this are processes such as milling, acid and/or thermal digestion, as well as steam treatment. These represent net energy inputs which must be taken into account when considering the overall economy of the total process. Alternatives to these physical treatments are based on biodegradation which involve the use of bacterial and fungal enzymes (Kirk, 1981). Fermentation processes make use of naturally occurring, or genetically engineered, micro-organisms, which tend to require lower energy inputs compared with those of other conversion systems. Furthermore, the end products formed from microbial, or thermal conversion of biomass tend to have a higher energy per unit weight than the original biomass itself. In addition, the liquid fuels formed are more convenient both to store and transport. Table 8.1 shows a number of energy-rich chemicals which could be produced by microbial conversion of biomass.

Table 8.1. Fuels and energy-rich chemicals produced by fermentation of biomass.

Ethanol	Acetic acid
Butanol	Citric acid
Glycerol	Lactic acid
Acetone	Propionic acid

Ethanol production

One fuel product capable of production from biomass, by processes which are relatively well understood, but which are still capable of significant improvement, is ethanol. Ethanol is both a high grade fuel as well as an excellent raw material for the chemical and plastic industries, though the use of ethanol as a fuel oil is neither a new concept nor a new technology. Henry Ford's Model T was designed to run on either ethanol or petroleum or any mixture of them. With the decrease in availability of petroleum oils which occurred in the 1970s, the possibility of supplementing petrol with home-produced alternatives received attention. In the US, the federal government aims to have increased fuel alcohol production from the 80–120 million gallons produced in 1980 to 1·8 billion gallons by the mid 1980s.

Alcohol production proceeds through a number of steps (Table 8.2), the first of which includes a pretreatment of the raw materials in order to obtain fermentable sugars. For crops already containing readily fermentable sugars, such as sugar-cane and sugar-beet, all that may be necessary to recover the sugars is extraction and recrystallization. The by-products of these processes, e.g. molasses, can also be utilized in alcohol production. When starch is used as a substrate it must first be gelatinized by heating. On cooling, α-amylase is added which results in the formation of dextrose. The addition of amyloglucosidases to saccharify (i.e. to reduce polysaccharides to mono- and oligosaccharides) the mash, can be accompanied by the addition of fermenting yeasts. With cellulosic biomass as a starting material, several pretreatments can be used. These are physical, chemical (Fig. 8.1) and enzymatic (Fig. 8.2).

In the next stage, fermentation, the sugar is utilized by yeast, or other micro-organisms as a carbon source to produce alcohol and carbon dioxide. The alcohol produced is concentrated by distillation to yield 100% alcohol, and the spent mash is removed and processed to provide animal feed.

In the production of ethanol, the cost of the substrate is the major expense representing 60–70% of the manufacturing overheads. Therefore, any increase in the efficiency of the use of substrate would be

Table 8.2. Biomass to ethanol.

Raw material	Pretreatment	Process	Substrate	Fermenting organism	Product
Sugar	Extraction	Sucrose inversion	Glucose, Fructose	Yeast, anaerobic bacteria, *Zymomonas*	Fuel ethanol and Feed residue
Starch	Gelatinization	Saccharification	Glucose, Maltose	Yeast, anaerobic bacteria	
Lignocellulose biomass	Grinding, milling	Hydrolysis: acid or enzymatic	Glucose, Xylose	Yeast, anaerobic bacteria	

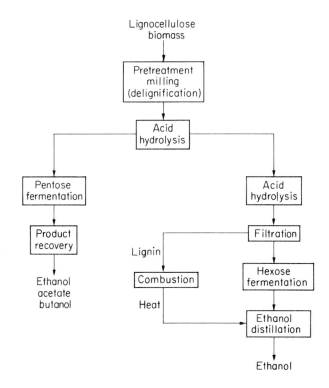

Fig. 8.1. Ethanol production from lignocellulose via acid hydrolysis.

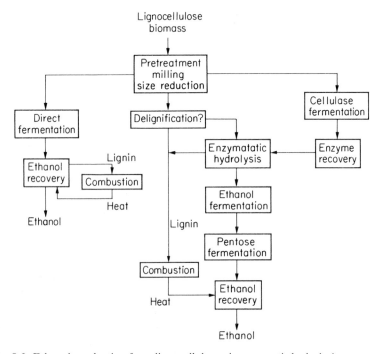

Fig. 8.2. Ethanol production from lignocellulose via enzymatic hydrolysis.

beneficial. In this respect, it is worth noting that the theoretical yield of ethanol from glucose, sucrose, and starch or cellulose is 0·51, 0·54 and 0·57 grams of ethanol per gram of substrate, respectively. Yields currently achieved are 90–95% of the theoretical maximum. Ways in which substrate utilization could be improved range from developing processes for the utilization of pentose sugars to increasing the ratio of ethanol produced per unit cell weight by increasing the cell's tolerance to alcohols and other fermentation products, perhaps by using ethanol producers other than yeast (Lee *et al.*, 1979).

The second major proportion of the production cost, 20–30%, involves factors concerned with the operation of the production unit, e.g. the supply of chemicals and fuels, labour, administration and factory overheads. The major input is fuel for the various operations such as pumping, sterilization, grinding, heating and distillation. These costs can be reduced by using coal as the heating source or better still cellulose biomass. Further, the use of continuous fermentation rather than the traditional batch operations might lead to increases in productivity and thus a reduction in overall costs. In the production of ethanol, investment in specialized equipment represents the third major manufacturing cost (4–12%). In this respect, the development of micro-organisms which require minimum substrate pretreatment, and which can produce ethanol at a high rate could reduce the investment.

Clearly, the application of the developing technologies described earlier in this book have a role to play in increasing the overall efficiency of production of ethanol and other chemical feedstocks. The development of more easily accessible starting materials, especially cellulose, will decrease costly pretreatments and lead to an overall more efficient use of substrates. Similarly, the study and development of the micro-organisms used to ferment the alcohol, particularly by recombinant DNA techniques, will lead to overall increases in process efficiency. In this respect, the closer evaluation and study of *Zymomonas* strains would appear to have great potential.

Finally, with regard to where the plant biomass for use in the production of ethanol and other chemicals, is to be produced, it is worth noting that those countries now producing ethanol as a fuel lie between latitudes 40°N and 40°S. Only here can the advantages of growing sugarcane as a feedstock be capitalized on. Unless lignocellulose can be efficiently used it seems unlikely that the temperate countries will make use of this technology to produce alcohol for fuel. Even if processes involving lignocellulose are developed, few of these countries have sufficient forestation to sustain such a programme. This then brings us back to the use of marginal land and the development of plants capable of growth and high yield under such conditions. The alternative is a situation where food resources from developing countries are diverted to fuel production, with obvious consequences for poorer nations.

Methane production

Any biomass which is placed in a closed tank in the absence of air and in the presence of suitable bacteria will be digested, degraded and eventually converted into a mixture of 40% carbon dioxide and 60% methane — biogas. Such systems operate on a small local scale in India and China, where an estimated eight million are in operation, and they serve to produce a cheap source of high energy fuel. These systems operate by converting animal, plant or more usually a mixture of these wastes to biogas. Mixing plant and animal wastes in a biogas system has the advantage of complementing the highly nitrogenous animal waste with the nitrogen-poor, but carbon-rich plant residue (Hashimoto, 1983). By operating this system at 35°C, a mixture containing up to 40% straw may be fermented, and at 55°C the proportion of straw can be raised to 75% of the mix. The free ammonia concentration is important as regards its effect on fermentation stress. It has been found that physical pretreatments of the plant waste, such as milling or rolling, do not enhance the yield of methane and that dilute wastes such as those obtained from food processing are not efficiently digested.

The production of methane from biomass is complex, involving three major communities of micro-organisms. The first is that containing fermentative micro-organisms which solubilize complex organic mixtures of proteins, fats and cellulose and provide the organic raw material. This is then converted to organic acids, mainly acetic acid, by the second community which contains obligate reducing organisms. These acids are specifically decomposed to methane and carbon dioxide by the third community which contains methanogenic bacteria (Bryant, 1979). The inter-relationships of these communities of bacteria in reactors is not well understood. However, in those cases where fermentors have been studied in great detail, the sustained high output of methane requires continuous monitoring as well as the accurate control of variables such as temperature, pH, liquid level, and raw material input. Future developments will depend upon a more intimate understanding of the parameters which control the various microbial conversion steps, and they may lead to the possibility of developing a single organism capable of performing more than one step in the production of methane.

Chemical resource

Plants are sources of an extremely wide range of chemical substances. The main groups of plant compounds of use to industry are listed in Table 8.3. More exhaustive lists are to be found in the further reading material, particularly in Staba (1980).

Value and exploitation of this resource

The majority of compounds of commercial importance (see Tables 8.4

Table 8.3. Major groups of compounds with commercial importance which are derived from plants.

Compound group	Type and examples
Pharmaceuticals	Alkaloids, steroids, anthraquinones
Enzymes	Proteases (e.g. papain)
Latex	Isoprenoids (e.g. rubber)
Waxes	Wax esters (e.g. jojoba)
Pigments	Stains and dyes
Oils	Fatty acids (e.g. seed oils)
Agrochemicals	Insecticides (e.g. pyrethrins)
Cosmetic substances	Essential oils (e.g. monoterpenes)
Food additives	Flavour compounds, non-nutritive sweeteners (e.g. thaumatin)
Gums	Polysaccharides (e.g. gum arabic)

Table 8.4. Natural products from plants and their associated industries (after Fowler, 1983).

Industry	Plant product	Plant species	Industrial uses
Pharmaceuticals	Codeine (alkaloid)	*Papaver somniferum*	Analgesic
	Diosgenin (steroid)	*Dioscorea deltoidea*	Anti-fertility agents
	Quinine (alkaloid)	*Cinchona ledgeriana*	Antimalarial
	Digoxin (cardiac glycoside)	*Digitalis lanata*	Cardiatonic
	Scopolamine (alkaloid)	*Datura stramonium*	Antihypertensive
	Vincristine (alkaloid)	*Catharanthus roseus*	Antileukaemic
Agrochemicals	Pyrethrin	*Chrysanthemum cinerariaefolium*	Insecticide
Food and drink	Quinine (alkaloid)	*Cinchona ledgeriana*	Bittering agent
	Thaumatin (chalcone)	*Thaumatococcus danielli*	Non-nutritive sweetener
Cosmetics	Jasmine	*Jasminum* sp.	Perfume

and 8.5) are secondary metabolites produced by plants as a consequence of different stages of cell, tissue and organ differentiation. Many of these metabolites are chemically complex and in many cases synthesized substitutes (when obtainable in commercially useful quantities and at a reasonable cost) are not as effective as the natural substances.

The importance of plants as sources of chemicals for various industries makes improvement of the crop species or plants involved a most important consideration. This is especially true of those cases where reliance is placed on the collection and the utilization of wild plant species and in cases where large amounts of mature plant tissue have to be processed in order to obtain small amounts of a drug. The

Table 8.5. The ten most prescribed medicinals from plant sources (after Fowler, 1983).

Medicinal agent	Activity	Plant source
Steroids from diosgenin	Anti-fertility agents	*Dioscorea deltoidea*
Codeine	Analgesic	*Papaver somniferum*
Atropine	Anticholinergic	*Atropa belladonna*
Reserpine	Antihypertensive	*Rauwolfia serpentina*
Hyoscyamine	Anticholinergic	*Hyoscyamus niger*
Digoxin	Cardiatonic	*Digitalis lanata*
Scopolamine	Anticholinergic	*Datura metel*
Digitoxin	Cardiovascular	*Digitalis purpurea*
Pilocarpine	Cholinergic	*Pilocarpus jabonandi*
Quinidine	Antimalarial	*Cinchona ledgeriana*

continuing decline in the natural habitats of some of these wild plants underlines the importance of some of the techniques of clonal propagation and crop breeding discussed in previous chapters. It must not be overlooked that these *in vitro* techniques have an important role to play in their application to plants of special significance to chemical industries. There are now many situations in which micropropagation has played an important part in increasing stocks of wild plant species

Table 8.6. Substances reported from plant cell cultures.

Alkaloids	Insecticides
Allergens	Latex
Anthraquinones	Lipids
Antileukaemic agents	
Antitumour agents	Naphthoquinones
Antiviral agents	Nucleic acids
Aromas	Nucleotides
Benzoquinones	Oils
	Opiates
Carbohydrates (including polysaccharides)	Organic acids
Cardiac glycosides	
Chalcones	Peptides
	Perfumes
Dianthrenes	Phenols
	Pigments
Enzymes	Plant growth regulators
Enzyme inhibitors	Proteins
Flavanoids, flavones	
Flavours (including sweeteners)	Steroids and derivatives
Fluranocoumarins	Sugars
Hormones	Tannins
	Terpenes and terpenoids
	Vitamins

used as sources of industrial compounds, particularly medicinal plants, e.g. the steroid producing species of *Dioscorea* yams and *Solanum* (Chaturvedi *et al.*, 1982).

In another context, plant tissue culture has particularly important applications to certain industries like the pharmaceutical and food industries which require specific, highly purified substances. These may be produced by (i) biosynthesis of specific groups of compounds in cell cultures of species known already as conventional sources, or (ii) biotransformation of specific compounds to ones of a more desirable (valuable) type taking advantage of specific enzymes in living cells.

Use of plant cell cultures for biosynthesis of plant compounds

Provided that plant cells are cultured under conditions which will allow the expression of a certain degree of differentiation, they have the potential to produce, either by *de novo* synthesis or by biotrans-formation of specific precursors, an impressive range of secondary plant compounds (Table 8.6). One major problem currently limits the use of plant cell cultures on an industrial scale. Plant cells cannot be grown in large enough volumes in a sufficiently productive state to make them economically suitable sources of commercial compounds except in a few instances in which high value, low market volume chemicals (as in the case of some medicinals) are being manufactured. Although plant cells can be grown in multilitre vessels as described in Chapter 5, their inherently slow rates of metabolism and growth, as compared to microbial cell systems, and their specific requirement for specialized bioreactor designs which will create the required mixing levels but will not damage the cells' relatively fragile structure, has so far impeded the rapid development of large-scale cultivation of plant cells (see Fowler, 1982, 1983). Even in those cases where multilitre systems have been developed, only trace amounts of the desired chemicals have been produced. Table 8.7 contains examples of the most successful levels of plant metabolite production yet produced in culture systems. It should be noted that the levels of production given in this table only act as a guide for approximate comparisons and it should be realized that some of the data presented in it were obtained from some of the smaller scale experimental systems. Also, it is extremely difficult to compare yields of a specific substance produced in cultured cells or tissues with those produced in whole plant tissues, since some metabolites are often synthesized in one tissue and then transported through the plant to others where they accumulate. For example, many alkaloids are synthesized in the roots, e.g. tobacco and poppy alkaloids like nicotine and morphine, respectively. During plant development, these sub-stances are then translocated either in final form or in conjugate forms such as glycosides, to the upper parts of the plant. In the case of these

Table 8.7. Yields of some natural products in cell cultures and their equivalent amounts in whole plant tissue.

Natural product	Species	Yield	
		Cell culture	Whole plant
Anthraquinones	*Morinda citrifolia*	900 nmol g^{-1} dry wt	Root, 110 nmol g^{-1} dry wt
Anthraquinones	*Cassia tora*	0·334% fresh wt	0·209% seed, dry wt
Ajmalicine and serpentine	*Catharanthus roseus*	1·3% dry wt	0·26% dry wt
Diosgenin	*Dioscorea deltoidea*	26 mg g^{-1} dry wt	20 mg g^{-1} dry wt tuber
Ginseng saponins	*Panax ginseng*	0·38% fresh wt	0·3–3·3% fresh wt
Nicotine	*Nicotiana tabacum*	3·4% dry wt	2–5% dry wt
Thebaine	*Papaver bracteatum*	130 mg g^{-1} dry wt	1400 mg g^{-1} dry wt leaf and 3000 mg g^{-1} dry wt root
Ubiquinone	*Nicotiana tabacum*	0·5 mg g^{-1} dry wt	16 mg g^{-1} dry wt leaf

two alkaloids, nicotine accumulates in leaves while morphine accumulates in greatest quantities in maturing fruit capsules.

Despite these limitations, there are also some potential advantages with using plant tissue cultures as sources of industrially important compounds instead of producing them by traditional means. The main advantages are as follows.

(a) Independence from various environmental factors, including climate, pests and diseases and geographical and seasonal constraints.

(b) The relative degree of control afforded by culturing cells under controlled conditions mean that production levels could be geared more accurately to market demands.

(c) A more consistent product quality could be assured with use of characterized cell lines.

(d) The intensive nature of the production of compounds in cultures might release lands for the production of food and cash crops.

(e) There would be greater control over production levels since they would not be so much at the mercy of political interference.

(f) Production of substances in chemically controlled environments facilitates later downstream processing and product recovery steps.

There are also some more specific advantages of plant cell cultures.

(a) New routes of synthesis can be recovered from deviant or mutant cell lines. These routes of synthesis can lead to novel products not previously found in whole plants.

(b) Culture of cells may prove more suitable in cases where plants are difficult or expensive to grow in the field due to their long life cycle, e.g. *Papaver bracteatum*, the source of thebaine takes two to three seasons to reach maturity.

(c) Some cell cultures have the capacity for biotransformation of specific substrates to more valuable products by means of single or multiple step enzyme activity (see later section).

Increasing the yields of secondary metabolites in cultures

As previously mentioned, yields of secondary metabolites are generally much lower in cell cultures (both cells and medium yields combined) than in equivalent synthetic tissues of the whole plant.

Several reasons are put forward for this situation. The most usual one is the lack of tissue and organ differentiation in most callus and liquid cell suspension cultures. This is believed to either prevent sufficient compartmentalization of enzymes required for synthesis and accumulation (storage) of secondary metabolites (see Böhm, 1980), or simply to be a reflection of the non-totipotent state of the majority of the cells grown in such cultures. Thus, root-differentiating calluses of *Atropa belladonna* are capable of producing tropane alkaloids like atropine, whilst non-differentiated calluses are not (Thomas & Street, 1970). Numerous other examples of this type of situation can be found in Butcher (1977). Some secondary metabolites accumulate in the vacuoles of cells; others are formed elsewhere in the cell and either accumulate at these sites or are actively excreted from cells via the vacuole system or by other means. Failure to excrete a metabolite from cells might lead to a cessation of biosynthesis, in some cases by feedback regulation mechanisms. Alternatively, the presence of metabolites in a culture medium may come about by lysis of cells during stationary phase growth (see later). As a general routine, cell suspensions have usually been established from the more friable, faster growing types since these have tended to generate fine suspensions of cells. Thus, it has frequently been the case that cell lines were selected either intentionally or non-intentionally for their suitability for growth and not necessarily for their ability to produce secondary metabolites. This fast growth ability is linked in most cases with little obvious tissue and/or biochemical differentiation so that it was believed that cell suspensions capable of good growth in bioreactors were not suitable for product formation. Over the last 10 years, however, a better appreciation has emerged of some of the characteristics of plant cell cultures. Firstly, it is clear that under some culture conditions there are various degrees of cell differentiation in expressed cell suspension cultures. In some cases different cell types are produced and frequently aggregates of cells form even in the finest of cell suspensions. Aggregates can consist of anything up to 200 cells so that some types of differentiation are in fact proceeding in these cultures. Secondly, the cultural conditions which operate during the various stages of the culture cycle have been found to have a profound effect on the productivity of cell cultures (for a summary see Mantell & Smith, 1983).

By optimization of different cultural factors, it has been shown possible to increase accumulations of certain secondary metabolites in cell cultures without any need for high levels of tissue differentiation. Because secondary metabolites are produced in whole plants as a consequence of cell, tissue and organ differentiation, it is becoming clear that production of reasonable levels in culture is best achieved under cultural conditions which favour slow or declining growth rather than rapid growth.

Asynchronously dividing batch cultures consist of a heterogenous mixture of cells at different stages of biochemical and morphological differentiation such that during initial and middle phases of culture varying proportions of cells are in rapid division. As substrates in the medium become more limiting, the proportion of cells undergoing cell divisions decreases until eventually during the stationary phase (Fig. 5.12), the majority of cells become quiescent and ageing processes occur in more and more cells. It is during these later stages of batch culture growth that more secondary metabolites are produced by cells. The accumulation of metabolite at any one particular instant in the culture

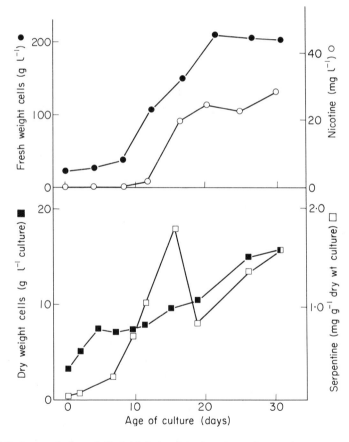

Fig. 8.3. Accumulation of alkaloids in batch suspension cultures of *Nicotiana tabacum* (top) and *Catharanthus roseus* (bottom) (after Mantell *et al.*, 1983 and Fowler, 1983).

cycle is the result of a dynamic balance between the rate of its bio-synthesis and of its biodegradation. Therefore, cultural conditions that promote biosynthesis of the desired compound while at the same time limiting those parts of metabolism involved with biodegradation, are obviously best striven for. In general, most secondary metabolites accumulate during late rather than early stages of growth of batch cultures (e.g. nicotine accumulation by tobacco cultures) although it should be noted that under some conditions certain metabolites (e.g. serpentine) can accumulate rapidly even during log phase growth (Fig. 8.3). There is no hard and fast rule as to the best time in the culture cycle at which to harvest cells in order to obtain maximum yield of metabolites. This is not surprising in view of the wide diversity of metabolism involved with the biosynthesis and biodegradation of the many secondary plant compounds, as detailed in Bell & Charlwood (1980), Vickery & Vickery (1981) and Conn (1981). Experience is showing that it is frequently best to produce large amounts of biomass under rapid growth conditions (relatively high auxin/cytokinin levels, high phosphate, nitrogen and potassium) and then to transfer the accumulated biomass to a second stage of culture in which conditions are created that promote secondary metabolite accumulation. Slower growth rates are induced by reducing levels of auxin and cytokinin and certain key macronutrients, particularly phosphate, in the culture media. By way of example, nicotine production by tobacco cell cultures is best achieved by a two-stage approach. The growth phase (Stage I) is supported on MS medium containing 10^{-5} M NAA and 10^{-6} M kinetin while the production phase (Stage II) is optimal in MS medium con-taining reduced levels of growth factors (10^{-6} M NAA and 10^{-7} M kinetin) and by omitting casein hydrolysate (which supports rapid cell growth) from the medium.

By reducing levels of phosphate in the production phase medium, the patterns of nicotine accumulation can also be manipulated to a significant degree (Fig. 8.4). Semi-continuous culture systems, in which large volumes of culture are removed from bioreactors and then replaced with an equivalent volume of fresh medium, can be operated successfully as chemostats to either generate biomass (e.g. tobacco cells of up to 20 g l^{-1} dry weight were produced by Kato *et al.*, 1977 in 15, 360 and 1500 l capacity bioreactors with sucrose as the carbon source) or for producing certain metabolites (e.g. different levels of anthocyanin were produced in carrot cell lines by Dougall & Weyrauch (1980) when cultured under phosphate-limiting conditions at different dilution rates). There are an increasing number of reports of plant cells producing secondary metabolites when immobilized in a variety of supports including agarose, starch, alginate and polyacrylamide (Lindsey & Yeoman, 1983). For instance, immobilized *C. roseus* cells showed not only continued but initially enhanced alkaloid biosynthesis (Brodelius &

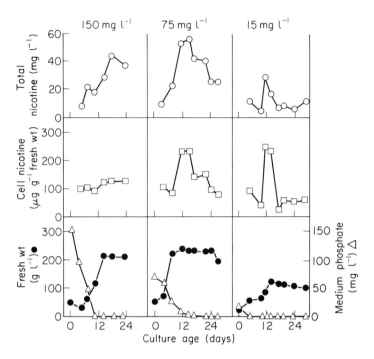

Fig. 8.4. Alkaloid accumulation and cell growth in tobacco cell cultures grown in 4-l batch reactors (after Mantell & Smith, 1983). Cells were grown in MS medium containing 150 mg l^{-1}, 75 mg l^{-1} and 15 mg l^{-1} phosphate in an auxin (from 10^{-5} M to 10^{-6} M NAA)/cytokinin (from 10^{-6} to 10^{-7} M kinetin) stepdown.

Nilsson, 1980). Cells raised in suspension cultures are immobilized in a selected matrix, e.g. alginate, or in fibre supports which are then placed in an aerated column (Fig. 8.5) through which suitable media are passed. Products can be released periodically from immobilized cells in the presence of permeabilizing agents such as DMSO so that the productive life of a column unit can be prolonged. Viability of cells in matrices has been surprisingly good and immobilized cell cultures can remain productive for six to ten times longer than comparable batch suspension cultures. An alternative system of culture is by means of attachment of cells to alginate beads which are held in fluidized beds, similar to the type widely used on an industrial scale for microbial and enzyme immobilization. At present, immobilized plant cells have not been used on an industrial scale for biosynthesis of plant metabolites. However, their potential is considerable; they provide novel experimental opportunities and they have been used in one instance for the pilot industrial scale biotransformation of β-methyldigitoxin to the more valuable β-methyldigoxin by Alfermann *et al.* (1983). Before dealing with biotransformation reactions, however, there are several important considerations with regard to the productivity of plant cell cultures and their potential for industrial use which must first be appreciated.

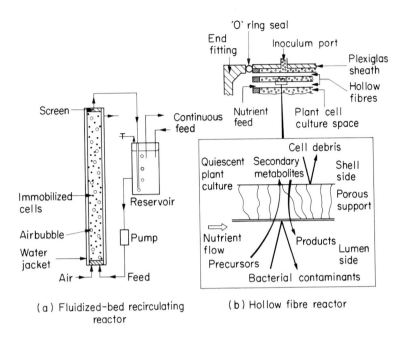

(a) Fluidized-bed recirculating   (b) Hollow fibre reactor
           reactor

Fig. 8.5. Small-scale immobilized plant cell reactors (after Prenosil & Pederson, 1983). (a) Fluidized bed recirculating reactor system for use with alginate-immobilized plant cells. Cells are entrapped in alginate by dripping a mixture of cell culture and alginate (3–4% w/v) into a medium containing at least 50 mM calcium. Beads of alginate containing entrapped cells form immediately upon contact with the high calcium concentration. These are transferred to a reactor of the type shown in which air-sparging levitates the beads in a column. Addition or withdrawal of medium from the reservoir allows for the provision of substrates for specific biotransformation reactions and for the harvesting of desired products. (b) Schematic diagram of a hollow-fibre reactor. Plant cells are entrapped by a two-step procedure. First, a concentrated plant cell suspension is loaded into a sterile syringe and introduced via ports to the shell side of the reactors. Second, the ports are hermetically sealed and aerated medium is supplied through the fibre lumen using a flow arrangement similar to that shown in (a). An asymmetric fibre membrane allows the flow of precursors and products but not cell debris or any other solid contaminants.

Variation and instability in metabolite production

A common observation has been the wide variability in amounts and types of secondary metabolite produced by cell cultures raised from different mother plants and even from a single mother plant. Evidence indicates that the genotype of the mother plant determines the relative productivity of cell cultures. Kinnersley & Dougall (1980) found that isogenic lines of tobacco, differing only in their ability to produce nicotine, gave cultures which correlated well with their respective nicotine genotypes, i.e. high-yielding mother plants tended to give high-yielding cultures whilst low-yielding mother plants gave low-yielding cultures with respect to nicotine, However, even within a high-yielding strain, culture lines are generally produced which vary significantly from the mean levels of metabolite expected under a given set of cultural conditions. Most frequently, it is a loss of productivity which occurs and the reasons for this are still not known (see Böhm, 1982). One method which has been found to be successful for generating productive cell lines (clones) from declining cultures has been single-cell clonal selection (Fig. 8.6). With metabolites that can be detected visibly (such as anthocyanins, quinones, betacyanins and carotenoids) it is possible to easily distinguish high from low producers and to positively screen very high numbers of cell colonies and so generate more productive cell lines. In other cases, quantitative analysis of cellular accumulation patterns of specific metabolites, e.g. rosmarinic acid and cinnamoyl putrescines, has been attempted with some success using microspectrophotometry in the

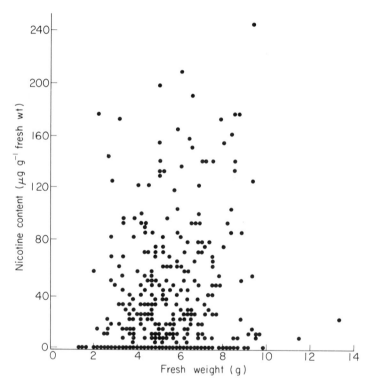

Fig. 8.6. The relationship between cell fresh weight and nicotine content of single cell-derived clines of tobacco from which high and low nicotine-producing lines were isolated (unpublished data of Dr. D. W. Pearson). Cell suspension cultures were filtered to obtain fine suspensions which were then diluted with fresh and conditioned medium to suitable densities for plating out. Single cell-derived colonies were taken at random, transferred to a nicotine production medium and then after 50–60 days growth screened for nicotine content. The figures shows the alkaloid-growth distributions of single cell-derived clones obtained from a low-producing cell suspension culture of *Nicotiana tabacum cv.* NC2512.

visible and u.v. range (B. Ellis, 1982). In both situations, stable high-yielding lines are not frequently encountered, though when these are they are clearly of great value to any production system. The requirement for the appropriate use of cryopreservation techniques with which selected cell lines could be held indefinitely for future production purposes is clear.

Problems with mass cultivation of plant cells

Several fundamental properties of plant cells must be taken into account when considering their possible use in mass growth and metabolite production. To begin with, plant cells are of the order of 10–100 times larger than bacterial or fungal cells, being generally between 20 μm and 150 μm in diameter. They are more dense and exhibit a wide variety of shapes and sizes during culture. Cell volumes during culture may vary by as much as 10^5, cells being typically small and densely cytoplasmic at the beginning of log growth and large with peripheral cytoplasm during the stationary phase. The cell walls of plant cells are of high tensile strength but of low shear resistance. This reduces the use of conventional microbial fermentation vessels which are usually designed to develop high levels of shear and which make use of impellers or stirring paddles to aid gas transfers. A wide variety of vessels has been used to grow plant cells (see review by Fowler, 1982). Vessels range from 2 l to 20,000 l in size. Figure 8.7 illustrates some of the types that have been developed over recent years to cope with these specific problems posed

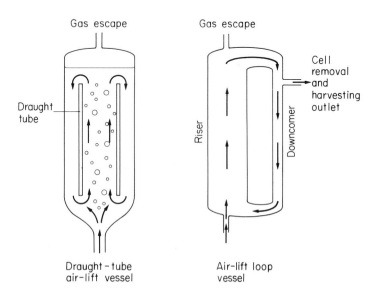

Fig. 8.7. Basic types of air-lift bioreactors adapted specifically for large-scale plant cell culture.

by plant cells. Various types of airlift system can support biomass levels of 30 g l^{-1} dry weight without the development of stagnant zones. One important consideration with air-lift systems is that mixing capacity is linked with gassing; merely increasing aeration rate does not solve a problem of poor mixing since high gassing levels can be inhibitory to growth and metabolite formation. One solution for this is to use complex mixtures of gases for aeration and to optimize the relative gas levels used at different total gassing levels. Data available for biomass productivity from plant cell cultures are encouraging from the point of view of potential industrial use. Levels of 3·82 g $l^{-1}d^{-1}$ and 6·9 g $l^{-1}d^{-1}$ have been obtained for tobacco cells grown in 1500 and 35 l vessels, respectively (Fowler, 1983).

At present, there are few examples of plant compounds which are being produced on a large industrial scale using plant cell cultures. The ones which have been publicized are the production of a phosphodiesterase and ubiquinone-10 from tobacco cells and the production of shikonin from *Lithospermium* sp. Other processes are now reaching pilot-scale industrial levels, such as the production of antitumour alkaloids by productive cell strains of *Catharanthus roseus*. Many others have been patented for potential industrial use should future economic or political pressures warrant it.

Biotransformation using plant cell cultures

Besides accumulating secondary metabolites of commercial significance, plant cells can be used to great advantage to accomplish certain changes in the structure and composition of industrially important chemicals. This conversion of a small part of a molecule by means of biological systems is termed biotransformation and has been utilized on a massive industrial scale in the steroid industry. Certain species of bacteria and fungi raised in fermentors have been used for many years to accomplish the specific alterations in the phenanthrene ring structure and side-chain composition of several plant-derived steroids, e.g. diosgenin, to produce the steroid sex hormones and anabolics (Aharonowitz & Cohen, 1981). Similar types of biotransformation have been achieved on a laboratory scale using plant cell cultures (for review see Stohs, 1977); the major types of biotransformation reported in plant cell cultures are summarized in Table 8.8. To date, plant tissue cultures have been used in only one instance for achieving a specific biotransformation on a large scale. This is in the production of the cardiovascular steroid, digoxin from digitoxin obtained from *Digitalis* spp. (foxglove). Although undifferentiated cell cultures of *D. lanata* do not produce cardiac glycosides, they are nevertheless able to perform special biotransformations on cardenolide glycosides added to the medium (Fig. 8.8). Various cell lines of *Digitalis* have been isolated and identified from plants which

Table 8.8. Biotransformations which can be achieved by plant cell cultures.

Reactions	Substrate	Product
Reduction	$C = C$	$CH_2 - CH_2$
	$C = C - CO$	$CH_2 - CH_2 - CO$
		or $CH_2 - CH_2 - CHOH$
	CO	$CHOH$
	CHO	CH_2OH
Oxidation	CH_3	CH_2OH
		or $COOH$
	CH_2OH	CHO
	$CHOH$	CO
	$= S$	$S = O$
Hydroxylation	CH	$C - OH$
	CH_2	$CH - OH$
	NH_2	$NH - OH$
Epoxidation	$CH = CH$	$- HC - CH -$
		$\diagdown\diagup$
		O
Glycosylation	OH	$O - glucose$
	$COOH$	$COO\text{-glucose}$
	CH	$C - glucose$
	N	$N^+ - arabinose$
Esterification	OH	$O - palmitate$
	$COOH$	$COO\text{-malate}$
	NH	$N\text{-acetate}$
Methylation	OH	$O - CH_3$
and demethylation	N	$N^+ - CH_3$
	$N^+ - CH_3$	$= NH$
Isomerization	trans	cis
	dextra	Laevo-rotation
	$\beta - OH$	$\alpha - OH$

were rich in digoxin and which perform these conversions (with the exception of the possible lanatoside to digoxin conversion) and these have been shown to be capable of biotransformation (via the 12β-hydroxylation step) of various forms of digitoxin, especially methylated digitoxin, on a large (200 l) scale (Fig. 8.9). Air-lift bioreactors of the down-draft type were used. It has also been demonstrated that these biotransformation reactions can be achieved successfully using immobilized cells of *Digitalis* (Alfermann *et al.*, 1983). This demonstrates the great potential for immobilization of plant cells since when appropriately applied, the plant cells are capable of functioning over a much longer time period (Fig. 8.10) thus helping to reduce the overall costs of the process. However, as discussed in the last section, plant cell cultures still suffer from the major disadvantages that scaling-up processes are expensive and slow due to the inherently slow growth rates of plant cell fermentations. There is, therefore, great scope for the development of

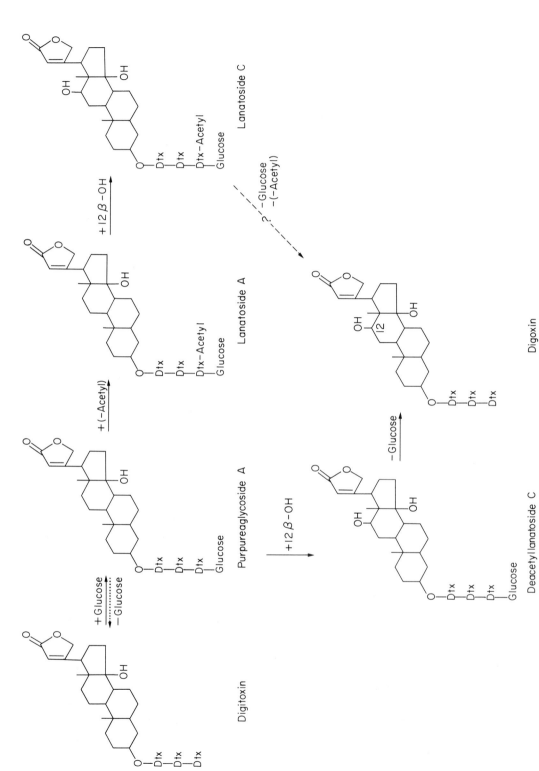

Fig. 8.8. Biotransformation steps involved in the production of digoxin from digitoxin by cell cultures of *Digitalis* spp. (after Alfermann *et al.*, 1983).

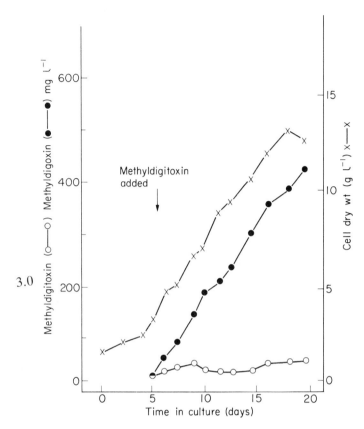

Fig. 8.9. Biotransformation of β-methyldigitoxin to β-methyldigoxin by *Digitalis* cells in a 200-l airlife reactor (after Alfermann *et al.*, 1983).

microbes which would be capable of some of these specific biosynthetic and biotransformation reactions through the insertion of specific plant genes into microbes using recombinant DNA techniques; the possibility is discussed in the last section of this chapter.

Enzymes from plants

Any living organism can be considered as a potential source of enzymes. However, only a limited number of plant and animal species yield commercially important enzymes. The greatest diversity and volume of enzymes come from micro-organisms, and these are now replacing plant and animal products in industrial processes on economic grounds.

In 1981, the amount of commercial industrial enzymes available on the world market was approximately 65,000 tonnes, with a value of 400 million dollars. This market is predicted to reach 75,000 tonnes by 1985 with a value of 600 million dollars. Surprisingly, all the available enzymes are produced by approximately twenty-five companies, of

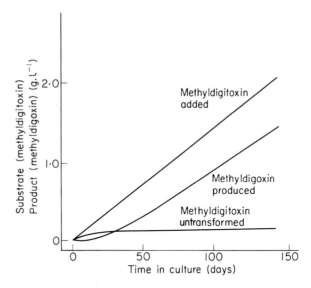

Fig. 8.10. Biotransformation of β-methyldigitoxin to β-methyldigoxin achieved by *Digitalis* cells immobilized in alginate beads (after Alfermann & Reinhard 1980). Immobilization in alginate is usually achieved by mixing cells with alginic acid (3–4% w/v) and then dripping the mixture into culture media containing relatively high levels of $CaCl_2$. The high Ca sets the dripping mixture to a solid gel on contact thus forming beads containing entrapped cells. After entrapment beads are washed free of excess Ca^{++} before culture in conventional plant cell bioreactors or ones of the type shown in Fig. 8.5(a).

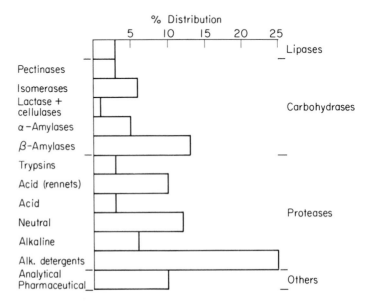

Fig. 8.11. Distribution of industrial enzymes by general type.

which about six are dominant both in terms of their annual volume and value of production. Among the western nations, Denmark accounts for 50% of all enzymes produced, Holland 20%, and the USA 12%. In the case of the US this is for local use. The remaining 18% is produced by Japan, W. Germany, Switzerland, France, the UK and Eire. Enzyme produced by Eastern Bloc countries does not reach the world market.

Figure 8.11 shows a breakdown of the general types of industrial enzymes. Over 80% of these are hydrolytic in nature, of which the proteases are used mainly in the dairy, detergent and leather industries. The carbohydrases are used in the brewing, baking, distilling and textile industries. It should be noted that the categories of enzymes listed, representing about thirty activity types, consititute only a small fraction of the thousands of identified and characterized enzymes. The inference to be made from this is that a lot of research and development has to take place before the production of an enzyme becomes a commercially viable proposition.

The bulk of enzymes used commercially are obtained from microbial sources, and are produced by fermentation processes. There are many reasons why production from microbes is preferred; the supply can be changed rapidly to meet market needs, the cost is low, and the product is available usually in several grades. Plant and animal enzyme supply tends to be erratic and can often be influenced adversely by climate, season, agricultural policy and political unrest. However, there are still several plant enzymes which have not yet been replaced by substitutes from micro-organisms. Among these are the plant sulphydryl proteases which include the papaya proteases from *Carica papaya* (Arnon, 1970), the main member of which is papain; bromelain from pineapple (*Ananas comosus*) (Murachi, 1970) and ficin from fig (*Ficus glabrata*) (Liener & Friedenson, 1970). Other enzymes derived from plants — including the amylolytic enzymes from cereals, α and β-amylase, the lipoxygenases of soya bean, and the pectic enzymes of citrus fruits — are all used in industrial processes, although they have now tended to be replaced by similar bacterial and fungal enzymes. Nevertheless, a knowledge of their action is essential when considering the processing of plant food products which contain these enzymes.

Sulphydryl proteases

As the name implies, these most important plant enzymes have a sulphydryl group at their active site, at which a histidine residue is also involved. Furthermore, the amino acid sequence around this active site is highly conserved (Fig. 8.12; Ramshaw, 1982). These proteases are all activated by oxidizing agents, are inactivated by reducing agents, are all of similar molecular weight, have conserved amino acid sequences, are all basic, and exhibit high isoelectric points. A few of the properties of

	20					25					
Papain	gly	ser	cys	gly	ser	cys	trp	ala	phe	ser	ala
Bromelain	asn	pro	cys	gly	ala	cys	trp	gly	phe	ala	ala
Ficin	gly	gly	cys	gly	ser	cys	trp	–	–	–	–

	160				165		
Papain	lys	val	asp	his	ala	val	ala
Bromelain	lys	leu	asn	his	ala	val	thr
Ficin	ser	leu	asp	his	ala	val	ala

Fig. 8.12. Conservation of amino acid sequence at the active site of sulphydryl proteases.

the sulphydryl proteases are summarized in Table 8.9. The proteases are isolated from plant latex or from the juice of the fruit, as in the case of bromelain from pineapple. Some confusion in nomenclature has arisen since names for these enzymes have often been given to either a mixture of enzymes, or the individual enzymes after purification from a mixture. Proteases obtained from many sources are used in industrial processes, but those from papaya, particularly papain, are most widely used. This is due to a number of factors; namely its availability, reasonable cost and biochemical effectiveness. The biochemical characteristics of this enzyme which make it particularly suitable for industrial application are as follows. Papain has a very broad substrate specificity (Table 8.10) with most bonds in protein substrates being hydrolysed and degraded more fully than with pepsin, trypsin or chymotrypsin. Cleavage of a particular peptide bond may not be indiscriminate and the amino acid residue one removed from the carboxyl bond may be important, particularly if it is tyrosine or phenylalanine. Papain is highly stable even under extreme conditions, and this enhances its storage properties. The enzyme is stable at high temperatures, and it resists dry heat at 100°C for 3 hours, which accounts for its application in certain processes discussed below. Papain is also unaffected by denaturing agents, retains

Table 8.9. Some general properties of the sulphydryl proteases.

Protease	Mol. wt	Isoelectric pt	Amino acid seq.	Glycolsylation
Papain	23,426	8·75	complete	–
Bromelain	33,500	9.55	partial	+
Ficin	25,500	>9·55	partial	+/−

Table 8.10. Preferential cleavage sites of the sulphydryl proteases.

Protease	Preferential cleavage
Papain	Arg-, Lys-, Phe-X-, Tyr-X-.
Bromelain	Lys-, Ala-, Gly-, Tyr-.
Ficin	Lys-, Ala-, Gly-, Tyr-, Leu-, Val-, Asn-.

its activity in 8M urea, and can be crystallized from 70% methanol. It also has a wide pH stability, pH 4–10, the optimum for most substrates being pH 5–7.

Bromelain and ficin have similar substrate specificity to that of papain but are generally less stable, particularly at elevated temperatures when dried and at extremes of pH.

The major industrial use of papain is in the brewing industry where it is used to stabilize and chill-proof beers mainly to prevent haze production, a major factor which determines the shelf life of some beers (MacLoed, 1977). Hazes form when polyphenols, proteins and possibly carbohydrates form complexes which are insoluble. Chill hazes occur when these complexes come out of solution at low temperatures. These can be removed by filtration at low temperature, but eventually permanent haze forms even at room temperature. The method of choice is to add a proteolytic enzyme, usually papain, at about 1–5 g of liquid product per 100 litres of beer. This treatment hydrolyses the proteins, derived from barley, hops and yeast, and leaves no insoluble residue. The mechanism of hydrolytic action is unclear. Often the enzyme is added before pasteurization of the beer takes place and it appears to be active during this process at 60–70°C.

The second largest use of papain is in meat tenderization, carried out by the housewife or, commercially, by the meat industry where it usually involves pre-slaughter injection of animals. The protease is most effective at between 40°C and 70°C during cooking; even collagen which undergoes unfolding of the triple helix structure at 55–65°C is attacked.

Proteases find use in the following industries:
(a) bread-making, to improve the handling properties of dough;
(b) leather, to remove undesirable proteins adhering to hides;
(c) textiles, in the treatment of wool to produce shrink-resistant yarn;
(d) laundries, as a stain remover.

There have also been several medicinal applications of the sulphydryl proteases:
(a) as a digestive aid in the treatment of dyspepsia;
(b) as de-worming agents;

(c) as an intraperitoneal to prevent post-operative adhesions;
(d) as a 'biological' scalpel in the treatment of burns to remove scar tissue.

A summary of the industrial applications of the sulphydryl proteases is given in Table 8.11.

Table 8.11. Industrial applications of the sulphydryl proteases.

Enzyme	Industry	Permitted in or on	pH optimum range	Operating temperature (Max) °C
All three	Meat tenderizing	Beer; ale; porter; stout; collagen sausage casings; hydrolysed protein, animal, vegetable, milk; meat tenderizing preparations; meat cuts; pumping pickle for curing meat cuts.		
Papain	Protein hydrolysates Beer chill-proofing Baking	Meat before slaughter; instant cereal;	5–7	65–70
Bromelain	Digestive aid Clinical applications	Bread; flour; whole wheat flour.	5–7	50
Ficin	Protein hydrolysates		5–7·5	50

The amylolytic enzymes

The main plant amylolytic enzymes α- and β-amylase are found in germinated barley (malt). The malting process leads to increases in the content of α- and β-amylase and, as a result, the starchy endosperm of barley seed is converted to sugars. These are then fermented by yeasts to make beer. The action of the two enzymes during the mashing process of beer-making converts the starch to a mixture of maltose and glucose, yielding approximately 80% fermentable products from the original starch. Starch is not homogeneous but consists of two high molecular weight polysaccharides: amylose which has a linear structure, and amylopectin which has a branched structure. α-amylase is an endoamylase, i.e. it hydrolyses α-1, 4-glucosidic bonds in the substrate interior but no closer than a few glucose units from the α-1, 6 branch point; whereas β-amylase is a sulphydryl exoamylase, i.e. it hydrolyses alternate α-1, 4-glucosidic bonds. Both enzymes are unable to hydrolyse the α-1, 6-glucosidic linkage characteristic of amylopectin, and in the brewing process this is achieved by using bacterial pullulanases, in addition to fungal amyloglucosidases (Lyons, 1983).

Lipoxygenases

These enzymes, originally called unsaturated fatty acid oxidases, are important not for their commercial applications, but for their endogenous action on a wide variety of processed foodstuffs. The enzymes were first isolated from, and thought to be restricted to, the legumes. Table 8.12 shows a few of the plant species in which they have now been found. They are also present in animals, particularly vertebrates.

The lipoxygenases are a large group of diverse enzymes (Axelrod, 1974). The soybean lipoxygenase is a globular protein of approximately 100,000 MW and it is now known to contain one molecule of iron per molecule. Lipoxygenase is a dioxygenase which catalyses the hydro-peroxidation of cis−cis pentadienes, and it is selective both for certain substrates and for positions in substrates. These include straight chain fatty acids, esters, alcohols and halides. The 1,4-pentadiene structure is found in essential polyunsaturated fatty acids, for example linolein, linolenic and arachidonic acid.

This ability of lipoxygenase to promote the peroxidation of the nutritionally essential polyunsaturated fatty acids can affect a number of properties of a plant product, such as taste, odour and colour, as well as influencing ripening and abcission. In soybean, there is a direct correlation between bitterness and the activity of lipoxygenase during development and maturation. In preparation of soybean meal, the mixture must be heated in order to inactivate trypsin inhibitor, haemag-glutinins, and this also inactivates the lipoxygenase. Similarly, lipoxy-genase activity also causes 'off' flavours in green peas, particularly unblanched frozen and stored peas (Wagenknecht & Lee, 1956), and underblanched sweet corn (Wagenknecht, 1959). One of the first reactions associated with lipoxygenase is the bleaching of yellow pig-ments in flour. Many pigments are destroyed such as chlorophyll, carotene, xanthophylls, cholesterol and vitamin A. The loss of carotenes and vitamin A is, however undesirable (Frey *et al.*, 1936). In contrast, lipoxygenase may also have beneficial effects. These include the improvement of dough's rheological and baking properties through the

Table 8.12. Some lipoxygenase containing plants.

Tomato	Egg plant
Soybean	Peas
Wheat	Peanut
Maize	Potatoes
Barley	Rape
Beans	Squash
Apple	Cauliflower
Alfalfa	

indirect oxidation of protein sulphydryl groups by lipoxygenase (Irvine, 1955).

Finally, this group of enzymes has been implicated in ethylene production in various fruits, mainly apple, in a reaction involving linolenic acid (Lieberman & Mapson 1964). At the climacteric stage lipoxygenase activity increases in parallel with rises in both respiration and ethylene production.

Pectic enzymes

Pectic enzymes are responsible for the degradation of plant pectic substances, which have an important structural role in both the primary cell wall and the middle lamella. Breakdown of these substances leads to plant tissue maceration. These enzymes occur in the plant and are involved in natural ripening processes (Spencer, 1965), and in abscission (LaMotte *et al.*, 1969). They are also produced by various plant pathogens and spoilage organisms.

One of the group of pectic enzymes, the pectinesterases, are found in many fruits and vegetables, with large amounts being present in tomato and citrus fruits. They are specific for pectin (esterified α-1,4 linked galacturonic acid) which is hydrolysed to polygalacturonate and methanol. De-esterification of fruit and vegetable tissue by pectinesterase during ripening, or storage, is thought to preceed degradation by polygalacturonase, which leads to fruit softening (Deuel & Stutz, 1958).

Polygalacturonases, another group of pectic enzymes, degrade the polygalacturonate produced by the action of pectinesterase on pectin, the products being oligo- or mono-galacturonate depending on whether the enzyme is an endo-(Rombouts & Pilnik, 1972) or an exo-(Hatanaka & Ozawa, 1963) polygalacturonase. The pectic enzymes which occur naturally in plants can influence commercial processes. If the enzymes are not inactivated, deleterious softening of canned fruit and increased viscosity of the suspending syrup can result. In jams and jellies, degradation of pectin in over-ripe fruit can result in loss of gel formation. However, in preparation of citrus fruit and tomato juices it is essential that pectins are degraded to some extent, and measurement of the pectinesterase and polygalacturonase activities often provide solutions to some of the problems encountered in production.

Genetic resource

Transfer of plant genes to micro-organisms

The technique of recombining DNA *in vitro* and of transferring DNA to bacterial host cells has, over the last few years, contributed greatly to our understanding of both the structure and function of the genomes of many organisms. There are several reasons why the transfer of genes from plants to micro-organisms is desired. By exploiting known mechanisms of gene expression in bacteria, the possibility of increasing the expression of eukaryotic proteins, which generally occurs at very low levels in their natural situations, has become reality. A classical example of this has been the recombinant DNA manipulation of the α and β interferon genes (Scott & Tyrrell, 1980). Other products from eukaryotes can be studied in the same way and their production in microbes maximized. There would also exist the possibility of making precise changes in polypeptides, by altering the nucleotide composition of genes thereby changing, for example, selected amino acids at the active site of an enzyme as outlined by Lathe *et al.*, 1983, and as discussed below.

Most if not all genes which are cloned using recombinant DNA techniques are inserted into micro-organisms, usually *E. coli*. This is simply because the methods used to manipulated DNA clones in this bacterium are so well practised. The amino acid sequence of proteins encoded by genes can be determined much more quickly by sequencing the nucleic acid than by conventional amino acid sequencing techniques. Also the structure and position of the 3' and 5' controlling signals can be elucidated and compared with other eukaryotic and prokaryotic cloned and studied genes. The accumulation of this information alone helps to build up a picture of the structure and organization of the genomes of different organisms. What plant genes are we likely to want to transfer to micro-organisms? The list of genes one would like to clone would be very extensive. Reference to Table 3.2 shows the plant genes which have currently been cloned. From a purely practical experimental point of view, plant genes which have been cloned are those which are relatively easy to manipulate, either because gene products are known, or because they are chloroplast or mitochondrial genes. These organelles are relatively easy to isolate, and most of their major polypeptide genes are expressed, either at high levels or preferentially in particular tissues at certain stages of development. Cloning other genes coding for products which are present at low levels in cells will be more problematical.

Microbial production of plant products

Currently only two plant genes have actually been shown to be expressed in *E. coli*. These are genes coding for (prepro) thaumatin (Edens *et al.*, 1982) and the large subunit of ribulose bisphosphate carboxylase (RuBPCase) (Gatenby *et al.*, 1981; Gatenby & Castleton, 1982). Thaumatin is the sweet-tasting protein isolated from *Thaumatococcus daniellii*, a West African shrub, and is encoded in the nuclear genome. In contrast, the large subunit of RuBPCase is encoded in the chloroplast genome.

There are several problems associated with the expression of eukaryotic DNA in *E. coli*, consequent on the differences in organization of prokaryotic and eukaryotic genes. The most important difference is the presence in genes of higher eukaryotes of intervening sequences or introns. Bacteria have no mechanism for the removal of these sequences from the primary transcript (as occurs in eukaryotes), so that eukaryotic DNA cannot in general be expressed in bacteria. As described in this chapter, the problem can be circumvented either by the use of cDNA cloning procedures or, where the amino acid sequence of the protein is known, the use of an artificial gene which is synthesized chemically (Edge *et al.*, 1981). The second difference is that prokaryotes and eukaryotes do not make use of the same transcription signals; see Breathnach & Chambon 1981 and Appendix I. However, by insertion of the constructed DNA adjacent to a strong prokaryotic promoter in the cloning vector, transcription can be controlled. To this end four bacterial promoters have been utilized. The *lac* promoter from the *E. coli lac* operon (Glass, 1982) has been used in the construction of vector plasmids (Itakura *et al.*, 1977; Fuller, 1982), and was used in the expression of thaumatin (Edens *et al.*, 1982) and numerous animal gene products such as those of rat proinsulin (Talmadge *et al.*, 1981) and chicken ovalbumin (Baty *et al.*, 1981) in bacterial cells. The *trp* promoter of the *E. coli trp* operon (Glass, 1982) has also been used in the construction of expression vectors (Hallewell & Emtage, 1980) again for the purpose of achieving expression of thaumatin, as well as of numerous other viral and mammalian gene products (Harris, 1983). Another promoter which has often been used is the strong leftward promoter P_L of bacteriophage λ (Derynck *et al.*, 1980; Derom *et al.*, 1982). This promoter has also been used in transcriptional fusions with the gene which codes for the chloroplast RuBPCase (Gatenby *et al.*, 1981; Gatenby, 1983). Finally, the weak constitutive β-lactamase (penicillinase) promoter present on plasmid pBR322 has also been used, particularly in the synthesis of fusion proteins (Villa-Komaroff *et al.*, 1978). This particular construction may be particularly useful as the fusion protein contains the β-lactamase NH_2-terminal signal sequence, and consequently the hybrid protein may be secreted into the bacterial periplasmic space.

Increased expression from vectors can be achieved by using high copy number plasmids in their construction, thereby increasing the gene dosage and hence the amount of product obtainable (O'Farrell *et al.*, 1978). Transcription termination is achieved by incorporating a termination site after the cloned gene (Nakamura & Inowye, 1982; Rosenberg & Court, 1979). Other problems arise with regard to the translation of eukaryotic-derived mRNA in prokaryotes. Eukaryotic mRNA does not have the equivalent of the prokaryotic ribosome binding site (rbs), which consists of the initiation codon (AUG) and the Shine–Dalgarno (SD) sequence of 3–9 bases which are complementary to the 3' end of the 16S rRNA (Shine & Dalgarno, 1975), and which are believed to be involved in the binding of the 30S ribosomal subunit. These problems may be overcome either by fusing the inserted foreign gene, in the correct reading frame, to a prokaryotic gene the rbs of which is used to initiate translation (Backman & Ptashne, 1978), or by using the rbs of the eukaryotic gene, as was done in the case of the large subunit of RuBPCase (Gatenby, 1983) However, the expression of chloroplast genes in bacteria represents a special case since these genes have a ribosome binding site of their own. Termination of transcription is usually not a problem as prokaryotes and eukaryotes both use one or more of the three termination codons. However, one problem which may affect the efficiency of translation is that of codon usage. The codons used in the mRNA of highly expressed prokaryotic genes are not random (Grosjean & Fiers, 1982), and these appear to correlate with the abundances of specific tRNA species (Ikemura, 1981). In addition, bacterial cells do not perform the post-translation modifications which occur to many eukaryotic proteins, and besides that, many factors which affect the stability, folding and degradation of proteins in bacteria are still not well understood.

Modification of plant genes

Over recent years recombinant DNA techniques have become more widely available, enabling scientists to manipulate specific pieces of DNA in a precise manner. This ability applies to eukaryotic DNA because it can be inserted into a prokaryote in which manipulation is much easier. The next logical step after having cloned genes from higher organisms, and engineered their expression in bacteria, would be to alter that gene with a view to studying the properties of any altered product. The purpose of this would be to study enzymic protein subunit interactions, and any functional changes in enzyme specificity or enzymatic properties which might occur as a consequence of gene manipulation. The techniques involved in this type of work have been recently reviewed by Lathe *et al.* (1983) and Smith & Gillam (1981). They include generalized mutagenesis, a technique which bacterial geneticists have employed with success for a number of years. However, the ability to manipulate DNA means that site mutations can now be more precisely made. Indeed, techniques are now available to specifically change a chosen base sequence under some circumstances. Oligonucleotide-directed mutagenesis provides the only precise means for achieving a desired mutation (Fig. 8.13). This is due to the ease with which defined oligonucleotide sequences can now be acquired. The method has certain basic requirements; the gene obviously must have

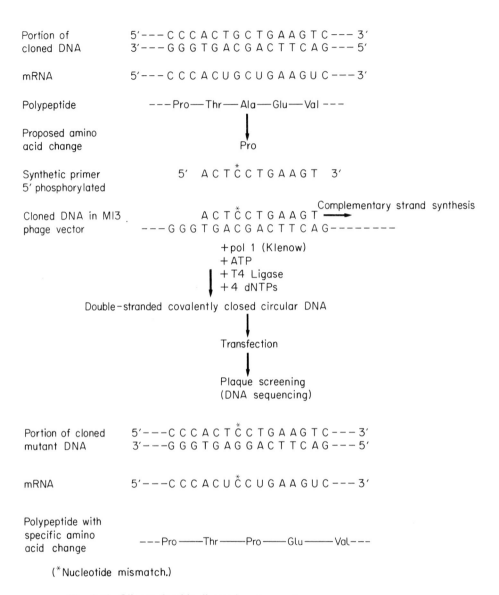

Portion of
cloned DNA

5′‒‒‒C C C A C T G C T G A A G T C ‒‒‒ 3′
3′‒‒‒G G G T G A C G A C T T C A G ‒‒‒ 5′

mRNA

5′‒‒‒C C C A C U G C U G A A G U C ‒‒‒ 3′

Polypeptide

‒‒‒Pro‒‒Thr‒‒Ala‒‒Glu‒‒Val ‒‒‒

Proposed amino
acid change

Pro

Synthetic primer
5′ phosphorylated

5′ A C T C̊ C T G A A G T 3′

Cloned DNA in MI3
phage vector

A C T C̊ C T G A A G T ‒‒‒‒‒‒‒► Complementary strand synthesis
‒‒‒G G G T G A C G A C T T C A G‒‒‒‒‒‒‒

+ pol 1 (Klenow)
+ ATP
+ T4 Ligase
+ 4 dNTPs

Double‒stranded covalently closed circular DNA

Transfection

Plaque screening
(DNA sequencing)

Portion of cloned
mutant DNA

5′‒‒‒C C C A C T C̊ C T G A A G T C ‒‒‒ 3′
3′‒‒‒G G G T G A G G A C T T C A G ‒‒‒ 5′

mRNA

5′‒‒‒C C C A C U C̊ C U G A A G U C ‒‒‒ 3′

Polypeptide with
specific amino
acid change

‒‒‒Pro‒‒‒‒Thr‒‒‒‒Pro‒‒‒‒Glu‒‒‒‒Val‒‒‒

(*Nucleotide mismatch.)

Fig. 8.13. Oligonucleotide-directed mutagenesis.

been cloned and sequenced, and the precise portion of the region of DNA in which the alteration is to be made must be known. For instance, in the case of an enzyme, it would be desirable to know the amino acid sequence, the three-dimensional structure of the molecule (through X-ray crystallography) as well as details of the active site. Next, the DNA to be mutagenized has to be present on a single-stranded DNA vector, such as bacteriophages ØX174, M13 or fd, since the short synthetic 5′ phosphorylated oligonucleotide must be complementary to the wild type sequence except for the mismatch which is to produce the desired mutation. This mutation may be one or two or more nucleotides in length, and deletions of up to 14 bases can be introduced (Gillam *et al.*, 1980; Wallace *et al.*, 1980). Three properties of the oligonucleotide primer are crucial: its length, its constituent sequences and the degree of mismatch. The primer must only hybridize to the site where the mutation is to be introduced, and no other site on the vector of the inserted gene sequence. With this in mind a knowledge of the complete nucleotide sequence of the inserted gene and the cloning vector is desirable. The primer will thus be at least 7, though preferably 10–12 nucleotides long, and the position of the mismatch must be at least three bases from the 3′ end of the primer. This will ensure that elongation of the primer by the *E. coli* DNA polymerase 1 Klenow fragment takes place, and that the proof-reading excision function of this enzyme will be avoided. Mutant progeny are identified from plaques after transfection of the bacterial host. A recent modification of the basic technique has improved the mutation isolation frequency (Kramer *et al.*, 1982). This powerful technique has so far been applied mainly to enzyme studies. In the case of tyrosyl-tRNA synthetase it has been possible to substitute individual amino acids at the active site and study their effect on the properties of this enzyme. Some changes are obviously deleterious but others did enhance certain properties of the enzyme. It is only a matter of time before such mutagenesis is applied to plant proteins which have been cloned.

Modified gene transfer to plants

The next step will be the transfer of genes, which have been cloned and modified in bacteria, back to the plant from which they were first isolated. However, there are several problems which must first be considered. As noted above, the control sequences specifying transcription and translation in eukaryotes and prokaryotes are not identical, although this problem has to a large extent already been recognized and solved in the construction of the Ti plasmid vectors (see Chapter 4). Therefore, there already exists a suitable means of transferring modifed genes into plants, or their cells in tissue culture.

One problem remains: integration of the altered gene into the site it would normally occupy on the host genome. When dealing with bacteria, their viruses and plasmids, and even simple eukaryotes, genetic 'tricks' can be used to ensure that there is *in vivo* homologous recombination; this has yet to be achieved in the case of higher eukaryotes. Where exogenous DNA has been stably integrated into eukaryotic host chromosomes, its location is random, and is often at multiple sites (Anderson *et al.*, 1982; Scangos *et al.*, 1981). For some applications and genes, this lack of homologous recombination may not be important.

However, it may be that the study of expression of the mutant gene is complicated and masked by the resident wild type allele. Also, the chromosomal location of the incoming mutant gene may greatly affect its behaviour and expression. This of course applies to any gene introduced into a plant whether or not its wild type partner is present.

Further reading

Alferman A.W. Reinhard E. (1980) Biotransformation by plant tissue cultures. *Bull. Soc. Chim. France*, **1–2**, 35–44.

Conn E.E. (1981) (Ed.) Secondary Plant Products. In: *The Biochemistry of Plants*, Vol. 7. Academic Press, New York.

Prenosil J.E. & Pederson H (1983). Immobilized plant cell reactors. *Enzyme Microb. Technol.* **5**, 323–331.

Staba E.J. (1980) (Ed.) *Plant Tissue Cultures a Source of Biochemicals*. CRC Press, Boca Raton, Florida.

Appendices

Appendix 1: Basic information for molecular biology

Structure of nucleic acids

Nucleic acids are built up from a sugar, a phosphate group and five nitrogenous bases: adenine (A), cytosine (C), guanine (G), uracil (U) and thymine (T). DNA contains A, C, G and T and the sugar is deoxy-D-ribose whereas RNA contains U instead of T and the sugar is D-ribose. These molecules have the following structures.

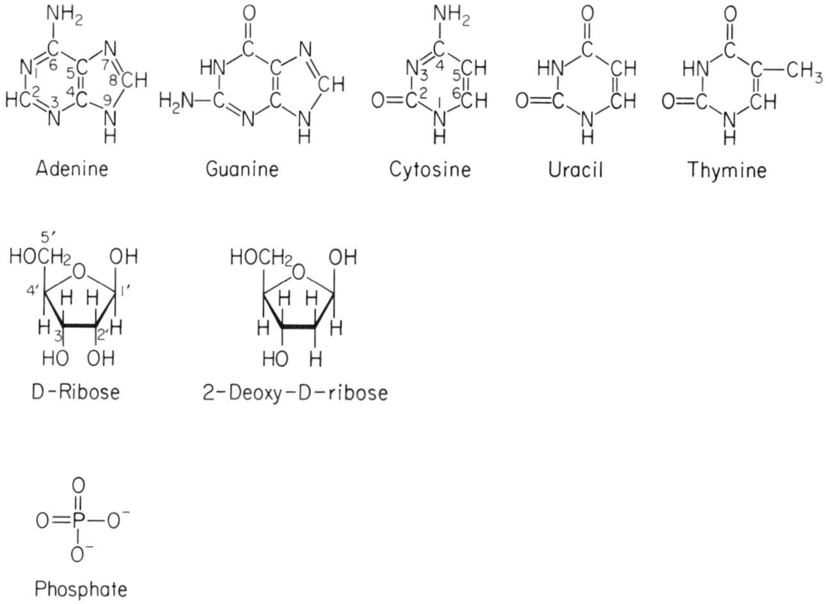

Fig. A1.1. Structure of the components of nucleic acids. The atoms of the bases are numbered 1, 2, 3 etc, whereas those of the sugars are numbered 1' to 5'.

The sugar residues are linked via the 1-hydroxyl group to the bases to form ribo- and deoxyribonucleosides which are called adenosine, guanosine, uridine and cytidine. The phosphate group is linked to the 5'-hydroxyl of the sugar, and this combination of sugar, base and phosphate is termed a ribo- or deoxyribo-nucleotide. These structures are illustrated below.

Nucleic acid chains are built up from the nucleotide triphosphates. During the process two phosphate groups (linked as pyrophosphate) are eliminated and the single phosphate group remaining on the 5'-hydroxyl group is linked to the 3'-hydroxyl group of the next residue. A nucleic acid chain has, therefore, a polarity; the 5' end has a free hydroxyl or phosphate group in the 5' position and the 3' end has it in the 3' position. Transcription of genes and translation of mRNA always takes

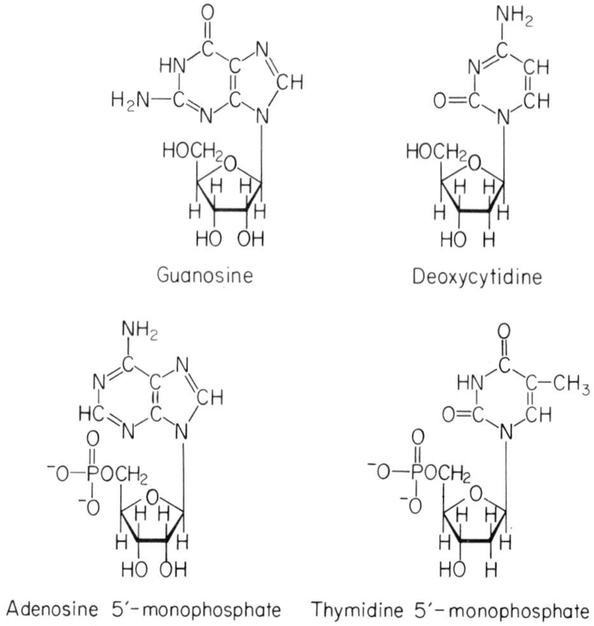

Fig. A1.2. Structure of ribo- and deoxyribo-nucleotides.

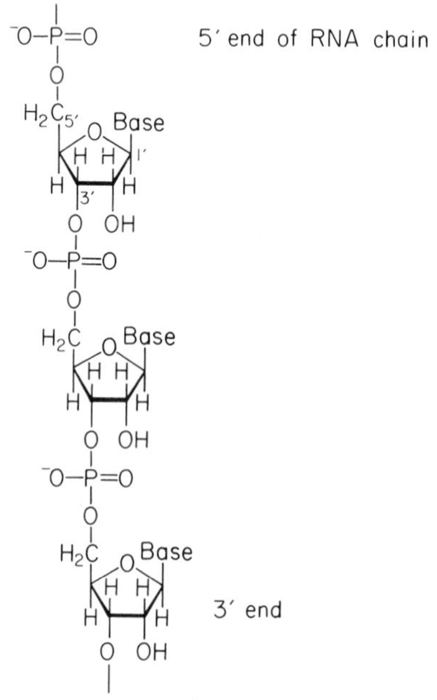

Fig. A1.3. Nucleic acid chain showing the linkages between nucleotides.

place from 5′ to 3′. The sugar and phosphate groups form the backbone of the molecule and in double-stranded DNA the bases interact in the centre of the helix to hold the structure together.

DNA specifies a protein by coding for the sequence of amino acids using triplets of residues. The code is the same for all organisms except for the DNA of the mitochondria which shows some variation. The table below shows the universal genetic code.

First position (5′ end)	Second position				Third position (3′ end)
	U	C	A	G	
U	Phe	Ser	Tyr	Cys	U
	Phe	Ser	Tyr	Cys	C
	Leu	Ser	Stop	Stop	A
	Leu	Ser	Stop	Trp	G
C	Leu	Pro	His	Arg	U
	Leu	Pro	His	Arg	C
	Leu	Pro	Gln	Arg	A
	Leu	Pro	Gln	Arg	G
A	Ile	Thr	Asn	Ser	U
	Ile	Thr	Asn	Ser	C
	Ile	Thr	Lys	Arg	A
	Met	Thr	Lys	Arg	G
G	Val	Ala	Asp	Gly	U
	Val	Ala	Asp	Gly	C
	Val	Ala	Glu	Gly	A
	Val	Ala	Glu	Gly	G

Fig. A1.4. The universal genetic code. Some variations occur in mitochondrial genomes; these are detailed in Chapter 2.

Many eukaryotic and prokaryotic genes have now been isolated and sequenced, and some general conclusions have been drawn about the nature of the sequences which control gene expression. Diagrams below show the structure of a typical gene from the two types of organisms with the various domains shown. Prior to the point where the mRNA chain is initiated there are promoter regions at which RNA polymerase binds. Between the initiation point of the mRNA and the initiation codon of the protein sequence there is a ribosome binding site which shows homology with one of the ribosomal RNAs (16s in prokaryotes, 18s in eukaryotes). At the end of the coding region there is a stop codon, often two together, specifying chain termination and, in eukaryotes, there is commonly a site which indicates the position of addition of the poly-adenylic acid tail which is a common feature of many mRNAs.

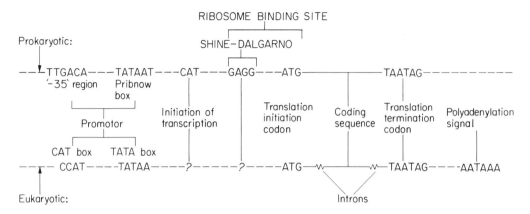

Fig. A1.5. Typical gene structures; in each case just one strand of the double-stranded DNA is shown. This one has the same 'sense' as the mRNA. The sequences shown are consensus sequences which are averages of which nucleotides most frequently occur at these sites. These precise sequences do not occur in every gene. There are not well-defined consensus sequences for the ribosome binding site and transcription initiation point of eukaryotic genes, although the sequence TAC has been observed at the initiation point in a number of genes. In eukaryotes, this is often called the 'cap' site, as it is believed that the transcript is capped (see Chapter 2) at the 5′ end (i.e. the initiation point) without the prior removal of any bases.

Appendix 2: Plasmid cloning vectors

Many plasmids have been constructed for molecular cloning bearing in mind needs for insertion sites, selectable drug resistance markers and biological safety (Brammar, 1982). One of the most widely used vectors is pBR322 (Fig. A2.1) which is a derivative of naturally occurring plasmid Col El. The attraction of pBR322 is that it is of low molecular weight (and therefore easy to handle), relatively high copy number within the cell and has a number of unique restriction sites allowing cloning with *Pst* I, *Hind* III, *Bam* HI, *Sal* I and *Eco* RI, among others.

A useful vector derived from pBR322 is pAT153 which was produced by deletion of two *Hae* II fragments (see Fig. A2.1). This plasmid has a 1·5−3 times higher copy number than pBR322, and the copy number can be increased greatly in the presence of a protein synthesis inhibitor such as chloramphenicol. This technique greatly enhances plasmid yield but is not applicable to pBR322. A second advantage of pAT153 is that it lacks DNA sequences essential for conjugal transfer, whereas pBR322, although itself non-transmissible, can be mobilized from cells carrying other combinations of plasmids. There is a greater degree of biological safety with pAT153, with less likelihood of recombinant plasmids, possibly carrying dangerous sequences, escaping into the environment.

The two plasmids share properties of drug resistance. Cloning into the *Pst* I site inactivates Ampicillin resistance (Ap^R) and cloning into

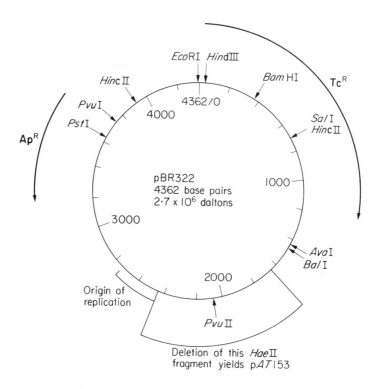

Fig. A2.1. Map of plasmid pBR322.

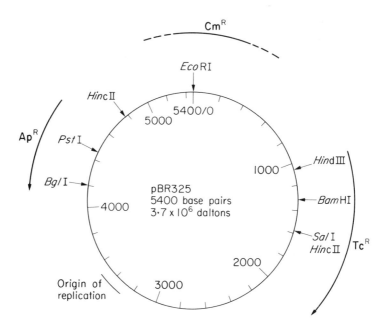

Fig. A2.2. Map of plasmid pBR325.

the *Bam* HI or *Sal* I sites inactivates tetracycline resistance (Tc^R). The *Hind* III site is in the promotor of the Tc^R gene and cloning often inactivates the gene. Inactivation of one drug resistance allows selection of recombinant plasmids over transformants carrying no plasmid or the native plasmid.

A slightly larger plasmid sometimes used is pBR325 (Fig. A2.2) which carries a chloramphenicol resistance gene (Cm^R) in addition to Tc^R and Ap^R. The single *Eco* RI site is found in the Cm^R gene enabling drug resistance selection of clones after cloning into this site. The position of the *Eco*RI site in pAT153 does not allow such selection.

These are three commonly used plasmids but are by no means all of them. Many other plasmids have been developed for specialist uses; for example, to facilitate sequencing or for use in other bacteria such as *Bacillus subtilis*. A glance through any molecular biologicals catalogue will demonstrate the multiplicity of available plasmids.

Appendix 3. Some media commonly used in plant tissue culture.

Ingredients (mg l^{-1})	MS	B5	White	Heller
$(NH_4)_2SO_4$		134		
$(NH_4)NO_3$	1650			
$NaNO_3$				600
KNO_3	1900	2500	80	
$Ca(NO_3)_2$			300	
$CaCl_2 . 2H_2O$	440	150		75
$MgSO_4 . 7H_2O$	370	250	720	250
Na_2SO_4			200	
KH_2PO_4	170			125
$NaH_2PO_4 . H_2O$		150	16·5	
KCl			65	750
$FeSO_4 . 7H_2O$	27·8	27·8		
Na_2EDTA	37·3	37·3		
$FeCl_3 . 6H_2O$				1·0
$Fe_2(SO_4)_3$			2·5	
$MnSO_4 . 4H_2O$	22·3		7	0·01
$MnSO_4 . H_2O$		10		
$ZnSO_4 . 7H_2O$	8·6	2	3	1
H_3BO_3	6·2	3	1·5	1
KI	0·83	0·75	0·75	0·01
$Na_2MoO_4 . 2H_2O$	0·25	0·25		
$CuSO_4 . 5H_2O$	0·025	0·025		0·03
$CoCl_2 . 6H_2O$	0·025	0·025		
$NiCl_2 . 6H_2O$				0·03
$AlCl_3$				0·03
Myo-inositol	100	100		
Nicotinic acid	0·5	1·0	0·5	
Pyridoxine . HCl	0·5	1·0	0·1	
Thiamine . HCl	0·1	10·0	0·1	1·0
Glycine	2·0		3·0	
Ca D-pantothenic acid			1·0	
Sucrose	30,000	20,000	20,000	20,000
Kinetin/BAP/2iP/*Zea*	0·04–10	0·1		
2,4-D		0·1–1·0	6·0	
IAA/NAA/IBA	1·0–30			
pH*	5·7–5·8	5·5	5·5	

* Prior to autoclaving.

Appendix 4. Sterilizing agents commonly used in plant cell and tissue culture.

Sterilizing agent	Levels used	Time of sterilization (mins)	Effectiveness
Calcium hypochlorite	9–10%	5–30	V. good
Sodium hypochlorite*	1–2%	5–30	V. good
Hydrogen peroxide	10–12%	5–15	Good
Mercuric chloride	0·1–1·0%	2–10	Satisfactory
Antibiotics	4–50 mg l^{-1}	30–60	Good

* 10–20% commercial bleach usually suffices.

Appendix 5. Four media commonly used in anther and pollen culture*.

Ingredients (mg l^{-1})	½ strength MS	H Medium	MM Medium	K Medium
KNO_3	950	950	2830	2500
$NH_4.NO_3$	825	720		
$(NH_4)_2SO_4$			463	134
$Ca(NO_3)_2.4H_2O$	220	166	166	750
KCl				
$MgSO_4.7H_2O$	185	185	185	250
KH_2PO_4	85	68	400	
$NaH_2PO_4.H_2O$				150
$MnSO_4.4H_2O$	11·2	25	4·4	10
H_3BO_3	3·1	10	1·6	3
$ZnSO_4.7H_2O$	4·3	10	1·5	2
KI	0·4		0·8	0·75
$Na_2MoO_4.2H_2O$	0·13	0·25		0·25
$CuSO_4.5H_2O$	0·013	0·025		0·025
$CoCl_2.6H_2O$	0·013			0·025
$FeSO_4.7H_2O$	14	27·8	27·8	†
Na_2EDTA	19	37·5	37·5	†
Thiamine HCl	0·05	0·5	1·0	10·0
Pyridoxine HCl	0·25	0·5	0·5	1·0
Nicotinic acid	0·25	5·0	0·5	1·0
Folic acid		0·5		
Biotin		0·05		
Glycine	1·0	2·0	2·0	
Glutamine				800
Myo-inositol	50	100		100
Sucrose	30,000	20,000	50,000	100,000
pH	5·5	5·5	5·8	5·8

* Other details quoted in Sunderland & Dunwell (1977).
† 40 mg l^{-1} sesquestrene 330 Fe used as Fe source.

Appendix 6. Examples of explant type and growth regulator requirement for callus formation, shoot initiation and multiplication and root development of herbaceous species propagated *in vitro*.

Species	Explant	Growth regulators used	Response
Freesia	Young flower buds	NAA (5) + BAP (2)	Callus
		Kin (5)	Shoots
Gladiolus	Axillary buds from new corms	BAP (0·12–0·5)	Shoots
		BAP (0·03)	Roots
Hyacinth	Bulb scales, bulb basal tissue, leaf, stem	None	Bulbils
Carnation	Shoot tips	Kin (2) + NAA (0·02)	Shoots
Gerbera	Lateral shoots	Kin (10) + IAA (0·5)	Shoots
		IAA (10)	Roots
African violet	Leaf lamina	Kin (2) + NAA (1)	Shoots/roots
	Petiole	IAA (0·01)	Callus
		BAP (0·5) + NAA (0·1)	Shoots
		Low light	Roots
	Floral parts	BAP (0·02) + NAA (0·2)	Callus
		BAP (0·1) + NAA (0·1)	Shoots
		Kin (0·1)	Roots
Rhubarb	Shoot tip from lateral buds	Kin (2·56) + NAA (8)	Shoots
		NAA (8)	Roots
Strawberry	Lateral buds	BAP (1)	Shoots
		None	Plantlets
Asparagus	Spear slices	NAA (0·5) + CM (15%) + Adenine sulphate (50)	Shoots
	Lateral buds	Kin (0·1) + NAA (0·1)	Shoots

Figures in parentheses are levels in mg l^{-1}.

Appendix 7. Examples of growth regulator requirements for shoot multiplication and rooting of woody fruit species propagated *in vitro* from shoot cultures.

Species/cultivar	Shoot multiplication	Rooting
Malus domestica		
Seedling (McIntosh)	Kinetin (5·8), IAA (57) and 15% CM	IAA (57)
Cox's Orange Pippin	Kinetin (0·5−4·7)	IBA (0·5) (8 h dip)
M.26	BA (4·4), IBA (5), GA (0·3) and phloroglucinol (1·26 mM)	IBA (5), GA (0·3) and phloroglucinol (1·26 mM)
M.7	BA (2·2)	IBA (10)
Prunus spp.	BA (4·4), 2,4-D (0·05) and GA (0·3)	IBA (5), GA (0·3) or IBA (5) dip
Pyrus communis		
Barlett	BA (5)	NAA (10)
Vitis vinifera		
Sylvaner Riesling	BA (10)	None
Cabernet Sauvignon	BA (5) or BA (8·8)	NAA (0−25) None
Rubus idaeus		
Malling Exploit	2,4-D (0·09), GA (0·3−3·0)	None (direct potting)
R. occidentalis		
Smoothstem	BA (4·4), IBA (5·0), GA (3·0)	IBA (5)
Actinidia chinensis	Zeatin (5)	IBA (5) or IAA (5·7) dip

Figures shown in parentheses are levels in mg l^{-1}.

Appendix 8. Examples of freeze preservation protocols devised from plant meristems, shoot apices, seedling, anthers or pollen embryos of different crop species.

Species	Material	Treatment	Freezing regime (°C)	Viability
Peanut	Meristems	Preculture on medium for 3–5 days with 5% each of sucrose, glycerol and DMSO	Rapid in LN$_2$	23–31% regrowth
Carnation	Shoot-tips	5% DMSO	Rapid in LN$_2$	15–33%
Strawberry	Meristems	Preculture for 2 days in 5% DMSO. Frozen in 50% DMSO	0·84°.min^{-1} to −40° LN$_2$	95%
Tomato	Seedlings	10–15% DMSO	LN$_2$ vapour	30%
Cassava	Meristems	Glycerol 10% + Sucrose 5%	Rapid in LN$_2$	8–13%
Pea	Meristems	Preculture for 2 days in medium containing 5% DMSO. Frozen in 5% DMSO	0·6°.min^{-1} to −40° LN$_2$ storage	60%
Potato	Meristems	5% glycerol	Rapid in LN$_2$	18%
Tobacco	Anthers	Preculture for 3–4 weeks. Frozen in 7% DMSO	2°.min^{-1}	1·5%
	Pollen embryos	5–7% DMSO	1–3°.min^{-1}	31%

Abbreviations

Auxins:

2,4-D	2,4-Dichlorophenoxyacetic acid
IAA	indole-3-acetic acid
IBA	indole-3-butyric acid
NAA	naphthaleneacetic acid

Cytokinins:

BAP	benzylaminopurine
2ip	2-isopentyladenine

Viruses:

BGMV	Bean golden mosaic
CaMV	Cauliflower mosaic
CTV	Curly top
MSV	Maize streak

Others:

ABA	abscisic acid
AT	3-amino-1,2,4-triazole
DCMU	3-(3,4-dichlorophenol)-1,1-dimethyl urea
DMSO	dimethylsulphoxide
DS	double-stranded
ELISA	enzyme-linked immunosorbent assay
EMS	ethylmethanesulphonate
GA	gibberellic acid
kb (p)	Kilobase (pairs)
Mdal	megadalton
NEU	N-ethyl-N-nitrosourea
NG	N-methyl-n'-nitrosoguanidine
PAGE	polyacrylamide gel electrophoresis
RuBPCase	ribulose 1,6-bisphosphate carboxylase oxygenase
SS	single-stranded
Ti	tumour-inducing plasmid of *Agrobacterium tumefaciens*

Glossary

Adventitious Adjective used to describe organs developing from positions on the plant from which they would not normally be derived, e.g. shoots from roots, leaves or callus and embryos from any cell other than a zygote.

Androgenesis Development of plants from male gametophytes.

Aneuploidy The loss or gain of chromosomes by various processes which result in abnormal chromosome complements at metaphase.

Angiosperms Flowering plants belonging to the Angiospermae, a subdivision of Spermatophyta. Distinguished from the other subdivision, the Gymnospermae, by having ovules borne within a closed cavity, the ovary. The Angiospermae includes two classes, the Monocotyledoneae and the Dicotyledoneae, distinguished by the number of seed leaves (cotyledons) in the embryo.

Annealing The repairing of complementary strands of DNA after denaturation.

Anticodon The tRNA molecule carries a triplet of bases which are complementary to the codon in the mRNA.

Apical dominance The phenomenon of suppression of growth of an axillary bud in the presence of the terminal bud on the branch.

Auxins A class of plant growth regulators which cause cell elongation, apical dominance and root initiation amongst other things. Indoleacetic acid (IAA), naphthaleneacetic acid (NAA) and 2,4-dichlorophenoxyacetic acid (2,4-D) are some of the auxins commonly used in plant cell and tissue culture work.

Axillary An adjective describing the relative position of a bud, i.e. axillary bud, in the axil of leaves.

Batch culture A suspension culture in which cells are grown in a finite volume of nutrient medium and follow a sigmoid pattern of growth.

Callus A tissue consisting of dedifferentiated cells generally produced as a result of tissue wounding or of culturing tissues in the presence of auxins in particular.

Cap The structure found on the 5'-end of eukaryotic mRNA consisting of an inverted, methylated guanosine residue.

Chemostat An open continuous culture in which cell growth rate and cell density are held constant by a fixed rate of input of a growth limiting nutrient.

Clone An assemblage of individuals derived by vegetative (asexual) means from a single mother plant or tissue.

Codon A group of three nucleotides coding for an amino acid.

Cohesive ends DNA with single-stranded ends which are complementary to each other, enabling the molecules to join, Bacterophage λ has cohesive ends (the 'cos' site) which allows the formation of concatamers.

Complementary DNA DNA synthesized by reverse transcriptase from an RNA template.

Concatamer DNA made up of repeated unit length DNAs.

Cybrid Product of somatic hybridization in which the chloroplast and mitochondrial genomes of one or other of the two partners fused are altered such that various mixtures of cytoplasmic genomes occur in the presence of a common nuclear genome.

Cytokinins A class of plant growth regulators which cause cell division, cell differentiation, shoot differentiation, and the breaking of apical dominance amongst other things. Some of the cytokinins commonly used in tissue culture are kinetin, benzylaminopurine (BAP), 2-isopentenyl-adenine (2iP) and zeatin.

Embryogenesis A pathway of differentiation which is characterized by the formation of organized structures that resemble zygotic embryos.

Embryoids Embryo-like structures produced as a consequence of differentiation processes such as embryogenesis and androgenesis.

Epigenetic changes Extranuclear heritable alterations in phenotype.

Exon The coding regions of a gene which are represented in the final mRNA.

Explant A piece of tissue used to initiate a tissue culture.

Flow cytometry A technique used to sort cells or other biological materials by means of flow through apertures of defined size.

Gametophyte Cells and tissues of the haploid stage of the life cycle of plants.

Gene Unit of the material of inheritance. Genes are composed of DNA and are arranged linearly on chromosomes. The DNA composing a gene unit occasionally undergoes a localized change in its sequence of nucleotides. This mutant form is replicated and inherited in the case of a genuine mutation.

Glycosylation Addition of sugar residues to proteins after translation.

Gymnosperms Cone-bearing plants of the Sporophyta.

Habituation The acquired ability of cells to grow and divide independently of growth regulators.

Haploid Having a single set of unpaired chromosomes in each nucleus. Characteristic of gametes.

Heterokaryon A cell in which two or more nuclei of unlike genetic make-up are present.

Histone Basic proteins found in close association with DNA in chromatin.

Immobilized cells Cells entrapped in matrices such as alginate, polyacrylamide and agarose designed for use in flatbed or column bioreactors.

Intron Sequence of DNA interrupting the coding sequence of a gene.

M13 A single-stranded DNA bacteriophage used as a vector for DNA sequencing.

Meristem Localized region of active cell division in plants from which permanent tissue is derived. The principal meristems in the flowering plants occur at the tips of the stems and roots (apical meristems), between xylem and phloem of vascular bundles (cambium) in the cortex (cork cambium), in young leaves and, in many grasses, at the bases of internodes (intercalary meristems).

Micrococcal nuclease A nuclease active only in the presence of calcium ions.

Microplasts Vesicles produced by subdivision and fragmentation of protoplasts or thin-walled cells.

Minitubers Small tubers (5–15 mm in diam.) formed on cuttings of tuber-forming crops such as potato and yams.

Morphogenesis Developmental pathways in differentiation which result in the formation of recognizable tissues.

Nick translation A procedure for radiolabelling DNA *in vitro*.

Operon A number of contiguous genes under co-ordinate control.

Organogenesis Type of morphogenesis which results in the formation of roots, shoots and/or floral organs.

Packed cell volume (PCV) The percentage volume of cells in a set volume of culture after sedimentation (packing) by means of low speed centrifugation.

Petiole Leaf stalk.

Peduncle Flower stalk.

Polyadenylation Post-transcriptional addition of a polyadenylic acid tail to mRNA.

Pribnow box Consensus sequence near the mRNA start-point of prokaryotic genes. There is also a conserved region known as the '-35' region.

Probe A radiolabelled nucleic acid molecule used to detect the presence of its complementary strand by hybridization.

Promoter Region of the DNA which is recognized by RNA polymerase in order to initiate transcription.

Protoplast A plasmalemma-bound vesicle consisting of a 'naked' cell formed as a consequence of the removal of the cell wall by mechanical or enzymatic means.

Shoot tip Terminal (0·5−2·0 mm) portion of a shoot comprising the meristem dome (0·01−0·3 mm) together with primordial and developing leaves and the adjacent stem tissues.

Signal peptide N-terminal addition to a protein which enables the passage of the protein across a membrane. The signal peptide is degraded during transport.

Somaclonal variation Variability in the idiotypes generated from a single mother stock by tissue culture. Protoclones or calliclones are produced from either single protoplasts or single cells, respectively, and these often produce regenerated plants which show variations in phenotypes as compared to the original mother plant.

Somatic Referring to the vegetative or non-sexual stages of a life cycle.

Somatic hybridization A technique of fusing protoplasts from two contrasting genotypes for production of hybrids or cybrids which contain various mixtures of nuclear and/or cytoplasmic genomes, respectively.

Splicing Removal of introns from the primary transcript during the maturation of eukaryotic mRNA.

Subculture Subdivision of a culture and its transfer to fresh medium.

Suspension culture A culture consisting of cells or cell aggregates initiated by placing callus tissues in an agitated liquid medium.

Synchronous culture A culture in which the cell cycles (or a specific phase of the cycle) of the majority of the cells are synchronous.

TATA box Eukaryotic promoter region analogous to the Pribnow box.

Totipotency The ability of individual cells to express the phenotype of the whole plant from which it is derived.

Transcription Copying of a gene into RNA by a DNA-dependent RNA polymerase.

Translation Copying of mRNA into protein.

Turbidostat An open continuous culture into which fresh medium flows in response to an increase in the turbidity of the culture.

Vegetative propagation The asexual propagation of plants by detachment of some part of the plant, e.g. a cutting, and its subsequent development into a complete plant.

Virus-tested Description of a plant stock certified as being free of certain specified viruses following recognized procedures of virus diagnosis.

References

Aharonowitz Y. & Cohen G. (1981) The microbiological production of pharmaceuticals. *Sci. Amer.,* **245**, 106–119.

Alfermann A.W., Bergmann W., Figur C., Helmbold U., Schwantag D., Schuller I. & Reinhard E. (1983) Biotransformation of β-methydigitoxin to β-methyldigoxin by cell cultures of *Digitalis lanata.* In *Plant Biotechnology* (Eds S.H. Mantell & H. Smith), pp. 67–74. Cambridge University Press, Cambridge.

Alfermann A.W. & Reinhard E. (1980) Biotransformation by plant tissue cultures. *Bull. Soc. Chim. France,* **1–2**, 35–45.

Alwine J.C., Kemp D.J., Parker B.A., Reiser J., Renart J., Stark G.R. & Wahl G.M. (1980) Detection of specific RNAs or specific fragments of DNA by fractionation in gels and transfer to diazobenzyl-oxymethyl paper. *Methods in Enzymology,* **68**, 220–245.

Anderson R.A., Krakauer T. & Camerini-Otero R.D. (1982) DNA-mediated gene transfer. Recombination between cotransferred DNA sequences and recovery of recombinants in a plasmid. *Proc. Natl. Acad. Sci. USA,* **74**, 2748–2752.

Appels R., Bouchard R.A. & Stern H. (1982) Complementary DNA clones of meiotic-specific polyadenylic acid containing RNA in *Lilium*: Homology with sequences in wheat, rye and maize. *Chromosoma,* **85**, 591–602.

Arcioni S., Davey M.R., Dos Santos A.V.P. & Cocking E.C. (1982) Somatic embryogenesis in tissues from mesophyll and cell suspension protoplasts of *Medicago coerulea* and *M. glutinosa. Z. Pflanzenphysiol.,* **106**, 105–110.

Arnon R. (1970) Papain. *Methods in Enzymol.,* **XIX**, 226–244.

Aviv H. & Leder P. (1972) Purification of biologically active globin mRNA by chromatography on oligothymidylic acid-cellulose. *Proc. Natl. Acad. Sci. USA,* **69**, 1408–1412.

Axelrod B. (1974) Lipoxygenases. In *Food Related Enzymes.* (Ed. J.R. Whitaker), pp. 324–348. Advances in Chemistry Series 136. American Chemical Society, Washington.

Backman K. & Ptashne M. (1978) Maximizing gene expression on a plasmid using recombination *in vitro. Cell,* **13**, 65–71.

Backman K., Ptashne M. & Gilbert W. (1976) Construction of plasmids carrying the Cl gene of bacteriophage. *Proc. Natl. Acad. Sci. USA.* **73**, 4174–8.

Bantle J.A., Maxwell I.H. & Hahn W.E. (1976) Specificity of oligo (dT)-cellulose chromatography in the isolation of polyadenylated RNA. *Analytical Biochem.,* **72**, 413–427.

Barbier M. & Dulieu H. (1983) Early occurrence of genetic variants in protoplast cultures. *Pl. Sci. Lett,* **29**, 201–206.

Barton K.A. & Brill W.J. (1983) Prospects in plant genetic engineering. *Science,* **219**, 671–675.

Baty D., Mercereau-Puijalon O., Perrin D., Kourilsky P.L. & Lazdunsky C. (1981) Secretion into the bacterial periplasmic space of chicken ovalbumin synthesized in *Escherichia coli. Gene,* **16**, 79–87.

Bayliss M.W. (1980) Chromasomal variation in plant tissues in culture. In *Perspectives in plant cell and tissue cultures* (Ed. I.K. Wasil) *Int. Rev. Cytol. Suppl. 11A* pp. 113–144. Academic Press, New York.

Beachy R.N., Jarvis N.P. & Barton K.A. (1981) Biosynthesis of subunits of the soybean *Glycine max* 7s storage protein. *J. Mol. Appl. Genet,* **1**, 19–28.

Beasley C.A. & Eaks I.L. (1979) Ethylene from alcohol lamps and natural gas burners. *In Vitro* **13**, 263–269.

Bedrook J.R., Jones J., O'Dell M., Thompson R.D. & Flavell R.B. (1980a) A molecular description of telomeric heterochromatin in secale species. *Cell,* **19**, 545–560.

Bedbrook J.R. & Kolodner R. (1979) The structure of chloroplast DNA. *Ann. Rev. Plant Physiol.,* **30**, 593–620.

Bedbrook J.R., Smith S.M. & Ellis R.J. (1980b) Molecular cloning and sequencing of com plementary DNA encoding the precursor to the small subunit of ribulose bis-phosphate carboxylase. *Nature,* **287**, 692–697.

Bell E.A. & Charlwood B.V. (1980) (Eds) *Secondary Plant Products.* Springer-Verlag, Berlin.

Belliard G., Pelletier G., Vedel F. & Quetier F. (1978) Morphological characteristics and chloroplast DNA distribution in different cytoplasmic parasexual hybrids in *Nicotiana tabacum, Molec. Gen. Gen.* **165**, 231–237.

Belliard G., Vedel F. & Pelletier G. (1979) Mitochondrial recombination in cytoplasmic hybrids of *Nicotiana tabacum* by protoplast fusion. *Nature,* **281**, 401–403.

Bennett J. (1981) Biosynthesis of the light-harvesting chlorophyll *a/b* protein. Polypeptide turnover in darkness. *Eur. J. Biochem.,* **118**, 61–70.

Benoist C., O'Hare K., Breathnach R. & Chambon P. (1980) The ovalbumin gene-sequence of putative control regions. *Nucleic Acids Res.,* **8**, 127–145.

Bergmann L. (1977) Plating of plant cells. In *Plant Tissue Culture and its Biotechnological Application.* (Eds W. Barz, E. Reinhard & M.H. Zenk), pp. 213–225. Springer-Verlag, Berlin.

Bevan M., Barnes W.M. & Chilton M.D. (1983) Structure and transcription of the nopoline synthase gene region of T-DNA. *Nucleic Acids Res.,* **11**, 369–385.

Beversdorf W.D., Weiss-Lerman J., Erickson L.R. & Souza Machado V. (1980) Transfer of cytosplasmically-inherited triazene resistance from bird's rape to cultivated oilseed rape (*Brassica campestris* and *B. napus*) *Can. J. Genet. Cytol.,* **22**, 167–172.

Bewley J.D. (1982) Protein and nucleic acid synthesis during seed germination and early seedling growth. In *Encyclopedia of Plant Physiology*, Vol 14A (Eds D. Boulter & B. Parthier), pp. 559–586. Springer-Verlag, Berlin.

Bilkey P.C. & Cocking E.C. (1982) A non-enzymatic method for the isolation of protoplasts from callus of *Saintpaulia ionantha* (African Violet) *Z. Pflanzenphysiol.,* **105**, 285–288.

Bilkey P.C., Davey M.R. & Cocking E.C. (1982) Isolation, origin and properties of enucleate plant microplasts. *Protoplasma* **110**, 147–151.

Bingham J. (1981) The achievements of conventional plant breeding. *Phil. Trans. Roy. Soc.,* **292**, 441–454.

Bingham E.T., Hurley L.V., Kaatz D.M. & Saunders J.W. (1975) Breeding alfalfa which regenerates from callus tissue in culture. *Crop Science,* **15**, 719–721.

Binns A.N. (1981) Developmental variation in plant tissue culture. *Env. Expt. Eot.,* **21**, 325–332.

Binns A.N. & Meins F. Jr. (1980) Chromosome number and the degree of cytokinin habituation of cultured tobacco path cells. *Protoplasma,* **103**, 179–187.

Blobel G. (1980) Intracellular protein topogenesis. *Proc. Natl. Acad. Sci. USA,* **77**, 1496–1500.

Blobel G., Walter P., Chang G.N., Goldman B.M., Erickson A.H. & Lingappa V.R. (1979) Translocation of proteins across membranes: the signal hypothesis and beyond. *Symp. Soc. Exp. Biol.,* **33**, 9–36.

Bogorad L. (1975) Evolution of organelles and eukaryotic genomes. *Science,* **188**, 891–898.

Böhm H. (1980) The formation of secondary metabolites in plant tissue and cell cultures. *Int. Rev. Cytol. Suppl.,* **11B**, 183–208.

Böhm H. (1982) The inability of plant cell cultures to produce secondary substances. In *Plant Tissue Culture 1982* (Ed. A. Fujiwara), pp. 325–328. Tokyo, Jap. *Assoc. Pl. Tiss. Cult.*

Bohnert H.J. & Crouse E.J. (1981) A simple, inexpensive general method for the isolation of high molecular weight chloroplast DNA. *Plant Molecular Biology Newsletter,* **2**, 70–72.

Bohnert H.J. Crouse E.J. & Schmitt J.M. (1982) Organization and expression of plastid genomes. In *Encyclopedia of Plant Physiology*, Vol. 14B (Ed. B. Parthier & D. Boulter). Springer-Verlag, Berlin.

Bokelmann G.S. & Roest S. (1983) Plant regeneration from protoplasts of potato.

(*Solanum tuberosum cv* Bintje). *Z. Pflanzenphysiol.* **109**, 259–265.

Bonga J.M. & Durzan D.J. (1982) (Eds) Tissue Culture in Forestry. Nijhoff/Junk, The Hague.

Boulter D. & Parthier B. (1982) Nucleic acids and proteins in plants. *Encyclopedia of Plant Physiology*, Vols 14A & 14B. Springer-Verlag, Berlin.

Brammar W.J. (1982) Vectors based on bacteriophage lambda. In *Genetic Engineering*, Vol. 3 (Ed. R. Williamson), pp. 53–81. Academic Press, London.

Branton R. & Blake J. (1983) A lovely clone of coconuts. *New Scientist*, **98**, 554–557.

Breathnach R. & Chambon P. (1981) Organisation and expression of eukaryotic split genes coding for proteins. *Ann. Rev. Biochem.*, **50**, 349–383.

Breathnach R., Mandel J.C. & Chambon P. (1977) Ovalbumin gene is split in chicken DNA. *Nature*, **270**, 314–318.

Brettell R.I.S., Thomas E. & Ingram D.S. (1980) Reversion of Texas male-sterile cytoplasm maize in culture to give fertile, T-toxin resistant plants. *Theor. appl. Gen.*, **58**, 55–58.

Bright S., Jarrett V., Nelson R., Creissen G., Karp A., Franklin J., Norbury P., Kneln J., Rognes S. & Miflin B. (1983). Modification of agronomic traits using *in vitro* technology. In *Plant Biotechnology* (Eds S.H. Mantell & H. Smith), pp. 251–165. Cambridge University Press, Cambridge.

Brisson N. & Verma D.P.S. (1982) Soybean leghemoglobin gene family: normal genes, pseudogenes and truncated genes. *Proc. Natl. Acad. Sci. USA*, **79**, 4055–4059.

Britten R.J. & Davidson E.H. (1976) Studies on nucleic acid reassociation kinetics: Empirical equations describing DNA reassociation. *Proc. Natl. Acad. Sci. USA*, **73**, 415–419.

Brodelius P. & Nilsson K. (1980) Entrapment of plant cells in different matrices. A comparative study, *FEBS Lett.*, **122**, 312–326.

Broglie R., Bellemare G., Bartlett S.G., Chua N-H & Cashmore A.R. (1981) Cloned DNA sequences complementary to messanger RNA encoding precursors to the small subunit of ribulose 1.5. bisphosphate carboxylase and a chlorophyll *a/b* binding polypeptide. *Proc. Natl. Acad. Sci. USA*, **78**, 7304–8.

Brown S., Wetherell D.F. & Dougall D.K. (1976) The potassium requirement for growth and embryogenesis in wild carrot suspension cultures. *Physiol. Plant.*, **37**, 73–79.

Bryant J.A. (1982) DNA replication and the cell cycle. In *Encyclopedia of Plant Physiology*, Vol 14B (Eds B. Parthier & D. Boulter), pp. 75–110. Springer-Verlag, Berlin.

Bryant M.P. (1979) Microbial methane production — theoretical aspects. *J. Animal Sci.*, **48**, 193–201.

Bukhari A.I., Shapiro J.A. & Adhaya S.L. (1977) (Eds). *DNA Insertion Elements, Plasmids, and Episomes*. Cold Spring Harbor, New York.

Burr B., Burr F.A., St. John T.P., Thomas M. & Davis R.W. (1982) Zein storage protein gene family of maize: an assessment of teterogeneity with cloned messenger RNA sequences. *J. Mol. Biol.*, **154**, 33–50.

Butcher D.N. (1977) Secondary Products in Tissue Culture. In *Plant Cell Tissue and Organ Cultures* (Eds J. Reinhert & Y.P.S. Bajaj), pp. 668–693. Springer-Verlag, Berlin.

Caboche M. (1980) Nutritional requirements of protoplast-derived, haploid tobacco cells grown at low cell densities in liquid medium. *Planta*, **149**, 7–18.

Capecchi M.R. (1980) High efficiency transformation by direct microinjection of DNA into cultured mammalian cells. *Cell*, **22**, 479–488.

Chaleff R.S. (1981) *Genetics of Higher Plants: Applications of Cell Culture. Developmental and Cell Biology*, Vol. 9. Cambridge University Press, Cambridge.

Charnay P., Perricauclet M., Galibert F. & Tiollais P. (1978) Bacteriophage λ and plasmid vectors, allowing fusion of cloned genes in each of the three translation phases. *Nucleic Acids Res.*, **5**, 4479−94.

Chaturvedi H.C., Sharma A.K., Sharma M. & Prasad R.N. (1982) Morphogenesis, micropropagation and germplasm preservation of some economic plants by tissue culture. In *Plant Tissue Culture 1982* (Ed. A. Fujiwara), pp. 687−688. Jap. *Assoc. Pl. Tiss. Cult.*, Tokyo.

Cheng T.Y. (1975) Adventitious bud formation in culture of Douglas Fir (*Pseudotsuga menziesii* (Mirls.) Franco) *Plant Sci. Lett.*, **5**, 97−102.

Chilton M.D., Drummond M.H., Merlo D.J., Sciaky D., Montoya A.L., Gordon M.P. & Nester E.W. (1977) Stable incorporation of plasmid DNA into higher plants: the molecular basis of crown gall tumorigenesis. *Cell*, **11**, 263−271.

Chirgwin J.M., Przybyla A.E., MacDonald R.J. & Rutter W.J. (1979) Isolation of biologically active ribonucleic acid from sources enriched in ribonuclease. *Biochemistry*, **18**, 5294−5299.

Christianson M.L. & Warnick D.A. (1983) Competence and determination in the process of *in vitro* shoot organogenesis. *Developmental Biol.*, **95**, 288−293.

Chu C-C. (1982) Haploids in plant improvement. In *Plant Improvements and Somatic Cell Genetics* (Eds I.K. Vasil, W.R. Scowcroft & K.J. Frey), pp. 129−158. Academic Press, New York.

Chu N.M., Oishi K.K. & Tewari J.K. (1981) Anatomy of the pea chloroplast ribosomal DNA. *J. Cell. Biol.*, **91**, 283A.

Clarke L. & Carbon J. (1980) Isolation of a yeast centromere and construction of functional small circular chromsomes. *Nature*, **287**, 504−509.

Cocking E.C. (1960) A method for the isolation of plant protoplasts and vacuoles. *Nature*, **187**, 917−929.

Cocking E.C. (1981) Opportunities from the use of protoplasts. *Phil. Trans. R. Soc.* **B292**, 557−568.

Cocking E.C., Davey M.R., Pental D. & Power J.B. (1981) Aspects of plant genetic manipulation. *Nature*, **293**, 265−270.

Cohen S.N., Chang A.C.Y. & Hsu L. (1972) Nonchromosomal antibiotic resistance in bacteria; genetic transformation of *Escherichia coli* by R-factor DNA. *Proc. Natl. Acad. Sci. USA*, **69**, 2110−2114.

Collins G.B. & Genovesi A.D. (1982) Anther culture and its application to crop improvement. In *Application of Plant Cell and Tissue Culture to Agriculture and Industry* (Eds D.T. Tomes *et al.*), pp. 1−24. University of Guelph, Guelph.

Collins J. & Hohn B. (1979) Cosmids: a type of plasmid gene cloning vector that is packageable *in vitro* in bacteriophage λ heads. *Proc. Natl. Acad. Sci. USA*, **75**, 4242−6.

Conger B.C. (1981) (Ed.) *Cloning Agricultural Plants via In Vitro techniques*. CRC Press, Florida.

Conn E.E. (1981) (Ed.) *Secondary Plant Products*, Vol. 7 *The Biochemistry of Plants*. Academic Press, New York.

Constantin M.J. (1981) Chromosome instability in cell and tissue cultures and regenerated plants. *Env. Expt. Bot.*, **21**, 359−368.

Croughan T.P., Stavarek S.J. & Rains D.W. (1981) *In vitro* development of salt resistant plants. *Env. Expt. Bot.*, **21**, 317−324.

Crisp P. & Walkey D.G.A. (1974) The use of aseptic meristem culture in cauliflower breeding. *Euphytica*, **23**, 305−313.

Croy R.D.D., Lycett G.W., Gatehouse J.A., Yarwood J.N. & Boulter D. (1982) Cloning and analysis of cDNAs encoding plant storage protein precursors. *Nature*, **295**, 76−79.

Cuellar R.E. & Thompson W.F. (1981) Complex organization of repetitive DNA families as analyzed with cloned DNA fragments. Carnegie institute of Washington Yearbook, pp. 81−82.

Cullis C.A. & Goldsborough P.H. (1980) In *The Plant Genome* (Eds D.R. Davies & D.A. Hopwood), p. 91. John Innes Charity, Norwich.

D'Amato F. (1977) Cytogenetics of differentiation in tissue and cell cultures. In *Plant*

Cell, Tissue and Organ Culture (Eds J. Reinert & Y.P.S. Bajaj), pp. 343–357. Springer-Verlag, Berlin.

Davies D.R. (1972) Speeding up the commercial propagation of freesias. *Grower*, **77**, 711.

De Greve H., Dhaese P., Seurinck J., Lemmers M., Van Montagu M. & Schell J. (1982a) Nucleotide sequence and transcript map of the *Agrobacterium* tumefaciens Ti plasmid encoded octopine synthase gene. *J. Mol. Appl. Genet.*, **1**, 499–512.

De Greve H., Leemans J., Hernalsteens J.P., Thia-Toong L., De Beuckeleer M., Willmitzer L., Otten L., Van Montagu M. & Schell J. (1982b) Regeneration of normal and fertile plants that express octopine synthase, from tobacco crown gall after deletion of tumour-controlling functions. *Nature* (*London*) **300**, 752–755.

De Langhe E. & De Bruijne E. (1976) Continuous propagation of tomato plants by means of callus cultures. *Scientia Horticultivae*, **4**, 221–227.

Depicker A., Stachel S., Dhaese P., Zambryski P. & Goodman H.M. (1982) Nopaline synthase: transcript mapping and DNA sequence. *J. Mol. Appl. Genet.*, **1**, 561–574.

Derbyshire E., Wright D.J. & Boulter D. (1976) Legumin and vicillin, storage proteins of legume seeds. *Phytochemistry*, **15**, 3–24.

Derom C., Gheysen D. & Fiers W. (1982) High level synthesis in *E. coli* of the SV40 small -t antigen under control of the bacteriophage lambda P_L promoter. *Gene*, **17**, 45–54.

Derynck R., Remaut E., Saman E., Stanssens P., De Clercq E., Content J. & Fiers W. (1980) Expression of human fibroblast interferon gene in *Escherichia coli*. *Nature*, **287**, 193–197.

Deuel H. & Stutz E. (1958) Pectic substances and pectic enzymes. In *Advances in Enzymology* (Ed. F.F. Nord), pp. 341–382 XX. Interscience, New York.

Dhaliwal S. & King P.J. (1978) Direct pollination of *Zea mays* ovules *in vitro* with *Z. mays*, *Z. mexicana* and *Sorghum bicolor* pollen. *Theor. appl. Genet.*, **53**, 43–46.

Dixon R.A. & Postgate J.R. (1971) Transfer of nitrogen fixation genes by conjugation in *Klebsiella pneumoniae*. *Nature*, **234**, 47–48.

Dodds J.H. & Roberts L.W. (1982) *Experiments in Plant Tissue Culture*. Cambridge University Press, Cambridge.

Doll H., Kie B. & Eggum B.O. (1974) Induced high lysine mutants in barley. *Radiat. Bot.*, **14**, 73–80

Dos Santos A.V.P., Davey M.R. & Cocking E.C. (1983) Cultural studies of protoplasts and leaf callus of *Trigonella corniculata* and *T. foenum–graecum*. *Z. Pflanzenphysiol.* **109**, 227.

Dougall D.K. (1982) Plant cells grown in chemostats. In. *Plants Tissue Culture 1982* (ed. A. Fujiwara) p. 51–54. Japan. Assn. Plant Tiss. Cult., Tokyo.

Dougall, D.K. & Verma D.C. (1978) Growth and embryo formation in wild-carrot suspension cultures with ammonium ion as a sole nitrogen source. *In Vitro*, **14**, 180–182.

Dougall D.K. & Weyrauch K.W. (1980) Growth and anthocyanin production by carrot suspension cultures grown under chemostat conditions with phosphate as the limiting nutrient. *Biotech. Bioengin.*, **22**, 337–352.

Döring H.P., Tillman E. & Starlinger P. (1984) DNA sequence of the maize transposable element Dissociation. *Nature*, **307**, 127–130.

Drummond M., Clements J., Merrick M. & Dixon R. (1983) Positive control and autogenous regulation of the nif LA promoter in *Klebsiella pneumoniae*. *Nature*, **301**, 302–306.

Dublin P. (1981) Direct somatic embryogenesis on fragments of Arabusta coffee tree leaves. *Café Cacao Thé* (Paris) **25**, 237–242.

Duvick D.N. (1965) Cytoplasmic pollen sterility in corn. *Adv. Genet.*, **13**, 1–56.

Earl, C.D. & Ausubel F.M. (1983) The genetic engineering of nitrogen fixation. *Nutrition Reviews*, **41**, 1–6.

Earle E.D. & Langhans R.W. (1974) Propagation of *Chrysanthemum in vitro*, II. Production, growth and flowering of plantlets from tissue cultures. *J. Amer. Soc. Hort. Sci.*, **99**, 352–358.

Edens L., Heslinga L., Klok R., Lederboer A.M., Maat J., Toonen Y., Visser C. & Verrips C.T. (1982) Cloning of complementary DNA encoding the sweet-tasting plant protein thaumatin and its expression in *Escherichia coli*. *Gene*, **18**, 1–12.

Edge M.D., Greene A.R., Heathcliffe G.R., Meacock P.A., Schuch W., Scanlon D.B., Atkinson T.C., Newton C.R. & Markham A.F. (1981) Total synthesis of a human leukocyte interferon gene. *Nature*, **292**, 756–762.

Ellis, B. (1982) Cell-to-cell variability in secondary metabolite production within cultured plant cell populations. In *Plant Tissue Culture 1982*. (Ed. A. Fujiwara), pp. 395–396. Jap. Assn. Pl. Tiss. Cult., Tokyo.

Ellis R.J. (1982a) Promiscuous DNA — chloroplast genes inside plant mitochondria. *Nature*, **299**, 678–679.

Ellis R.J. (1983) Chloroplast protein synthesis: principles and problems. *Subcellular Biochem.*, **9**, 237–261.

Eriksson T. (1977) Technical advances in protoplast isolation and cultivation. In *Plant Tissue Culture and its Biotechnological Application* (Eds Barz W., Reinhard E. & Zenk M.H.), pp. 313–322. Springer-Verlag, Berlin.

Evans P.K. & Cocking E.C. (1977) Isolated plant protoplasts. In *Plant Tissue and Cell Culture* (Ed. H.E. Street), pp. 103–135. Blackwell Scientific Publications, Oxford.

Evola S.V., Earle E.D. & Chaleff R.S. (1983) The use of genetic markers selected *in vitro* for the isolation and genetic verification of intraspecific somatic hybrids of *Nicotiana tabacum*. *Mol. Gen. Genet.*, **189**, 441.

Faber M. (1983) Cornell scientists clone, express cellulose genes in *E. coli*. *Biotechnology*, **1**, 139.

Federoff N. (1982) Introduction to transposable controlling elements in maize. In *Maize for Biological Research* (Ed. W.F. Sheridan), pp. 203–211. Plant Mol. Biol. Assoc. Univ. Press, N. Dakota.

Fernandez S.M., Lurquin P.F. & Kado C.I. (1978) Incorporation and maintenance of recombinant-DNA plasmid vehicles pBR313 and pCR1 in plant protplasts. *Fed. Europ. Biochem. Soc. Lett.*, **87**, 277–282.

Fincham J.R.S. & Sastry G.R.K. (1974) Controlling elements in maize. *Ann. Rev. Genet.*, **8**, 15–50.

Fischer R.L. & Goldberg R.B. (1982) Structure and flanking regions of soybean seed protein genes. *Cell*, **29**, 651–660.

Fisher R., Tuli R. & Haselkorn R. (1981) A cloned cyanobacterial gene for glutamine synthetase functions in *Escherischia coli*, but the enzyme is not adenylated. *Proc. Natl. Acad. Sci. USA*, **78**, 3393–3397.

Flavell, R.B. (1980) The molecular characterization and organisation of plant chromosomal DNA sequences. *Ann. Rev. Plant Physiol.*, **31**, 569–596.

Flick C.E. & Evans D.A. (1983) Isolation, culture and plant regeneration from protoplasts isolated from flower petals of ornamental *Nicotiana* species. *Z. Pflanzenphysiol.*, **109**, 379.

Fonnesbech M. (1974) Temperature effects on shoot and root development from *Begonia × cheimantha* petiole segments grown *in vitro*. *Physiol. Plant.*, **32**, 282–286.

Forde B.G., Kreis M., Bahramian B., Matthews J.A., Miflin B.J., Thompson R.D., Bartels D. & Flavell R.B. (1981) Molecular cloning and analysis of cDNA sequences derived from poly-A$^+$ RNA from barley endosperm: identification of B-hordein clones. *Nucleic Acids Res.*, **9**, 6689–6707.

Fowler M.W., (1982) The large scale cultivation of plant cells. *Prog. Ind. Microbiol.*, **17**, 207–229.

Fowler M.W. (1983) Commercial applications and economic aspects of mass plant cell culture. In *Plant Biotechnology* (Eds S.H. Mantell & H. Smith), pp. 3–38. Cambridge University Press, Cambridge.

Fox T.D. & Leaver C.J. (1981) The *Zea mays* mitochondrial gene coding cytochrome c oxidase subunit II has an intervening sequence and does not contain TGA codons. *Cell*, **26**, 315–323.

Fraley R.T., Dellaporta S.L. & Papahadjopoulos D. (1982) Liposome-mediated delivery of tobacco mosaic virus RNA into tobacco protoplasts: A sensitive assay for monitoring liposome-protoplast interactions. *Proc. Natl. Acad. Sci. USA*, **79**, 1859–1863.

Framond A.J. de., Barton K.A. & Chilton M-D. (1983) Mini-Ti: a new vector strategy for plant genetic engineering. *Biotechnol.*, **1**, 262–269.

Frankel O.H. & Hawkes J.G. (Eds) (1975) *Crop Genetic Resources for Today and Tomorrow*. Cambridge University Press, Cambridge.

Frey C.N., Schultz A.S. & Light R.F. (1936) The effect of active soybean on vitamin A. *Ind. Eng. Chem.*, **28**, 1254.

Fuller F. (1982) A family of cloning vectors containing the *lac* UV5 promoter. *Gene*, **19**, 43–54.

Gallagher T.F. & Ellis R.J. (1982) Light-stimulated transcription of genes for two chloroplast polypeptides in isolated pea nuclei. *EMBO J.*, **1**, 1493–1498.

Galling G. (1982) Use (and misuse) of inhibitors of gene expression. In *Encyclopodia of Plant Physiology* (Eds Parthier B. & Boulter D.) Vol. **14B** pp. 663–673. Springer-Verlag, Berlin.

Galun E., Arzeegonen P., Fluhr R., Edelman M. & Aviv D. (1982) Cytoplasmic hybridization in *Nicotiana*-mitochondrial DNA analysis in progenies resulting from fusion between protoplasts having different organelle constitutions. *Molec. Gen. Genet.*, **186**, 50.

Gamborg O.L. Murashige T., Thorpe T.A. & Vasil I.K. (1976) Plant tissue culture media. *In Vitro*, **12**, 473–490.

Gamborg O.L., Shyluk J.P. & Shakin E.A. (1981) Isolation fusion and culture of plant protoplasts. In *Plant Tissue Culture: Methods and Applications in Agriculture* (Ed. T.A. Thorpe), pp. 115–153. Academic Press, New York.

Gautheret R.J. (1934) Culture du tissu cambial. *C. r. hebd. Séanc. Acad. Sci. Paris*, **198**, 2195–2196.

Gautheret R.J. (1982). Plant tissue culture: the history. In *Plant Tissue Culture 1982* (Ed. A. Fujiwara), pp. 7–11. Japan. Assn. Plant Tiss. Cult., Tokyo.

Gardner C.O., Melcher V., Shockey M.W. & Essenberg R.C. (1980) Restriction enzyme cleavage maps of the DNA of 2 cauliflower mosaic virus isolates. *Virology*, **103**, 250–254.

Gatenby A.A. (1983) The expression of eukaryotic genes in bacteria and its application to plant genes. In *Plant Biotechnology* (Eds S.H. Mantell & H. Smith), pp. 268–297. Soc. Exp. Biol. Seminar Series, 18. Cambridge University Press, Cambridge.

Gatenby A.A. & Castleton J.A. (1982) Amplification of maize ribulose bisphosphate carboxylase large subunit synthesis in *E. coli* by transcriptional fusion with the lambda N operon. *Mol. Gen. Genet*, **185**, 424–429.

Gatenby A.A., Castleton J.A. & Saul M.W. (1981) Expression in *E. coli* of maize and wheat chloroplast genes for large subunit of ribulose bisphosphate carboxylase. *Nature*, **291**, 117–121.

Gengenbach B.G., Connelly J.A., Pring D.R. & Conde M.F. (1981) Mitochondrial DNA variation in maize plants regenerated during tissue culture selection. *Theor. Appl. Gen.* **59**, 161–167.

Gengenbach B.G., Green C.E. & Donovan C.M. (1977) Inheritance of selected pathotoxin resistance in maize plants regenerated from cell cultures. *Proc. Nat. Acad. Sci. USA*, **74**, 5113–5117.

Gerlach W.L. & Bedbrook J.R. (1979) Cloning and characterisation of ribosomal

RNA genes from wheat and barley. *Nucleic Acids Res.*, **7**, 1869–1885.

Gerlach W.L., Pryor A.J., Dennis E.S., Ferl R.J., Sachs M.M. & Peacock W.J. (1982) Complementary DNA cloning and induction of the alcohol dehydrogenase gene ADH 1 in maize. *Proc. Natl. Acad. Sci. USA*, **79**, 2981–2985.

Gillam S., Astell C.R. & Smith M. (1980) Site-specific mutagenesis using oligodeoxyribonucleotides: isolation of a phenotypically silent ØX174 mutant, with a specific nucleotide deletion, at very high efficiency. *Gene*, **12**, 129–137.

Glass R.E. (1982) *Gene Function: E. coli and its Heritable Elements*. Croome Helm, London.

Gleba Y.Y. & Hoffmann F. (1979) 'Arabidobrassica' plant genome engineering by protoplast fusion. *Naturwissenschaften* **66**, 547–554.

Glimelius K. & Bonnett A.T. (1981) Somatic hybridization in *Nicotiana*: restoration of photoautotrophy to an albino mutant with defective plastids. *Planta*, **153**, 497.

Goeddel D.V., Kleid D.G. Bolivar F., Heyneker H.L., Yansura D.G., Crea R., Hirose T., Kraszewski A., Itakura K. & Riggs A.D. (1979) Expression in *Escherichia coli* of chemically synthesised genes for human insulin. *Proc. Natl. Acad. Sci. USA*, **76**, 106–110.

Goldberg R.B., Hoschek G., Ditta G.S. & Breidenback R.W. (1981) Developmental regulation of cloned superabundant embryo mRNAs in soybean. *Developmental Biology*, **83**, 218–321.

Goldberg R.B., Hoschek G. & Vodkin L.O. (1983) An insertion sequence blocks the expression of a soybean lectin gene. *Cell*, **33**, 465–475.

Goodman R.M. (1981a) Geminiviruses. In *Handbook of Plant Virus Infections and Comparative Diagnosis* (Ed. E. Kurstak), pp. 879–910. Elsevier/N. Holland Biomed. Press.

Goodman R.M. (1981b) Geminiviruses. *J. gen. Virol*, **54**, 9–21.

Gordon J.W., Scangos G.A., Platkin D.J., Barbosa J.A. & Ruddle F.H. (1980) Genetic transformation of mouse embryos by microinjection of purified DNA. *Proc. Natl. Acad. Sci. USA*, **77**, 7380–7384.

Gould A.R. (1982) Chromosome instability in plant tissue cultures studied with banding techniques. In *Plant Tissue Culture 1982* (Ed. A. Fujiwara), pp. 431–432. Japan. Ass. Plant Tiss. Cult., Tokyo

Gray R.E. & Cashmore A.R. (1976) RNA synthesis in plant leaf tissue: the characterization of messenger RNA species lacking and containing polyadenylic acid. *J. Mol. Biol.*, **108**, 595–608.

Green C.E. (1978) *In vitro* plant regeneration in cereals and grasses. In *Frontiers of Plant Tissue Culture* (Ed. T.A. Thorpe), *Int. Assoc. for Plant Tissue Culture*, Calgary pp. 411–418.

Grierson D. (1982) RNA processing and other post-transcriptional modifications. In *Encyclopedia of Plant Physiology*, Vol. 14B (Eds B. Parthier & D. Boulter), pp. 192–223. Springer-Verlag.

Grosjean H. & Fiers W. (1982) Preferential codon usage in prokaryotic genes. The optimal codon-anticodon interaction energy and selective codon usage in efficiently expressed genes. *Gene*, **18**, 199–209.

Grout B.W.W., Westcott R.J. & Henshaw G.G. (1978) Survival of shoot meristems of tomato seedlings frozen in liquid nitrogen. *Cryobiology*, **15**, 478–483.

Grünstein M. & Hogness D.S. (1975) Colony hybridization: a method for the isolation of cloned DNAs that contain a specific gene. *Proc. Natl. Acad. Sci. USA*, **72**, 3961–5.

Guha S. & Maheshwari S.C. (1964) *In vitro* production of embryos from anthers of *Datura*. *Nature*, **204**, 497.

Guilfoyle T.J. & Malcolm S. (1980) The amounts, subunit structure and template engaged activities of RNA polymerases from germinating soybean axis. *Dev. Biol*, **78**, 113–125.

Guilfoyle T.J., Olszewski N. & Zurfluh L. (1980) RNA polymerase during developmental transitions in soybean. In *Genome Organisation and Expression in Plants*.

(Ed. C.J. Leaver), pp. 93–104. Plenum, New York.

Gupta P.K., Nadgir A.L., Mascarhenas A.F. & Jagannathan V. (1980) Tissue culture of forest trees: Clonal multiplication of *Tectona grandis* (teak) by tissue culture. *Pl. Sci. Lett,* **17**, 259–268.

Haber S., Ikegami M., Bajet N.B. & Goodman R.M. (1981) Evidence for a divided genome in bean golden mosaic virus, a geminivirus. *Nature,* **289**, 324–326.

Hahlbrock K., Boudet A.M., Chappell J., Kreuzaler F., Kuhn D.N., Ragg H. & Schmelzer E. (1983) Selective and co-ordinate enzyme induction in cultured plant cells. *15th FEBS* meeting abstracts. p. 76.

Hall D.O. (1979) World biomass: an overview. In *Biomass for Energy,* pp. 1–14, UK-ISES, London.

Hall T.C., Ma. Y, Buchbinder B.U., Pyne J.W., Sun S.M. & Bliss F.A. (1978) Messenger RNA for GI protein of French bean seeds: Cell-free translation and product characterisation. *Proc. Natl. Acad. Sci. USA,* **75**, 3196–3200.

Hallewell R.A. & Emtage S. (1980) Plasmid vectors containing the tryptophan operon promoter suitable for efficient regulated expression of foreign genes. *Gene,* **9**, 27–47.

Harris T.J.R. (1983) Expression of eukaryotic genes in *E. coli.* In *Genetic Engineering 4* (Ed. R. Williamson). pp. 127–185. Academic Press, London.

Harney P.M. (1982) Tissue culture propagation of some herbaceous horticultural plants. In *Application of Plant Cell and Tissue Culture to Agriculture & Industry* (Eds Tomes D.T., Ellis B.E., Harney P.M., Kasha K.J. & Peterson R.L.). pp. 187–208. University of Guelph, Guelph.

Hartmann, H.T. & Kester, D.E. (1983) *Plant Propagation: Principles and Practices.* 4th Edn. Prentice-Hall, New Jersey.

Hasegawa P.M., Murashige T. & Takatori F.N. (1973) Propagation of *Asparagus* through shoot apex culture II. Light and temperature requirements, transplantability of plants and cytological characteristics. *J. Am. Soc. Hort. Sci.,* **98**, 143–148.

Hashimoto A.G. (1983) Conversion of straw-manure mixtures to methane at mesophilic and thermophilic temperatures. *Biotechnol. Bioeng.* **XXV**, 185–200.

Hatanaka C. & Ozawa J. (1963) On the saccharifying pectolytic enzymes of *Erwinia aroideae. Agric. Biol. Chem.,* **27**, 596–597.

Haugland R.A. & Cline M.G. (1978) Capping structures at the 5′-terminus of polyadenylated RNA in *Avena* coleoptiles. *Plant Physiol.,* **62**, 838-840.

Heberle-Bors E. & Reinert J. (1980) Isolated pollen cultures and pollen demorphism. *Naturwissenschaffen,* **67**, 311.

Heinz D.J., Krishamurthi M., Nickell L.G. & Maretzki A. (1977) Cell, tissue and organ culture in sugarcane. In *Plant Cell, Tissue and Organ Culture.* (Eds J. Reinert & Y.P.S. Bajaj), pp. 3–17. Springer-Verlag, Berlin.

Hemleben V. (1981) Characterization and cloning cf a satellite DNA of *Cucumis melo* (Cucurbitaceae). *Eur. J. Cell. Biol,* **24**, 330–331.

Henke R.R. (1981) Selection of biochemical mutants in plant cell cultures: some considerations. *Env. Expt. Bot.,* **21**, 347–357.

Henshaw G.G. & O'Hara J.F. (1983) *In vitro* approaches to the conservation and utilization of global plant genetic resources. In *Plant Biotechnology,* (Eds S.H. Mantell & H. Smith), pp. 219–238. Cambridge University Press, Cambridge.

Herrera-Estrella L., Depicker A., Van Montagu M. & Schell J. (1983) Expression of chimaeric genes transferred into plant cells using a Ti-plasmid-derived vector. *Nature,* **303**, 209–213.

Herrmann R.G., Bohnert H.J., Kowallik K.V. & Schmill J.M. (1975) Size, conformation and purity of chloroplast DNA from higher plants. *Biochim. Biophys. Act,* **378**, 305–317.

Heyser J.W. & Nabors M.W. (1982) Long term plant regeneration, somatic embryogenesis and green spot formation in secondary oat (*Avena sativa*) callus. *Z. Pflanzenphysiol.,* **107**, 153–160.

Hibberd K.A., Walter T., Green C.E. & Gengenbach B.G. (1980) Selection and characterization of a feed-back insensitive tissue culture of maize. *Planta*, **148**, 183–187.

Highfield P.E. & Ellis R.J. (1978) Synthesis and transport of the small subunit of ribulose biphosphate carboxylase. *Nature*, **271**, 420–424.

Higuchi R., Paddock G.V., Wall R. & Salser W. (1976) A general method for cloning eukaryotic structural gene sequences. *Proc. Natl. Acad. Sci. USA*, **73** 3146–50.

Hinnen A., Hicks J.B. & Fink G.R. (1978) Transformation of yeast. *Proc. Natl. Acad. Sci. USA*, **75**, 1929–1933.

Ho T.D. (1980) Hormonal and genetic regulation of α-amylase synthesis in barley aleurone cells. In *Genome Organisation and Expression in Plants* (Ed. C.J. Leaver), pp. 147–157. Plenum, New York.

Horner M. & Street H.E. (1978) Pollen dimorphism — origin and significance in pollen plant formation by anther culture. *Ann. Bot.*, **42**, 763–771.

Horsch R.B. & Jones G.E. (1980) A double filter paper technique for plating cultured plant cells. *In vitro*, **16**, 103–108.

Howe C.J., Bowman C.M., Dyer T.A. & Gray J.C. (1982a) Localization of wheat genes for beta and epsilon subunits of ATP synthase. *Mol. Gen. Genet.*, *186*, 525–530.

Howe C.J., Auffret A.D., Doherty A., Bowman C.M., Dyer T.A. & Gray J.C. (1982b) Location and nucleotide sequence of the gene for the proton-translocating subunit of wheat chloroplast ATP synthase. *Proc. Natl. Acad. Sci. USA*, **79**, 6903–6907.

Howell S.H. (1982) Plant molecular vehicles: potential vectors for introducing foreign DNA into plants. *Ann. Rev. Plant Physiol.* **33**, 609–650.

Howell S.H., Walker L.L., & Dudley R.K. (1980) Cloned cauliflower mosaic virus DNA infects turnips *Brassica rapa*. *Science*, **208** 1265–1267.

Hsiao C.-L. & Carbon J. (1981) Direct selection procedure for the isolation of functional centromeric DNA. *Proc. Natl. Acad. Sci. USA*, **78**, 3760–3764.

Hull R. & Covey S.N. (1983) Does cauliflower mosaic virus replicate by reverse transcription? *Trends in Biochem. Sci.*, **8**, 119–121.

Hussey G. (1983) *In vitro* propagation of *Narcissus*. *Ann. Bot.* **49**, 707–719.

Hutchinson J. & Londsdale D.M. (1982) The chromosomal distribution of cloned highly repetitive sequences from hexaploid wheat, *Triticum aestivum*. *Heredity*, **48**, 371–376.

Huth W. (1978) Culture of apple plants from apical meristems. *Gartenbauwissenschaft*, **43**, 163.

Ikemura T. (1981) Correlation between the abundance of *E. coli* transfer RNAs and the occurrence of respective codons in its protein genes. *J. Mol. Biol.*, **146**, 1–21.

Imamura J. & Harada H. (1980) Effects of abscisic acid and water stress on the embryo and plantlet formation in anther culture of *Nicotiana tobacum* cv. Samsun. *Z. Pflanzenphysiol.*, **100**, 285–289.

Ingram D.S. & Helgeson J.P. (1980) (Eds) *Tissue Culture Methods for Plant Pathologists*. Blackwell Scientific Publications, Oxford.

Irvine G.N. (1955) Some effects of semolina lipoxidase activity on macaroni quality. *J. Amer. Oil. Chem. Soc.*, **32**, 558–561.

Itakura K., Hirose T., Crea R., Riggs A.D., Heyreker H.L., Bolivar F. & Boyer H.W. (1977) Expression in *E. coli* of a chemically synthesised gene for the hormone somatostatin. *Science*, **198**, 1056–63.

Jacob H.E., Siegmund F., Bauer E., Muhlig P. & Berg H. (1982) Fusion of plant protoplasts by dielectrophoresis and electric field pulse technique. *Sbud Biophys.*, **94**, 99.

James E. (1983) Low-temperature preservation of living cells. In *Plant Biotechnology* (Eds S.H. Mantell & H. Smith), pp. 163–186. Cambridge University Press, Cambridge.

Jeffreys A.J. (1979) DNA sequence variants in the $^G\gamma$-, $^A\gamma$-, δ- and β-globin genes of man. *Cell*, **18**, 1–10.

Jeffreys A.J. & Flavell R.A. (1977) A physical map of the DNA regions flanking the rabbit β-globin gene. *Cell*, **12**, 429–439.

Jendrisak J. (1980) Purification, structures and functions of the nuclear RNA polymerases from higher plants. In *Genome Organization and Expression in Plants* (Ed. C.J. Leaver), pp. 77–92. Plenum, New York.

Jigeng L. & Yi-nong L. (1983) Chloroplast DNA and cytoplasmic male sterility. *Theor. Appl. Genet.*, **64**, 231–238.

Jones J.D.G. & Flavell R.B. (1982) The structure, amount and chromosomal localization of defined repeated DNA sequences in species of the genus *Secale*. *Chromosoma*, **86**, 613–642.

Jones O.P. (1983) *In vitro* propagation of tree crops. In *Plant Biotechnology* (Eds S.H. Mantell & H. Smith) *SEB Seminar Ser.* Vol. 18, pp. 139–159. Cambridge University Press, Cambridge.

Kadkade P.G. & Seibert M. (1977) Phytochrome regulated organogenesis in lettuce tissue culture. *Nature*, **170**, 49–50.

Kahl G., Schafer W. & Wechselberg M. (1979) Changes in non-histone chromosomal proteins during the development of potato tubers: their involvement in wound- and hormone-induced processes. *Plant Cell. Physiol.*, **20**, 1217–1228.

Kamaley J.C. & Goldberg R.B. (1980) Regulation of structural gene expression in tobacco. *Cell*, **19**, 935–946.

Kao K.N. & Michayluk M.R. (1974) A method for high frequency intergeneric fusion of plant protoplasts. *Planta*, **115**, 355–367.

Kartha K.K. (1982) Cryopreservation of germ plasm using meristem and tissue culture. In *Application of Plant Cell and Tissue Culture to Agriculture and Industry*, Tomes D.T. *et al.* (eds), pp. 139–161. University of Guelph, Guelph.

Kato A. (1978) The involvement of photosynthesis in inducing bud formation on excised leaf segments of *Helionopsis orientalis* (Liliaceae). *Plant Cell Physiol.*, **19**, 791–799.

Kato A., Kawozoe S., Iizima M. & Shimizu Y. (1976) Continuous culture of tobacco cells. *Journal of Fermentation Technology*, **54**, 52–57.

Kato A., Shiozawa Y., Yamada A., Nishida K. & Noguchi M. (1977) A jar fermentator culture of *Nicotiana tabacum* L. cell suspensions. *Agric. Biol. Chem.*, **36**, 899–904.

Kemble R.J., Mans R.J., Gabay-Laughnan S. & Laughnan J.R. (1983) Sequences homologous to episomal mitochondrial DNAs in the maize nuclear genome. *Nature*, **304**, 744–747.

King P.J. (1980) Cell proliferation and growth in suspension cultures. In *Perspectives in Plant Cell and Tissue Culture*, Vasil I.K. (ed) *Suppl. 11A, Int. Rev. Cytol.* pp. 25–54 Academic Press, New York.

King P.J. & Street H.E. (1977) Growth patterns in cell cultures. In *Plant Tissue and Cell Culture* (Ed, H.E. Street), pp. 307–387. Blackwell Scientific Publications, Oxford.

Kinnersley A.M. & Dougall D.K. (1980) Correlation between the nicotine content of tobacco plants and callus cultures. *Planta*, **149**, 205–206.

Kirk T. (1981) Lignases, mechanism of action. In *Trends in the Biology of Fermentations for Fuels and Chemicals*, (Ed. A. Holleander). pp. 131–149. Plenum Press, New York.

Klee H.J., Gordon M.P. & Nester E.W. (1982) Complementation analysis of *Agrobacterium tumefaciens* Ti plasmid mutations affecting oncogenicity. *J. Bacteriol*, **150**, 327–331.

Knapp G., Ogden R.C., Peebles C.J. & Abelson J. (1979) Splicing of yeast tRNA precursors: structure of the reaction intermediates. *Cell*, **18**, 37–45.

Knauss J.F. & Miller J.W. (1978) A contaminant, *Erwinia carotovara*, affecting commercial plant tissue cultures. *In Vitro*, **14**, 754–756.

Koch W., Edwards K. & Kossel H. (1981) Sequencing of the 16S–23S spacer in a ribosomal operon of *Zea mays* chloroplast DNA. *Cell,* **25,** 203–213.

Kohlenbach H.W., Wenzel G. & Hoffmann F. (1982) Regeneration of *Brassica napus* plantlets in cultures from isolated protoplasts of haploid stem embryos as compared with leaf protoplasts. *Z. Pflanzenphysiol.,* **105,** 131–142.

Kolodner R. & Tewari K.K. (1972) Physiochemical characterization of mitochondrial DNA from Pea leaves. *Proc. Natl. Acad. Sci. USA,* **69,** 1830–1834.

Kramer W., Schughart K. & Fritz H-J. (1982) Directed mutagenesis of DNA cloned in filamentous phage: influence of hemimethylated GATC sites on marker recovery from restriction fragments. *Nucl. Acids. Res.,* **10,** 6475–6485.

Krikorian A.D. (1982) Cloning higher plants from aseptically cultured tissues and cells. *Biol. Rev.* **57,** 151–218.

Krikorian A.D., Staicu S.A. & Kann R.P. (1981) Karyotype analysis of a daylily clone reared from aseptically cultured tissues. *Ann. Bot.* **47,** 121–131.

Krumbiegel G. & Schieder O. (1979) Selection of somatic hybrids after fusion of protoplasts from *Datura innoxia* Mill and *Atropa belladonna* L. *Planta,* **145,** 371–379.

Laemmli U.K. (1970) Cleavage of structural proteins during the assembly of the head of bacteriophage T4. *Nature,* **227,** 680–685.

LaMotte C.E., Gochnauer C., LaMotte L.R., Mothur J.R. & Davies L.L.R. (1969) Pectin esterase in relation to leaf abscission in *Coleus* and *Phaseolus. Plant Physiol,* **44,** 21–26.

Lang H. & Kohlenbach H.W. (1982) Differentiation of alkaloid cells in cultures of *Macleaya* mesophyll protoplasts. *Planta Medica,* **46,** 78–81.

Larkin P.J. & Scowcroft W.R. (1981) Somaclonal variation — a novel source of variability from cell cultures for plant improvement. *Theor. appl. Genet.,* **60,** 197.

Larkins B.A., Jones R.A. & Tsai C.Y. (1976) Isolation and *in vitro* translation of zein messenger ribonucleic acid. *Biochemistry,* **15,** 5506–5511.

Larkins B.A., Pedersen K., Handa A.K., Hurkman W.J. & Smith L.D. (1979) Synthesis and processing of maize storage proteins in *Xenopus laevis* oocytes. *Proc. Natl. Acad. Sci. USA,* **76,** 6448–6452.

Laskey R.A. & Mills A.D. (1975) Quantitative film detection of ^{3}H and ^{14}C in polyacrylamide gels by fluorography. *Eur. J. Biochem.,* **56,** 335–341.

Lathe R.F., Lecocq J.P. & Everett R. (1983) DNA engineering: the use of enzymes, chemicals and oligonucleotides to restructure DNA sequences *in vitro.* In *Genetic Engineering 4* (Ed. R. Williamson), pp. 1–56. Academic Press, London.

Lawrence, R.H. (1981). *In vitro* plant cloning systems. *Env. Expt. Bot.* **21,** 289–300.

Lazar G.B., Frankhauser H. & Potrykus I. (1983) Complementation analysis of a nitrate reductase deficient *Hyoscyamus muticus* cell line by somatic hybridization. *Mol. Gen. Genet.,* **189,** 359.

Leaver C.J. & Gray M.W. (1982) Mitochondrial genome organization and expression in higher plants. *Ann. Rev. Plant Physiol.,* **33,** 373–402.

Lee K.J., Tribe D.E. & Rogers P.L. (1979) Ethanol production by *Zymomonas mobilis* in continuous culture at high glucose concentrations, *Biotechnol. Lett.,* **1,** 421–426.

Leemans J., Deblaere R., Willmitzer L., De Greve H., Hernalsteens J.P., Van Montagu M. & Schell J. (1982) Genetic identification of functions of TL-DNA transcripts in octopine crown gall. *EMBO J.,* **1,** 147–152.

Lemmers M., De Beuckeleer M., Holsters M., Zambryski P., Depicker A., Hernalsteens J.P., Van Montagu M. & Schell J. (1980) Internal organization, boundaries and integration of Ti-plasmid DNA in nopaline crown gall tumours. *J. Molec. Biol.,* **144,** 353–376.

Lewin B. (1980) *Gene Expression 2.* 2nd edn. Wiley Interscience, London.

Lieberman M. & Mapson L.W. (1964) Genesis and biogenesis of ethylene. *Nature,* **204,** 343–345.

Liener I.E. & Friedenson B. (1970) Ficin. *Methods in Enzymol.* **XIX,** 261–273.

Lindsey K. & Yeoman M.M. (1983) Novel experimental systems for studying the production of secondary metabolites by plant tissue cultures. In *Plant Biotechnology* (Eds S.H. Mantell & H. Smith), pp. 39–66. Cambridge University Press, Cambridge.

Litz R.E. & Conover R.A. (1981) Effect of sex type, season and other factors on *in vitro* establishment and culture of *Carica papaya* L. explants. *J. Amer. Soc. hort. Sci.*, **106**, 792–794.

Lörz H., Paszhowski J., Dierks-Ventling C. & Potrykus I. (1981) Isolation and characterization of cytoplasts and miniprotoplasts derived from protoplasts of cultured cells. *Physiologia Plantarum*, **53**, 385–391.

Lu D.Y., Pental D. & Cocking E.C. (1982) Plant regeneration from seedling cotyledon protoplasts. *Z. Pflanzenphysiol.* **107**, 59–63.

Lyons T.P. (1983) Alcohol-power/fuel. In *Industrial Enzymology: The Application of Enzymes in Industry* (Eds. T. Godfrey & J. Reichelt), pp. 179–193. Nature Press, New York.

Lyttleton J.W. (1962) Isolation of ribosomes from spinach chloroplasts. *Expl. Cell. Res.*, **26**, 312–317.

McClintock B. (1951) Chromosome organization and genic expression. *Cold Spring Harbor Symp. Quant. Biol.*, **16**, 13–47.

McClintock B. (1956) Controlling elements and the gene. *Cold Spring Harbor Symp. Quant. Biol.*, **21**, 197–216.

McClintock B. (1965) The control of gene action in Maize. *Brookhaven Symp. Biol.*, **18**, 162–184.

McCormick S., Mauvais J. & Fedoroff N. (1982) Evidence that the two sucrose synthetase genes in maize are related. *Mol. Gen. Genet.*, **187**, 494–500.

McKenzie R.J. (1979) Organelle genetics. *Bio-Science*, **29**, 569–572.

MacLoed A.M. (1977) Beer. In *Alcoholic Beverages* (Ed. A.H. Rose), pp. 44–137. Academic Press, New York.

Maliga P. (1980) Isolation, characterization and utilization of mutant cell lines in higher plants. *Int. Rev. Cytol.* Suppl. 11A, 225–250.

Maliga P., Menczel L., Sidorov V., Marton L., Cseplo A., Medgyesy P., Dung T.M., Lazar G & Nagy F. (1982) Cell culture mutants and their uses. In *Plant Improvement and Somatic Cell Genetics* (Eds Vasil I., Scowcroft W.R. & Frey K.J.), pp. 221–238. Academic Press, New York.

Malmberg R. & Griesbach R.J. (1980) The isolation of mitotic and meiotic chromosomes from plant protoplasts. *Plant Sci. Lett.*, **17**, 141–147.

Maniatis T., Fritsch E.F. & Sambrook J. (1982) *Molecular Cloning: a Laboratory Manual.* Cold Spring Harbor.

Mantell S.H., Haque S.Q. & Whitehall A.P. (1978) Clonal multiplication of *Dioscorea alata* L. and *D. rotundata* Poir. yams by tissue culture. *J. Hort. Sci.*, **53**, 95–98.

Mantell S.H. & Smith H. (1983) (Eds) *Plant Biotechnology* SEB Seminar Ser. Vol. 18. Cambridge University Press, Cambridge.

Mantell S. H., Pearson D.W., Hazell L.P. & Smith H. (1983) The effect of initial phosphate and sucrose levels on nicotine accumulation in batch suspension cultures of *Nicotiana tabacum* L. *Plant Cell Reports*, **2**, 73–77.

Margara, J. (1969) Etude des facteurs de la reoformation de bourgeous en culture *in vitro* chez la choufleur (*Brassica oleraceae* L., Var. Botrytis) *Ann. Physiol. Veg.*, **11**, 95–112.

Martin C. & Northcote D.H. (1983) The action of exogenous gibberellic acid on polysome formation and translation of mRNA in germinating castor-bean seeds. *Planta*, **158**, 16–26.

Martin S.M. (1980) Environmental factors: B. Temperature, aeration, and pH. In *Plant Tissue Cultures as a Source of Biochemicals.* (Ed. E.J. Staba), pp. 143–160. CRC Press, Boca Raton, Florida.

Martinez J., Hugard H. & Jonard R. (1979) The different grafting of shoot tips realized *in vitro* between peach (*Prunus persica Batsch*) apricot (*Prunus armeniaca* L.) and myrobolan (*Prunus cesarifera* Ehrh.), *C.R. Acad. Sci. Ser. D*, **288**, 759–762.

Marton L., Dung T.M., Mendel R.R. & Maliga P. (1982) Nitrate reductase deficient cell lines from haploid protoplast cultures of *Nicotiana plumbaginifolia*. *Molec. Gen. Genetics*, **186**, 301.

Marton L., Wullems G.J., Molendyk L. & Schilperoort R.A. (1979) *In vitro* transformation of cultured cells from *Nicotiana tabacum* by *Agrobacterium tumefaciens*. *Nature*, **277**, 129–131.

Marx J.L. (1983) A transposable element of maize emerges. *Science*, **219**, 829–830.

Matsui C., Hasezawa S., Tanaka N. & Syono K. (1983) Introduction of *Escherichia coli* cells and Spheroplasts into *Vinca* protoplasts. *Plant cell Reports*, **2**, 30–32.

Matthews B.F. & Cress D.E. (1981) Liposome-mediated delivery of DNA to carrot protoplasts. *Planta*, **153**, 90–94.

Matthews J.A., Brown J.W.S. & Hall T.C. (1981) Phaseolin mRNA is translated to yield glycosylated polypeptides in *Xenopus* oocytes. *Nature*, **294**, 175–176.

Matthews J.A. & Miflin B.J. (1980) *In vitro* synthesis of barley storage proteins. *Planta*, **149**, 262–268.

Matze A.J.M. & Chilton M-D. (1981) Site-specific insertion of genes into T-DNA of the *Agrobacterium* tumor-inducing plasmid: an approach to genetic engineering of higher plant cells. *J. Mol. Appl. Genet.*, **1**, 39–49.

Maxam A.M. & Gilbert W. (1977) A new method for sequencing DNA. *Proc. Natl. Acad. Sci. USA*, **74**, 560–564.

Maxam A.M. & Gilbert W. (1980) Sequencing end-labelled DNA with base-specific chemical cleavages. *Methods in Enzymology* **65**, 499–599.

Miflin B.J., Burgess S.R. & Shewry P.R. (1981) The development of protein bodies in the storage tissues of seeds. *J. Exp. Bot.*, **32**, 119–219.

Meins F. (1986) Epigenetic phenomena in relation to differentiation. In *Plant Cell Culture Technology* Yeoman M.M. (ed), Blackwell Scientific Publications, Oxford.

Meins F. & Binns A.N. (1978) Epigenetic clonal variation in the requirement of plant cells for cytokinins. In *The Clonal Basis of Development* (Eds Subtelny S. & Sussex I.M., pp. 185–201. Academic Press, New York.

Meins F., Lutz J. & Foster R. (1980) Factors influencing the incidence of habituation for cytokinin of tobacco pith tissue in culture. *Planta*, **150**, 264–268.

Melchers G, Sacristan M.D. & Holder A.A. (1978) Somatic hybrid plants of potato and tomato regenerated from fused protoplasts. *Carlsberg Res. Commun.*, **43**, 203–218.

Mercerau-Puijalon O., Royal A., Cami B., Garapin A., Krust A., Gannon F. & Kourilsky P. (1978). Synthesis of an ovalbumin-like protein by *Escherichia coli* K12 harbouring a recombinant plasmid. *Nature*, **275**, 505–510.

Messing J., Crea R. & Seeburg P.H. (1981) A system for shotgun DNA sequencing. *Nucleic Acids Res.* **9**, 309–321.

Miller L.K., Lingg A.J. & Bulla L.A. (1983) Bacterial, viral and fungal insecticides. *Science*, **219**, 715–721.

Miller L.R. & Murashige T. (1976) Tissue culture propagation of tropical foliage plants. *In Vitro*, **12**, 797–813.

Minami S.A., Collins P.S., Young E.E., & Weeks D.P. (1981) Tubulin induction in *Chlamydomonas reinhardii*: requirements for tubulin mRNA synthesis. *Cell*, **24**, 89–96.

Møller B.L., Høyer-Hansen G. & Henry L.E.A. (1982) The use of chloroplast proteins in crop improvement. In *Plant cell Culture in Crop Improvement. Basic Life Sciences*, Vol. 22 (Eds S.K. Sen & K.L. Giles). Plenum, New York.

Monod J. (1950) La technique de culture continuee. Theorie et application. *Ann. Inst. Pasteur, Paris*, **79**, 390–410.

Muir W.H., Hildebrandt A.C. & Riker A.J. (1954) Plant tissue cultures produced from single isolated plant cells. *Science*, **119**, 877–878.

Muntz K., Bassuner R., Baumlein H., Manteuffel R., Puchel R., Schmidt P. & Wobus V. (1981) The biosynthesis of storage proteins in developing field bean seeds. In *Proc. 2nd Seed Protein Symposium: Regulation of protein biosynthesis and degredation during embryogenesis and germination of plant seeds* (eds K. Muntz, R. Manteuffel & G. Scholz), pp. 57–73. Akademie Verlag, Berlin.

Murachi T. (1970) Bromelain Enzymes. *Methods in Enzymol.*, **XIX**, 273–284.

Murai N., Sutton D.W., Murray M.G., Slightom J.L., Merlo D.J., Reichert N.A., Sengupta Gopalan C., Stock C.A., Barker R.F., Kemp J.D. & Hall T.C. (1983) Phaseolin gene from bean is expressed after transfer to sunflower via tumor inducing plasmid vectors. *Science*, **222**, 476–482.

Murashige T. (1974) Plant propagation through tissue cultures. *Ann. Rev. Plant Physiology*, **25**, 135–166.

Murashige T. & Nakano R. (1967) Chromosome complement as a determinant of the morphogenic potential of tobacco cells. *Ann. J. Bot.*, **54**, 963–970.

Murashige T. & Kakano R. (1968) The light requirement for shoot initiation in tobacco callus cultures. *Ann. J. Bot.*, **55**, 710.

Murashige T. & Skoog F. (1962) A revised medium for rapid growth and bioassays with tobacco tissue cultures. *Physiologia Pl.*, **15**, 473–497.

Murata M. & Orton T.J. (1982) Analysis of karyotypic changes in suspension cultures of celery. In *Plant Tissue Culture* (Ed. A. Fujiwara), pp. 435–436. Jap. Assoc. Pl. Tiss. Cult., Tokyo.

Murray A.W. & Szostak J.W. (1983) Construction of artificial chromosomes in yeast. *Nature*, **305**, 189–193.

Murray M.G., Palmer J.D., Cuellar R.E. & Thompson W.F. (1979) Deoxyribonucleic acid sequence organization in the mung bean genome. *Biochemistry*, **18**, 5259–5266.

Murray M.G. & Thompson W.F. (1980) Rapid isolation of high molecular weight plant DNA. *Nucleic Acids Res.*, **8**, 4321–4325.

Murray N.E. & Murray K. (1974) Manipulation of restriction targets in phage λ to form receptor chromosomes for DNA fragments. *Nature*, **251**, 476–481.

Muthukrishnan S., Maxwell E.S. & Chandra G.R. (1981) Molecular cloning of barley alpha-amylase complementary DNA sequences in pBR322. *Fed. Proc.* **40**, 1711.

Nabors M.W., Gibbs S.E., Bernstein C.S. & Meis M.E. (1980) NaCl-tolerant tobacco plant from cultured cells. *Z. Pflanzenphysiol.*, **97**, 13–17.

Nagl W. (1982) Nuclear chromatin. In *Encyclopedia of Plant Physiology*, vol. 14B (Eds B. Parthier & D. Boulter), pp. 1–45. Springer-Verlag, Berlin.

Nagl W., Jeanjour M., Kling H., Kuhner S., Michels I., Muller T. & Stein B. (1983) Genome and chromatin organization in higher plants. *Biologisches Zentralblatt*, **102**, 129–148.

Nakamura K. & Inowye M. (1982) Construction of versatile expression cloning vehicles using the lipoprotein gene of *E. coli*. *EMBO Journal*, **1**, 771–775.

Nakata K. & Oshima H. (1982) Cytoplasmic chimaericity in the somatic hybrids of tobacco. In *Plant Tissue Culture 1982* (Ed. A. Fujiwara), pp. 641–642. Japan. Assn. Plant Tiss. Cult., Tokyo.

Navarro L., Roistacher C.N. & Murashige T. (1975) Improvement of shoot-tip grafting *in vitro* for virus-free Citrus. *J. Ann. Hort. Sci.*, **100**, 471–478.

Nitsch C. (1977) Culture of isolated microspores. In *Plant Cell, Tissue and Organ Culture* (Eds J. Reinert & Y.P.S. Bajaj), pp. 268–278. Springer-Verlag, Berlin.

Noyes B.E., Mevarech M., Stein R. & Agarwal K.L. (1979) Detection and partial sequence analysis of gastrin mRNA by using an oligodeoxy-nucleotide probe. *Proc. Natl. Acad. Sci. USA*, **76**, 1770–1774.

O'Farrell P.H., Polisky B. & Gelfand D.H. (1978) Regulated expression by read-through translation from a plasmid-encoded β-galactosidase. *J. Bact.*, **134**, 645–654.

Ohgawara T., Uchimiya H. & Harada H. (1983) Uptake of liposome-encapsulated plasmid DNA by plant protoplasts and molecular fate of foreign DNA. *Protoplasma*, **116**, 145–148.

Old R.W. & Primrose S.B. (1981) *Principles of Gene Manipulation* (2nd Edn.) Blackwell Scientific Publications, Oxford.

Palmer J.D., Shields C.R., Cohen D.B. & Orton T.J. (1983) An unusual mitochondrial DNA plasmid in the genus *Brassica. Nature*, **301**, 725–727.

Palmer J.D. & Shields C.R. (1984) Tripartite structure of the *Brassica campestris* mitochondrial genome. *Nature*, **307**, 437–440.

Palmer J.D. & Thompson W.F. (1980) Studies on higher plant chloroplast and mitochondrial DNA. *Carnegie Institute Yearbook*, **79**, 120–122.

Passavant C.W., Stiegler G.L. & Hallick R.B. (1983) Location of the single gene for elongation factor Tu on the *Euglena gracilis* chloroplast chromosome. *J. Biol. Chem.*, **258**, 693–695.

Paterson B.M., Roberts B.E. & Kuff E.L. (1977) Structural gene identification and mapping by DNA-mRNA hybrid-arrested cell-free translation. *Proc. Natl. Acad. Sci. USA*, **74**, 4370–4374.

Patnaik G., Cocking E.C., Hamill J. & Pental D. (1981) A simple procedure for the manual isolation and identification of plant heterokaryons. *Plant Sci. Lett.* **24**, 105–110.

Paul J. (1975) *Cell and Tissue Culture* (5th Edn.) Churchill Livingstone, London.

Payne P.I. & Rhodes A.P. (1982) Cereal storage proteins: structure and role in agriculture and food technology. In *Encyclopedia of Plant Physiology*. Vol. 14A (Eds D. Boulter & B. Parthier) Springer-Verlag, Berlin.

Pedersen K., Devereux J., Wilson D.R., Sheldon E. & Larkins B.A. (1982) Cloning and sequence analysis reveal structural variation among related zein genes in maize. *Cell*, **29**, 1015–1026.

Pelham H.R.B. & Jackson R.J. (1976) An efficient mRNA dependent translation system from reticulocyte lysates. *Eur. J. Biochem.*, **67**, 247–256

Pellicer A., Robins D., Wold B., Sweet R., Jackson J., Lowy I., Roberts J.M., Sim G.K., Silverstein S. & Axel R. (1980) Altering genotype and phenotype by DNA-mediated gene transfer. *Science*, **209**, 1414–1422.

Perucho M., Hanahan D. & Wigler M. (1980) Genetic and physical linkage of exogenous sequences in transformed cells. *Cell*, **22**, 309–317.

Petit A., Delhaye S., Tempe J. & Morel G. (1970) Recherches sur les guanidines des tissues de crown gall. Mise en evidence d'une relation biochemique specifique entre les souches d'*Agrobacterium* et les tumeurs qu'elles induisent. *Physiol. veg.*, **8**, 205–213.

Pental D., Cooper-Bland S., Harding K., Cocking E.C. & Muller A.J. (1982) Cultural studies on nitrate reductase deficient *Nicotiana tabacum* mutant protoplasts. *Zeitsch. fur Pflanzen*, **105**, 219–227.

Pfeiffer P. & Hohn T. (1983) Involvement of reverse transcription in the replication of cauliflower mosaic virus: a detailed model and test of some aspects. *Cell*, **33**, 781–789.

Pirt S.J. (1975) *Principals of Microbe and Cell Cultivation*. Blackwell Scientific Publications, Oxford.

Power J.B., Berry S.F., Chapman J.V. & Cocking E.C. (1980) Somatic hybridization of sexually incompatible petunias: *Petunia parodii, Petunia parviflora. Theor. Appl. Genet.*, **57**, 1–4.

Prenosil J.E. & Pederson H. (1983) Immobilized plant cell reactors. *Enzyme Microb. Technol.* **5**, 323–331.

Pring D.R., Conde M.F. & Gengenbach B.G. (1981) Cytoplasmic genome variability in tissue culture-derived plants. *Env. Expt. Bot.*, **21**, 369–377.

Quak F. (1977) Meristem culture and virus-free plants. In *Plant Cell, Tissue and Organ Culture* (Eds Reinert J. & Bajaj Y.P.S.), pp. 598–615. Springer-Verlag, Berlin.

Quail P.H. (1984) Phytochrome: a regulatory photoreceptor that controls expression of its own gene. *Trends in Biochemical Sciences, **9**,* 450–453.

Rackwitz H.-R., Rohde W. & Sanger H.L. (1981) DNA-dependent RNA polymerase II of plant origin transcribes viroid RNA into full-length copies. *Nature,* **291**, 297–301.

Raghavan V. (1977) Applied aspects of embryo culture. In *Plant Cell, Tissue and Organ Culture* (Eds Reinert J. & Bajaj Y.P.S.), pp. 160–178. Springer-Verlag, Berlin.

Ramshaw J.A.M. (1982) Structures of plant proteins. In *Nucleic Acids and Proteins in Plants I.* (Eds D. Boulter & B. Parthier), pp. 229–290. Springer-Verlag, Berlin.

Rashid A. (1982) Induction of embryos in *ab initio* pollen cultures of *Nicotiana.* In *Plant Cell Culture in Crop Improvement.* (Eds S.K. Sen & K.L. Giles), pp. 141–144. Plenum Press, New York.

Reinert J., Bajaj Y.P.S. & Zbell B. (1977) In *Plant Tissue and Cell Culture.* (Ed. H.E. Street), pp. 389–427 Blackwell Scientific Publications, Oxford.

Reinert J. & Yeoman M.M. (1982) *Plant Cell and Tissue Culture: A Laboratory Mannual.* Springer-Verlag, Berlin.

Rice D., Mazur B.J. & Haselkorn R. (1982) Isolation and physical mapping of nitrogen fixation genes from the cyanobacterium *Anabena. J. Biol. Chem.,* **257**, 13157–13163.

Rigby P.W.J., Dieckmann M., Rhodes C. & Berg P. (1977) Labelling deoxyribonucleic acid to high specific activity *in vitro* by nick translation with DNA polymerase 1. *J. Mol. Biol.,* **113**, 237–251.

Rines H.W. & McCoy T.J. (1981) Tissue culture initiation and plant regeneration in hexaploid species of oats. *Crop Science,* **21**, 837–842.

Ris H. & Plaut W. (1962) Ultrastructure of DNA-containing areas in the chloroplast of *Chlamydomonas. J. Cell. Biol.,* **13**, 383–391.

Roberts B.E. & Paterson B.M. (1973) Efficient translation of Tobacco Mosaic virus RNA and rabbit globin 9s RNA in a cell-free system from commercial wheat germ. *Proc. Natl. Acad. Sci. USA,* **70**, 2330–2334.

Roca W.M., Bryan J.E. & Roca M.R. (1979) Tissue culture for international transfer of potato genetic resources. *Amer. Potato J.* **55**, 691–701.

Rombouts F.M. & Pilnik W. (1972) Research on Pectin Depolymerases in the Sixties: A Literature Review. *C.R.C. Crit. Rev. Food Technol.,* **3**, 1–26.

Rosenberg M. & Court D. (1979) Regulatory sequences involved in the promotion and termination of RNA transcription. *Ann. Rev. Genet.,* **13**, 319–353.

Royal Society (1980) A Joint Report ACARD., ABRC., H.M.S.O., London.

Rubin G.M. & Spradling A.C. (1982) Genetic transformation of *Drosophila* with transposable element vectors. *Science* **218**, 348–353.

Sahai O.P. & Shuler M.L. (1982) On the nonideality of chemostat operation using plant cell suspension cultures. *Can. J. Bot.* **60**, 692.

Sänger H.L., Klotz G., Riesner D., Gross H.J. & Kleinschmidt A.M. (1976) Viroids are single-stranded covalently closed circular RNA molecules existing as highly base-paired rod-like structures. *Proc. Natl. Acad. Sci. USA,* **73**, 3852–3856.

Sanger F., Nicklen S. & Coulson A.R. (1977) DNA sequencing with chain-termination inhibitors. *Proc. Natl. Acad. Sci. USA,* **74**, 5463–5467.

Scangos G.A., Huttner K.M., Juricek D.K. & Ruddle F.H. (1981) DNA-mediated gene transfer in mammalian cells: molecular analysis of unstable transformants and their progression to stability. *Mol. Cell. Biol.,* **1**, 111–120.

Schaffner W. (1980) Direct transfer of cloned genes from bacteria to mammalian cells. *Proc. Natl. Acad. Sci. USA,* **77**, 2163–2167.

Schell J. (1982). The Ti- plasmids of *Agrobacterium tumefaciens. Encyclopedia of Plant Physiology.* New Series, Vol. 14B, 455–474.

Scherer S. & Davis R.W. (1979) Replacement of chromosome segments with altered DNA sequences constructed *in vitro. Proc. Natl. Acad. Sci. USA,* **76**, 4951–4955.

Schoffl F. & Key J.R. (1982) An analysis of messenger RNA species for a group of heat-shock proteins of soybean using cloned complementary DNA. *J. Mol. Appl. Genetics.*, **1**, 301−314.

Schubert K.R. (1982) The energetics of biological nitrogen fixation. *American Society of Plant Physiologists Workshop Summaries*, I, p. 24.

Schwarz Z., Jolly S.O., Steinmetz A.A. & Bogorad L. (1981) Overlapping divergent genes in the maize chloroplast genome and *in vitro* transcription of the gene for histidyl tRNA. *Proc. Natl. Acad. Sci. USA*, **78**, 3423−3427.

Scott G.M. & Tyrrell D.A.J. (1980) Interferon: therapeutic fact or fiction for the '80's? *Brit. Med. J.*, **280**, 1558−1562.

Scowcroft W.R. & Larkin P.J. (1982) Somaclonal variation: a new option for plant improvement. In *Plant Improvement and Somatic Cell Genetics.* (Eds I.K. Vasil *et al.*), pp. 159−178. Academic Press, New York.

Seibert M. (1973) The effects of wavelength and intensity on growth and shoot initiation in tobacco callus. *In Vitro*, **80**, 435.

Shargool P.D. (1982) Biotechnological applications of plant cells. *Appl. Biochem. Biotechnol.* **7**, 239−257.

Shepard J.F., Bidney D., Barsby T. & Kemble R. (1983) Genetic transfer in plants through interspecific protoplast fusion. *Science*, **219**, 683−688.

Shepard J.F., Bidney D. & Shalvin E.A. (1980) Potato protoplasts in crop improvement. *Science*, **208**, 17−24.

Shepherd N.S., Schwarz-Sommer Z., Wienand U., Sommer H., Deumling B., Paterson P.A. & Saedler H. (1982) Cloning of a genomic fragment carry insertion element CIN-1 of *Zea mays. Mol. Gen. Genet.*, **188**, 266−271.

Sheridan W.F. (1968) Tissue culture of the monocot *Lilium. Planta*, **82**, 189−192.

Shine J. & Dalgarno L. (1975) Determinant of cistron specificity in bacterial ribosomes. *Nature*, **254**, 34−38.

Shine J., Fettes I., Lan N.C.Y., Roberts J.L. & Baxter J.D. (1980) Expression of cloned β-endorphin gene sequences by *Escherichia coli. Nature*, **285**, 456−461.

Shinozaki K. & Suguira M. (1982) The nucleotide sequence of the tobacco chloroplast gene for the large subunit of ribulose 1. 5. bisphosphate carboxylase oxygenase. *Gene*, **20**, 91−102.

Shull G.H. (1912) 'Phenotype' and 'clone'. *Science*, **35**, 182−183.

Sidorov V.A. & Maliga P. (1982) Fusion-complementation analysis of auxotrophic and chlorophyll-deficient lines isolated in haploid *Nicotiana plumbaginifolia* protoplast cultures. *Molec. Gen. Genetics*, **186**, 328.

Sieliwanowicz B., Kalinowska M. & Chmielewska I. (1977) Appearance of poly(A)-rich RNA in germinating pea seeds. *Acta Biochim. Pol.*, **24**, 59−64.

Skirvin R.M. (1978) Natural and induced variation in tissue culture. *Euphytica*, **27**, 241−266.

Skirvin R.M. & Janick J. (1976) Tissue culture-induced variation in scented *Pelargonium* spp. *J. Amer. Soc. Hort. Sci.*, **101**, 281−290.

Skoog F. & Miller C.O. (1957) Chemical regulation of growth and organ formation in plant tissues cultured *in vitro. Symp. Soc. Exp. Biol.*, **11**, 118−130.

Smith H. (1982) Light quality, total perception, plant strategy. *Annual Rev. Plant Physiology* **33**, 481−518.

Smith M. & Gillam S. (1981) Constructed mutants using synthetic oligodeoxyribonucleotides as site-specific mutagens. In *Genetic Engineering*, 3 (Eds J.K. Setlow & A. Holleander), pp. 1−32. Plenum Press, New York.

Smith S.M. & Ellis R.J. (1979) Processing of small subunit precursor of ribulose bisphosphate carboxylase and its assembly into whole enzyme are stromal events. *Nature*, **278**, 662−664.

Sorenson J.C. (1981) Cloning of the catalase genes from maize. *Genetics*, **97** (Suppl. 1), S100.

Southern E.M. (1975) Detection of specific sequences among DNA fragments separated by gel electrophoresis. *J. Mol. Biol.*, **98**, 503−517.

Southern E.M. (1979) Gel electrophoresis of restriction fragments. *Methods in Enzymology,* **68**, 152–176.

Spencer M. (1965) Fruit ripening. In *Plant Biochemistry* (Eds J. Bonner & J.E. Varner), pp. 793–825. Academic Press, New York.

Spencer R.W., Foard D.E. & Larkins B.A. (1982) Molecular cloning and analysis of sequences coding for the Bownan-Birk and related soybean protease inhibitors. *Plant Physiol.,* **69** (Suppl. 4), 140.

Spiegel S., Obendorf R.L. & Marcus A. (1975) Transcription of ribosomal and messenger RNAs in early wheat embryo germination. *Plant Physiol.,* **56**, 502–507.

Spruill W.M., Levings C.S. & Sederoff R.R. (1981) Organization of mitochondrial DNA in normal and Texas male sterile cytoplasms of maize. *Development Genetics,* **2**, 319–336.

Staba E.J. (1980) (Ed.) *Plant Tissue Culture as a Source of Biochemicals.* CRC Press, Boca Raton, Florida.

Starlinger P. (1980) A re-examination of McClintock's 'controlling elements' in maize in view of recent advances in molecular biology. In *Genome Organization and Expression in Plants* (Ed. C.J. Leaver), pp. 537–551. Plenum Press, New York.

Steinbiss H.H. & Stabel P. (1983) Protoplast-derived tobacco cells can survive capillary microinjection of the fluorescent dye lucifer yellow. *Protoplasma,* **116**, 223–227.

Stern D.B. & Lonsdale D.M. (1982) Mitochondrial and chloroplast genomes of maize have a 12 kilobase DNA sequence in common. *Nature,* **299**, 698–702.

Stewart J.M. (1981) *In vitro* fertilization and embryo rescue. *Env. expt. Bot.,* **21**, 301–315.

Stiekema W.J., Wimpee C.F., Silverthorne J. & Tobin E.M. (1983) Phytochrome control of the expression of two nuclear genes encoding chloroplast proteins in *Lemna gibba* L. G-3. *Plant Physiol.,* **72**, 717–724.

Stohs S.J. (1977) Metabolism of steroids in plant tissue cultures. In *Plant Tissue Culture and its Bio-technological Application* (Eds Barz W., Reinhard E. & Zenk M.H.), pp. 142–150. Springer-Verlag, Berlin.

Stout A.B. (1940) The nomenclature of cultivated plants. *Amer. J. Bot.,* **27**, 339–347.

Street H.E. (1977) (Ed.) *Plant Tissue and Cell Culture.* Blackwell Scientific Publications, Oxford.

Struhl K., Cameron J.R. & Davis R.W. (1976) Functional genetic expression of eukaryotic DNA in *Escherichia coli. Proc. Natl. Acad. Sci. USA,* **73**, 1471–1475.

Struhl K., Stinchcomb D.T., Sherer S. & Davis R.W. (1979) High-frequency transformation of yeast: Autonomous replication of hybrid DNA molecules. *Proc. Natl. Acad. Sci. USA,* **76**, 1035–1039.

Stuart R. & Street H.E. (1971) Studies on the growth in culture of plant cells, X. Further studies on the conditioning of culture media by suspensions of *Acer pseudoplatanus* L. *J. Exp. Bot.,* **22**, 96–106.

Sullivan D., Brisson N., Goodchild B., Verma D.P.S. & Thomas D.Y. (1981) Molecular cloning and organization of two leghemoglobin genomic sequences from soybean. *Nature,* **289**, 516–518.

Sun C-R., Endo T., Kusuda M. & Suguira M. (1982) Molecular cloning of the genes for ribosomal DNA from broad bean *Vicia faba* chloroplast DNA. *Jap. J. Genet.,* **57**, 397–402.

Sun S.M., Slightom J. & Hall T.C. (1981) Intervening sequences in a plant gene — comparison of the partial cDNA and genomic DNA of french bean phaseolin. *Nature,* **289**, 37–41.

Sundaresan V., Jones J.D.G., Ow D.W. & Ausubel F.M. (1983) *Klebsiella pneumoniae nif A* product activates the *Rhizobium meliloti* nitrogenase promoter. *Nature,* **301**, 728–731.

Sunderland N. (1977) Nuclear cytology. In *Plant Tissue and Cell Culture* (Ed. H.E. Street), pp. 177–205. Blackwell Scientific Publications, Oxford.

Sunderland N. & Dunwell J.M. (1977) Pollen and anther cultures. In *Plant Cell and Tissue Culture* (Ed. H.E. Street), pp. 205–239. Blackwell Scientific Publications, Oxford.

Szabados L., Hadlaczky G. & Dudits D. (1981) Uptake of isolated plant chromosomes by plant protoplasts. *Planta*, **151**, 141–145.

Takawa F. & Sugiura M. (1982) Nucleotide sequence of the 16s–23s spacer region in an rRNA gene cluster from tobacco chloroplast DNA. *Nucleic Acids Res.*, **10**, 2665–2675.

Takayama S. & Misawa M. (1982) Mass propagation of ornamental plants through tissue culture. In *Plant Tissue Culture 1982* (Ed. A. Fujiwara), pp. 681–682. Japan. Assn. Plant Tiss. Cult., Tokyo.

Takebe I. (1975) The use of protoplasts in plant virology. *Ann. Rev. Phytopathol.*, **13**, 105–125.

Talmadge K., Brosius J. & Gilbert W. (1981) An internal signal sequence directs secretion and processing of proinsulin in bacteria. *Nature*, **294**, 176–178.

Thomas D.S. & Murashige T. (1979) Volatile emissions of plant tissue cultures. I. Identification of the major components. *In Vitro*, **15**, 654–658.

Thomas E. & Street H.E. (1970) Organogenesis in cell suspension cultures of *Atropa belladonna* L. and *Atropa belladonna* cultivar *lactea* Doll. *Ann. Bot.* **34**, 657–669.

Thomashow M.F., Nutter R., Montoya A.L., Gordon M.P. & Nester E.W. (1980) Integration and organization of Ti plasmid sequences in crown gall tumors. *Cell*, **19**, 729–739.

Thompson W.F., Everett M., Polans N.O., Jorgensen R.A. & Palmer J.D. (1983) Phytochrome control of RNA levels in developing pea and mung bean leaves. *Planta*, **158**, 487–500.

Tobin E.M. (1981) Phytochrome-mediated regulation of messenger RNAs for the small subunit of ribulose 1, 5-bisphosphate carboxylase of *Lemna gibba*. *Plant Molec. Biol.* **1**, 35–51.

Torrey J.G. (1966) The initiation of organized development in plants. *Adv. Morphogen*, **5**, 39–91.

Tran Thanh Van K. (1977) Regulation of morphogenesis. In *Plant Tissue Culture and Its Bio-technological Application* (Eds Barz W., Reinhard E. & Zenk M.H.), pp. 367–385. Springer-Verlag, Berlin.

Tran Thanh Van K. (1980) Control of morphogenesis by inherent and exogenuously applied factors in thin cell layers. In *Perspectives in Plant Cell and Tissue* (Ed. I.K. Vasil) *Culture Suppl. 11A* Int. Rev. Cytol. pp. 175–194. Academic Press, New York.

Uchimiya H. & Harada H. (1981) Transfer of liposome-sequestering plasmid DNA into *Daucus carota* Protoplasts. *Plant Physiol.*, **68**, 1027–1030.

Uchimiya H. & Marashige T. (1974) Evaluation of parameters in the isolation of viable protoplasts from cultured tobacco cells. *Plant Physiol.*, **54**, 936–944.

Van Ee J.H., Vos Y.J., Bohnert H.J. & Planta R.J. (1982) Mapping of genes on the chloroplast DNA *Spirodela oligorhiza*. *Plant. Mol. Biol.*, **1**, 117–132.

Vasil I.K. (1976) The progress, problems and prospects of plant protoplast research. *Adv. Agron.*, **28**, 119–160.

Vasil I.K. (1982) Plant cell culture and somatic cell genetics of cereals and grasses. In *Plant Improvement and Somatic Cell Genetics.* (Eds I.K. Vasil, W.R. Scowcroft & K.J. Frey), pp. 179–203. Academic Press, New York.

Vasil I.K., Ahiya M.R. & Vasil V. (1979) Plant tissue cultures in genetics and plant breeding. *Advances in Genetics* **20**, 127–215.

Vasil V. & Vasil I.K. (1980) Isolation and culture of cereal protoplasts II. Embryogenesis and plantlet formation from protoplasts of *Pennisetum americanum*. *Theol. Appl. Genet.*, **56**, 97–99.

Verma D.P.S., Nash D.T. & Schulman H. (1974) Isolation and *in vitro* translation of soybean leghemoglobin. *Nature, New Biol.*, **251**, 74–77.

Verma D.P.S., Fuller F., Lee J., Künster P., Brisson N. & Nguyen T. (1983) A search for nodulin genes of soybean. In *Structure and Function of Plant Genomes* (Eds O. Ciferri & L. Dure), pp. 269–285. Plenum, New York.

Vickery M.L. & Vickery B. (1981) *Secondary Plant Metabolism.* Macmillan Press, London.

Vienken J., Zimmermann U., Gauser R. & Hampp R. (1983) Vesicle formation during electrofusion of mesophyll protoplasts of *Kalanchoe daigremontiana. Planta*, **157**, 331.

Villa-Komaroff L., Efstratiadis A., Broome S., Lomedico P., Tizard R., Naber S.P., Chick W.L. & Gilbert W. (1978) A bacterial clone synthesising proinsulin. *Proc. Natl. Acad. Sci. USA*, **75**, 3727–3731.

Viotti A., Abildsten D., Pogna N., Sala E. & Pirrotta V. (1982) Multiplicity and diversity of cloned zein complementary DNA sequences and their chromosomal localization. *EMBO J.*, **1**, 53–58.

Vodkin L.O. (1981) Isolation and characterisation of messenger RNAs for seed lectin and kunitz trypsin inhibitor from soybeans. *Plant. Physiol.*, **68**, 766–771.

Wareing, P.F. (1982) Determination and related aspects of plant development. In *The Molecular Biology of Plant Development* (Eds H. Smith & D. Grierson), pp. 517–539. Blackwell Scientific Publications, Oxford.

Wagenknecht A.C. (1959) Lipoxidase activity and off-flavour in underblanched frozen corn-on-the-cob. *Foods Res.*, **24**, 539–547.

Wagenknecht A.C. & Lee F.A. (1956) The action of lipoxygenase in frozen raw peas. *Foods Res.*, **21**, 605–610.

Walker J.C. & Key J.L. (1982) Isolation of cloned complementary DNA to auxin-responsive polyadenylated RNA of elongating soybean, Glycine max, hypotocyl. *Proc. Natl. Acad. Sci. USA*, **79**, 7185–7189.

Walkey D.G.A. (1978) *In vitro* methods for virus elimination. In *Frontiers of Plant Tissue Culture* (Ed. T.A. Thorpe), pp. 245–254. Univ. of Calgary, Calgary.

Wallace R.B., Johnson P.F., Tanaka S., Schold M., Itakura K. & Abelson J. (1980) Directed deletion of a yeast transfer RNA intervening sequence. *Science*, **209**, 1396–1400.

Webber H.J. (1903) New horticultural and agricultural terms. *Science*, **18**, 501–503.

Westcott R.J. (1981) Tissue culture storage of potato germplasm. 1. Minimal growth storage. *Potato Research*, **24**, 331–342.

White P.R. (1934) Potentially unlimited growth of excised tomato root tips in a liquid medium. *Pl. Physiol.*, 585–600.

Wielgat B., Wechselberger M. & Kahl G. (1979) Age-dependent variations in transcriptional response to wounding and gibberellic acid in a higher plant. *Planta*, **147**, 205–209.

Wienand U., Landridge P. & Feix G. (1981) Isolation and characterization of a genomic sequence of maize coding for a zein gene. *Mol. Gen. Genet.*, **182**, 440–444.

Wienand U., Sommer H., Schwarz Z., Shepherd N., Saedler H., Kreuzaler F., Ragg H., Fautz E., Hahlbrock K., Harrison B. & Peterson P.A. (1982) A general method to identify plant structural genes among genomic clones using transposable element induced mutations. *Mol. Gen. Genet.*, **187**, 195–201.

Wigler M., Sweet R., Sim G.K., Wold B., Pellicer A., Lacy E., Maniates T., Silverstein S. & Axel R. (1979; Transformation of mammalian cells with genes from prokaryotes and eukaryotes. *Cell*, **16,** 777–785.

Willecke K. (1978) Results and prospects of chromosomal gene transfer between cultured mammalian cells. *Theor. Appl. Genet.*, **52**, 97–104.

Willey D.L., Huttly A.K., Phillips A.L. & Gray J.C. (1983) Localization of the gene for cytochrome *f* in pea chloroplast DNA. *Mol. Gen. Genet.* **189**, 85–89.

Willmitzer L., Dhaese P., Schreier P. H., Schlmalenbach W., Van Montagu M., &

Schell J. (1983) Size, location and polarity of transferred DNA encoded transcripts in nopaline crown gall tumors: common transcripts in octopine and nopaline tumors. *Cell*, **32**, 1045–1056.

Wilson S.B., King P.J. & Street H.E. (1971) Studies on the growth in culture of plant cells XII. A versatile system for the large scale batch or continuous culture of plant cell suspensions. *J. Exp. Bot*, **21**, 177–207.

Withers L.A. (1983) Germplasm storage in plant biotechnology. In *Plant Biotechnology*. Mantell S.H. & Smith H. (eds), pp. 187–218. Cambridge University Press, Cambridge.

Withers L.A. (1982) The development of cryopreservation techniques for plant cell, tissue and organ cultures. In *Plant Tissue Culture* (Ed. A. Fujiwara), pp. 793–794. Jap. Assoc. Pl. Tiss. Cult., Tokyo.

Withers L.A. & Street H.E. (1977) The freeze-preservation of cultured plant cells: II The pregrowth phase. *Physiologia Plastarum*, **39**, 171–178.

Wright J.A., Lewis W.H. & Parfett C.L.J. (1980) Somatic cell genetics: a review of drug resistance and gene transfer in mammalian cells in culture. *Canadian Journal of Genetics and Cytology*, **22**, 443–496.

Wright N.A. & Alderson P.G. (1980) The growth of tulip tissues *in vitro*. *Acta Horticulturae*, **109**, 263–270.

Xu Z.H., Davey M.R. & Cocking E.C. (1982) Plant regeneration from root protoplasts of *Brassica*. *Plant Sci. Lett*, **24**, 117–121.

Yang H.Y. & Zhon C. (1982) *In vitro* induction of haploid plants from unpollinated ovaries and ovules. *Theor. Appl. Genet.*, **69**, 97.

Yeoman M.M. & Forche E. (1980) Cell proliferation and growth in callus cultures. In *Perspectives in Plant Cell and Tissue Culture* (Ed. I.K. Vasil), pp. 1–24. Int. Rev. Cytol. Suppl. 11A.

Yontsey C.O. (1978) A method for virus-free propagation of citrus-shoot tip grafting. *Citrus Ind.*, **59**, 39.

Zambryski P., Joos H., Genetello C., Leemans J., Van Montagu M. & Schell J. (1983) Ti plasmid vector for the introduction of DNA into plant cells without alteration of their normal regeneration capacity. *EMBO J.* **2**, 2143–2150.

Zelcer A., Aviv D. & Galnn E. (1978) Interspecific transfer of cytoplasmic male sterility by fusion between protoplasts of normal *Nicotiana sylvestris* and X-ray irradiated protoplasts of male sterile *N. tabacum*. *Z. Pflanzen Phys.*, **90**, 397–407.

Zimmerman, U. & Scheurich P. (1981) High frequency fusion of plant protoplasts by electric fields. *Planta*, **151**, 26–32.

Zurawski G., Bottomley W. & Whitfield P.R. (1982) Structure of the genes for the beta and epsilon subunits of spinach chloroplast ATPase indicate a dicistronic mRNA and an overlapping translation stop start signal. *Proc. Natl. Acad. Sci. USA*, **79**, 6260–6264.

Index